This volume is published with the cooperation of the
Great Smoky Mountains Natural History Association

May 1, 1963

NOTES ON THE BIRDS
OF GREAT SMOKY MOUNTAINS
NATIONAL PARK

BY ARTHUR STUPKA

Park Naturalist, 1935–60
Biologist, 1960–63

THE UNIVERSITY OF TENNESSEE PRESS

Preface

More than 20 years have passed since I first contemplated the preparation of a report on the birds of Great Smoky Mountains National Park. In the meantime the records have accumulated—lists and pertinent data submitted to me by interested observers, published information, and the notes from my own journals wherein natural history observations have been recorded. It was not until I was appointed to the newly-established position of Biologist, late in 1960, that sufficient time became available for the preparation of a summary such as the following.

Many persons, including a number of eminent ornithologists, have generously placed their records at my disposal; others have favored me by contributing specimens or in other ways have assisted with the project. To them is due the main credit for what is, essentially, a compilation. As the editor, I have had to decide whether to admit or exclude records based only on sight identifications and this I have done by combining what I know about the competence and reputation of the observer with the probability of the record. The primary objective has been to present as accurate a picture of the birds of the park as possible. If the inclusion of certain species appears questionable, my intention has been the presentation of a reasonably complete list—not a "big" list. The interpretation of the records, unless otherwise given, is my own.

Acknowledgments

First, I wish to express my indebtedness to Joe F. Manley of Gatlinburg, Tennessee, whose knowledge and interest, coupled with unusually keen vision, have resulted in records of birds too numerous to mention—with these he has favored me for the past 25 years.

Miss Mary Ruth Chiles, one of my Great Smoky Mountains National Park colleagues, deserves grateful acknowledgment for the long and arduous task of typing and indexing some 15 years of natural history records and notes, much of which was of a more or less extra-curricular nature. Her cooperation with other pertinent clerical work and her participation in the Christmas Bird Counts are likewise appreciated. I also wish to thank the many other National Park Service colleagues, most of whose names appear in a later list, for favoring me with information, with specimens of local birds, and in other ways. In particular, the cooperation of James O. Stevenson and the late Ned J. Burns is acknowledged for their examination of some 250 specimens of Great Smoky Mountains National Park birds in the collections of the Chicago Academy of Sciences.

Alexander Wetmore contributed materially by examining and determining approximately 100 specimens that were shipped to him by personnel of the Chicago Academy of Sciences, and to him and to the persons associated with the Academy I am deeply indebted.

Grateful acknowledgment is due the members of the Knoxville Chapter of the Tennessee Ornithological Society for their loyal participation in the Christmas Bird Counts and for other favors over a long period of years. In particular, I wish to thank James T. Tanner and Joseph C. Howell for their records of park birds, for their publications devoted to local birds, for their counsel in the initial stages of this report, and for other assistance.

Among those who contributed carefully-prepared lists of birds observed during visits to the park, I wish to give special thanks to John O. Watkins, Milton B. Trautman, and

Chandler S. Robbins. To the personnel of the Buffalo Springs Game Farm and to officials of the Tennessee State Game and Fish Commission I am indebted for data relating to the stocking of various kinds of game birds in the eastern part of Tennessee.

To my wife, Margaret Stupka, who spent more than a year in the typing and indexing of 12 years of my journals and in preparing detailed tabulations of all records pertaining to park birds, grateful acknowledgment is due. For a part of this undertaking she received financial compensation from the Great Smoky Mountains Natural History Association, and the aid of that organization is appreciated.

Gatlinburg, Tennessee   ARTHUR STUPKA
January, 1963

Contents

Introduction

Since practically all who are interested in birds possess a copy of Roger Tory Peterson's *A Field Guide to the Birds* or have other fine guide-books available, no description of the bird or detailed account of its habits is given. The information presented here concerns mostly the following:

1. Status of the bird in the park. If there is only one or a few records, these are given. Changes of status within the past several years or decades are noted, especially for some of the northern finches and for species whose population has changed as a result of natural reforestation.

2. Altitudinal range. In a mountainous region it is of interest to learn how high, as well as how low, certain species range. Here, as well as in high mountain regions everywhere, some birds perform a vertical migration.

3. Dates of arrival and departure. The earliest and latest such dates are given for most of the migrant species. If enough such records are available, data covering a span of years is presented.

4. Nesting data. All the records relating to eggs and young birds are presented.

5. For most of the wintering species, a brief review of the numbers listed on the annual one-day count of winter birds is given. This, also known as the Christmas Bird Count, is an undertaking familiar to most bird watchers. Results were published in *Bird Lore* and its successor, *Audubon Field Notes*, every year beginning with 1935.*

---

* Results were also published regularly in *The Migrant* (Journal of the Tennessee Ornithological Society) beginning with the March 1936 issue (Vol. 7, No. 1) and in *The Chat* (Bulletin of the Carolina Bird Club) beginning with the January 1940 issue (Vol. 4, No. 1).

The counts in 1935, 1936, and for the 5-year period 1957–61 were made in Cades Cove and vicinity; those for the 20-year period 1937–56 had their center on Mt. LeConte. In view of the variables involved in these excursions (the number of observers ranging from 2 to 40, for instance), a summary is not presented in this report.

6. The breeding-bird census conducted June 23–28, 1946, by Aldrich and Goodrum [1946] in the Greenbrier area of the park. The numbers of pairs located in a 23-acre stand of virgin hardwood forest are given with each of the 15 species involved.

7. Significant numbers of certain species of birds killed in the vicinity of ceilometer beacons at the Knoxville (McGhee-Tyson) airport on the nights of October 7–8, 1951 [Howell and Tanner, 1951] and again on October 5–8, 1954 [Tanner, 1954], are reported. This airport is located approximately 12 miles northwest of the park boundary. Mortality along park roads is mentioned for the few species that are involved.

8. Miscellaneous data for some species pertains to food habits, size of flocks, unusual occurrences, ecology, etc.

9. With but few exceptions, the matter of subspecies is relegated to footnote comments.

The journals referred to in the preface, pertaining to my observations on the park's flora and fauna, have been the source of many of the records used in this resumé.* These, beginning with my arrival in the park in October 1935, cover a period of approximately 25 years. During a part of that time the observation and recording of birds—more or less a habit since my middle 'teens—was closely related to my assignment of Park Naturalist, it being my good fortune to conduct groups of park visitors afield and to interpret what was seen and heard during the course of hiking trips. Thus many areas were visited time and again, and this is reflected in the records of birds. The Park Headquarters area in particular

* One copy is in the Park Naturalist's Office, Great Smoky Mountains National Park, and another in the Department of the Interior Library, Washington, D. C. All other records and data used in this report are on file and available for reference at the former location.

has a preponderance of records, for not only is my office located there but that has been the locale for numerous nature walks with groups of visitors. On the other hand, some of the more remote and relatively inaccessible parts of the park were visited but rarely. In later years, with increased administrative responsibilities, field trips (for me) became infrequent.

The records in this report are for the region comprising Great Smoky Mountains National Park and for the communities, coves, ridges, mountains, etc., immediately adjacent to or forming a part of its boundary. Records from places such as Pigeon Forge, Laurel Lake, and Maryville on the Tennessee side, and from Waynesville and Sylva on the North Carolina side, since they are not included in that area, are considered irrelevant and are given only if reference to them serves to throw further light upon the status of a species from the park area, as, for example, the reports of mortality at an airport ceilometer. The Black-crowned Night Heron, Redhead, Canvasback, Common Goldeneye, Bufflehead, White-winged Scoter, Semipalmated Sandpiper, and Black Tern were observed either in the Laurel Lake or Pigeon Forge areas, but since there are no park records for these birds they are not included in the list.

Since the Starling (*Sturnus vulgaris*) and the House Sparrow (*Passer domesticus*) breed within the park and are common permanent residents along its boundary, these foreign birds are included in this report. However, I am deleting the Ring-necked Pheasant (*Phasianus colchicus*), Chukar (*Alectoris graeca*), and Rock Dove (*Columba livia*) since these exotic species have not established themselves in a region quite unsuited to their requirements. The pheasant and Chukar (*persona non grata* in National Parks where non-native species are regarded as undesirable) invaded the area following their release on lands in the vicinity,* but these birds were few and, as far as could be determined, their tenure within the park was brief. The Rock Dove, a domesticated species on some farms and in communities near the park,

* The Ring-necked Pheasant was observed in 1936, 1938, 1941, 1955, and 1958; the Chukar in 1941, 1943, and 1944.

has been observed in the area very infrequently, and there are no "wild" colonies within the park.

The order in which the species are arranged and the common and scientific names are those used in the 5th (1957) edition of the American Ornithologists' Union *Check-list of North American Birds.*

Along with the more prosaic aspects of bird life, this report has also recorded some of the changes that have taken place during the past few decades. It is hoped that these notes will serve to stimulate others to observe and to record such data in the years to come.

The Area

Great Smoky Mountains National Park, comprising an area of approximately 800 square miles, extends for a distance of 54 miles east to west and averages about 15 miles in width north to south. The dominant topographic feature is the uninterrupted chain of mountains that bisect the area from its northeasternmost to its southwesternmost extremity. These mountains reach an elevation of 6643 ft. on Clingmans Dome, second-highest point in Eastern United States; for 36 miles the crest of this range remains more than 5000 ft. above sea level. Tennessee and North Carolina share a common boundary along this high ridge—from Davenport Gap (1902 ft.) near the Pigeon River at the northeastern extremity of the park to Deals Gap (1955 ft.) near the Little Tennessee River at the southwestern limits. The National Park occupies parts of three counties in Tennessee (Cocke, Sevier, and Blount) and parts of two counties in North Carolina (Haywood and Swain).

Some 600 miles of streams—mostly rather small, fast, rocky, and margined with vegetation—drain the heavily forested slopes of the mountains. All of these watercourses eventually make their way to the Tennessee River, a part of the Mississippi River drainage. The lowest point in the park, 857 ft. above sea level, is where Abrams Creek flows into Chilhowee Lake, near the westernmost extent of the area. No lakes or permanent ponds are located within the park; a few limestone sinkholes in Cades Cove become small temporary ponds.

From near Deals Gap to the central part of the southern boundary near Bryson City, the waters of Cheoah and Fontana Lakes determine the limits of the park for many miles. These are reservoirs created by the construction of Cheoah and Fontana Dams. On the Tennessee side northwest of Deals Gap the waters of two more reservoirs—Calderwood Lake and Chilhowee Lake—are near the park's boundary. None of these long narrow bodies of water has attracted any appreciable number of shore- and waterbirds, perhaps due, in part, to their newness, their fluctuating water levels (Fontana, in particular), and other reasons. Infrequent visits by birdwatchers during the spring and fall migrations is reflected in the scarcity of records.

Laurel Lake, a 40-acre impoundment located outside the park in Tuckaleechee Cove, lies approximately 5 miles north of Cades Cove; at one place (Ace Gap) the park boundary lies less than 2 miles from this little body of water. Since 1937 (1938?) when it was impounded, a number of shore- and waterbirds have appeared there during migration, and some, particularly American Coots and a few species of ducks, winter there regularly. As mentioned elsewhere, records of birds observed on Laurel Lake are given in this report only if there is a record of that species from within the park area.

Over 600 miles of horse and foot trails make much of the park accessible to the bird watcher. The transmountain road, from Gatlinburg, Tennessee, to Cherokee, North Carolina, crosses the main divide at Newfound Gap (5040 ft.) where birds characteristic of the Canadian zone prevail; a spur road from Newfound Gap to near Clingmans Dome reaches an elevation of 6311 ft. at its terminus—within one-half mile of the Clingmans Dome observation tower. Another road that has its terminus at a high altitude (5325 ft.) is the Heintooga Overlook spur from the Blue Ridge Parkway; this joins the transmountain road just north of Cherokee, North Carolina. Still another road follows the tortuous course of Little River with a spur whose terminus is represented by the scenic loop road around Cades Cove. A highway from Gatlinburg east to Cosby follows along or near the northern limits of the park for many miles. There are mountain roads along the eastern and western boundaries and a number of spur roads that penetrate the park for short distances near some of the larger watercourses.

Geology

Most of Great Smoky Mountains National Park is formed of rocks belonging to the Ocoee series of late Precambrian age. These are sedimentary rocks of unusual complexity, considerably folded and metamorphosed. This series, whose thickness has been estimated at 30,000 ft. or more, has no volcanic components and no fossils. It has minor intercalations of limestone and dolomite [King, Hadley, Neuman, and Hamilton, 1958]. To the northwest of the park the rocks are of Paleozoic age and these extend into the mountains in a few places [King and Stupka, 1950]. The limestones in Cades Cove and Whiteoak Sink within the park and in nearby Tuckaleechee Cove and Wear Cove are of Ordovician age and contain brachiopods, trilobites, and gastropods [Newman, 1947]; in these "coves" the older Ocoee rocks have been thrust over the younger.*

Climate

In a region where the range in altitude is from 857 ft. to 6643 ft. above sea level, climatic conditions vary considerably. In Gatlinburg (Park Headquarters) at 1460 ft., the annual precipitation is approximately 55 inches while at an altitude of 6250 ft. on Clingmans Dome the average precipitation is about 85 inches [Tennessee Valley Authority, 1961].** In a survey entitled "Climates of the Great Smoky Mountains," Shanks [1954b] reports that "the precipitation at the base of the mountains is not far different from that of the adjacent valley area, but . . . it increases sharply with altitude, and has increased by 50% by the time the lower limit of the spruce-fir zone is reached, at 4500 to 5000 feet." Summer is

* Readers interested in accounts relating to the geology of the park are referred to the articles cited. Between 1946 and 1955 a group of geologists with the U. S. Geological Survey prepared a geological map covering most of Great Smoky Mountains National Park and some adjacent areas. The first pertinent report to be published is by Hamilton [1961]; subsequent reports, now in preparation, are by Hadley and Goldsmith, P. B. King, and Neuman and Nelson. Each will appear as a *Geological Survey Professional Paper*.

** Figures based on records for periods of 35 to 25 years, respectively.

the season of greatest precipitation while fall is the driest time of the year.

There is a period of rapid warming during April and May; from October to November fast cooling takes place. Temperatures decrease with increase in altitude, Shanks [ibid.] reporting that this averages 2.23° F. per 1,000 ft. He concluded that in terms of both climate and vegetation the nearest low-altitude equivalent of the Great Smokies spruce-fir forest region lies about 1,000 miles to the northeast. For the period 1922–53, inclusive, at the Gatlinburg, Tennessee, station, the average temperature for January is 39.9° (F.); for July, 74.6°; annual, 57.0° [Henry and Dickson, 1959].

Previous Ornithological Activities

William Brewster's stay of 12 days in western North Carolina, beginning May 23, 1885, resulted in an exceptionally fine account of the bird life of that area [Brewster, 1886]. That eminent ornithologist did not visit the region which now comprises Great Smoky Mountains National Park, but he did come within 10 miles of the boundary (at Waynesville), and all who are interested in the bird life of the park are urged to read his outstanding pioneering report. A number of ornithologists followed Brewster into other sections of the Southern Appalachian Mountains shortly thereafter.

Arthur Lemoyne [1886] published a series of articles that ran in five consecutive numbers of the *Ornithologist and Oologist* beginning with the August (Vol. 11, No. 8) 1886 issue. Entitled "Notes on Some Birds of the Great Smoky Mountains," this series reported on a total of 21 species, one-third of that number being warblers. Lemoyne, having visited Cocke, Sevier, and Blount Counties in Tennessee (in addition to Greene, Roane, and Monroe Counties), appears to have been the first ornithologist to investigate and report on the birds of what is now a part of Great Smoky Mountains National Park. His itinerary, as given in the report, leaves the reader in doubt as to the locations of the birds and their nests and eggs. The second-hand account pertaining to securing a pair of Golden Eagles and their eggs is unconvincing. Lemoyne's visit extended from February 20, 1886, when he arrived at Newport, Tennessee, to June 1, 1886.

F. W. Langdon [1887], in his "August Birds of the Chilhowee Mountains, Tennessee," reports on observations "made chiefly in Blount County, East Tennessee, between August 11 and 21, 1886, inclusive. . . . excursions were made in various directions, notably one to the Great Smoky Mountains, about twenty miles southeast. . . . Our headquarters on Defeat Mountain [Defeat Ridge], a spur of the Smoky Range, was at a cattle-herder's camp, a small log cabin, situated at an altitude of perhaps 4000 feet . . ." Langdon's list of 63 species and subspecies "adds five species and two subspecies to the list of birds heretofore recorded from the state."

Rhoads [1895] depended largely on the findings of Lemoyne and Langdon for his information on the birds of the Great Smoky Mountains when he published his report on the birds of Tennessee in 1895; his own travels did not bring him closer to these mountains than Knoxville although the conditions he found on Roan Mountain were most like those that prevail here.

Albert F. Ganier, dean of Tennessee ornithologists, has maintained an interest in the birds of the Great Smoky Mountains since 1920, when his first visit was made to this area. From 1920 to 1933 he conducted a series of investigations "nearly every year" [Ganier, 1962] publishing, in the meantime, an article entitled "Summer Birds of the Great Smoky Mountains" [Ganier, 1926]. This, along with the article describing the foray he led to the park in June 1938 [Ganier and Clebsch, 1938], was the most extensive of a dozen or more reports in which some reference was made to park birds. In 1954 he pointed out [Ganier, 1954] that the breeding sapsuckers of the Southern Appalachians represented a distinct race,* and his designation finds acceptance in the 1957 edition of the *Check-list of North American Birds*.

Thomas D. Burleigh was stationed in Asheville, North Carolina, from January 1930 to September 1934 during which time one of his assignments for the U. S. Biological Survey

* *Sphyrapicus varius appalachiensis.*

was a distributional study of the birdlife of the Southern Appalachian Mountains. "During this interval," he writes, "I carried on field work from time to time in the Great Smoky Mountains and . . . collected there a total of 62 birds, largely to determine the subspecific identification of certain of the species recorded" [letter]. One of the birds he collected on Mt. Guyot on April 15, 1932, was designated as the type specimen of a new race of Black-capped Chickadees * by Oberholser [1937] a few years later. Specimens of Winter Wrens and Brown Creepers which Burleigh collected in the Great Smoky Mountains at that time formed the basis of his descriptions of new races ** of both these birds [Burleigh, 1935]. He made his extensive notes on the birds of the mountainous region of North Carolina available to Pearson, Brimley, and Brimley who make considerable use of them in their *Birds of North Carolina* [1942 and 1959 editions].

Under the auspices of the Chicago Academy of Sciences, E. V. Komarek had charge of a faunal survey of the Great Smoky Mountains that began investigations in the area in March 1931. After about six weeks, during which time a large number of vertebrates were collected, the party returned to Chicago. The following year and again in 1933 Komarek had charge of other parties that remained in the area for longer periods of time. Altogether approximately 250 specimens of birds were collected, and about 100 of these were later (1943) examined and identified by Wetmore. Sometime in 1934 Komarek prepared an "Incomplete Checklist of the Birds of The Smokies, based on sight records and specimens of any doubtful forms." This list, copies of which are in the park files, includes 147 species and subspecies; there are no annotations.

Raymond J. Fleetwood arrived in the park on May 27, 1934, where he served as Wildlife Technician attached to the camps of the Civilian Conservation Corps for a period of 13 months. Much of his time was spent in the field in a survey of park birds, and his daily journal is essentially a listing of the species of birds observed in the course of his hiking

* *Penthestes [Parus] atricapillus practicus.*
** *Nannus hiemalis [Troglodytes t.] pullus* and *Certhia familiaris nigrescens,* respectively.

trips.* On March 14, 1935, he submitted a briefly annotated list of 137 species and subspecies of birds which is in the park files. He also published three brief notes pertaining to the birds of the area—on the Red-cockaded Woodpecker, the American Woodcock, and the Blue Goose [Fleetwood, 1936, 1937, 1943].

A mimeographed *Check-list of Birds of Great Smoky Mountains National Park,* issued by the Wildlife Division of the National Park Service [1937], is based largely upon these lists prepared by Komarek and Fleetwood. It includes 181 species and subspecies with brief annotations.

On June 17, 1937, W. M. Perrygo and Carleton Lingebach of the U. S. National Museum arrived in the park and set up a camp four and one-half miles southwest of Cosby where, from an elevation of 2700 ft., they made collecting trips over a period of 18 days. Altogether 117 specimens of birds were obtained [Burleigh, letter], and these are discussed, often at some length, in Wetmore's excellent *Notes on the Birds of Tennessee* [1939].

John W. Aldrich and Phil Goodrum of the Division of Wildlife Research, U. S. Fish and Wildlife Service, conducted a census of breeding birds in the Greenbrier area of the park from June 23 to 28, 1946. In a 23-acre tract of virgin hardwood forest (2950–3200 ft.) they listed 15 species of birds [Aldrich and Goodrum, 1946].

James T. Tanner, who joined the staff of the Zoology Department of the University of Tennessee in 1947, published his studies on Blackcapped and Carolina Chickadees in 1952, "The Altitudinal Distribution of Birds in a Part of the Great Smoky Mountains" in 1955, and "Juncos in the Great Smoky Mountains" in 1958. Among the short notes he published was a "First Record of Swainson's Warbler in the Great Smoky Mountains" [1950a] and "Sight Record of a Saw-whet Owl in the Great Smoky Mountains" [1957c]. In the *Audubon Magazine* for May–June 1957, his article entitled "Adventures for Bird-watchers in the Great Smoky Mountains" is an excellent popular report on the birds of the park.

---

* Although some of his records appear throughout this report, others were not used due to lack of sufficient data pertaining to specific localities at which the birds were observed.

Henry M. Stevenson of Florida State University collaborated with me in a report on "The Altitudinal Limits of Certain Birds in the Mountains of the Southeastern States" in 1948. He published additional articles on the geographic and altitudinal distribution of southeastern birds in 1950 and 1957, respectively.

Among several short articles and notes I published are items relating to Pine Siskins [1937, 1938], the breeding of Red Crossbills [1938], the mortality of Screech Owls [1953] and initial park records of the Blue Grosbeak [1946], Snow Goose [1948], Evening Grosbeak [1954a], and Golden Plover [1954b]. Informa____ _____ ____ ___ part, deals with the bird life of the park is t_ __ __ _____ __ _my chapter "Through the Year in the Great S____ _____ins," in the book *The Great Smokies and the ____ _____ [__943], and in the *Natural History Handbook _____ ____ _y Mountains National Park* [Stupka, 1960].

Altogether there ar_ ____ ____)00 study skins of birds collected in the park ___ _____ These are located as follows: the Chicago Ac_____ __ ___ ____nces (approximately 250 specimens), the Uni___ _____ __ _____onal Museum (179 specimens), Great Smok_ _____ National Park (50 specimens), the Univers___ __ _____ee (32 specimens—chickadees only), and a _____ _____; comprising the personal collection of Albe__ __ _____ in Nashville, Tennessee.

Flora

Few areas in th_ _____ ____Zone of North America have as rich a flora as is to _._ ____1 in the Great Smoky Mountains. "More than 1300 kinds of flowering plants, almost 350 mosses and liverworts, 230 lichens, and more than 2,000 fungi have been found here" [Stupka, 1960]. The trees are notable for their variety and large size; should we include those shrubs, such as mountain-laurel, staghorn sumac, and witch-hazel that may attain arborescent proportions, one could find more than 100 kinds of native trees in the park. About 20 trees, including red spruce, eastern hemlock, cucumbertree, Fraser magnolia, yellow buckeye, and mountain silverbell, reach record size.

Plants occur in greatest variety at the low and middle altitudes; the numbers dropping out by the time the 3500–4000 ft. elevation is reached readily exceeding the numbers of Canadian zone species that occur only above that range. But the monotonous character of the high-altitude forests of spruce and fir is at variance with the fascination that such a boreal habitat holds for those interested in the fauna and flora of the Great Smoky Mountains. Here in the park, a few miles west of Clingmans Dome, is the southernmost extension of the Canadian zone in the Eastern United States, where the Red-breasted Nuthatch, Brown Creeper, Winter Wren, Golden-crowned Kinglet, Olive-sided Flycatcher, and Saw-whet Owl breed. Here the Black-capped Chickadee, Veery, and Slate-colored Junco are common birds, along with the Raven, Canada Warbler, Blackburnian Warbler and others which we ordinarily associate with the forests of northern New England and Canada. Since more than 90 percent of the virgin spruce stands of the Southern Appalachian region have disappeared as a result of lumbering and fires [Korstian, 1937], this remnant within the National Park becomes a particularly precious heritage. It represents the only clearly-defined "life zone" in the park, where 59 percent of the woody plants are made up of northern species [Cain, 1930].

Infiltrating the spruce-fir forests at altitudes mostly above 4000–4500 ft. and forming a band along its lower limits is the northern hardwood forest where yellow birch and beech are dominant. There we find the upper limits of such trees as yellow buckeye, black cherry, American beech, red and sugar maples, mountain silverbell, and eastern hemlock. Practically all the spruce-fir forest birds occur here along with the Yellow-bellied Sapsucker, Solitary Vireo, Rose-breasted Grosbeak, Chestnut-sided Warbler, Black-throated Blue Warbler, and others.

The cove hardwood forests, mostly at altitudes of 3000–4000 ft., "are doubtless among the most beautiful deciduous forests in the world" [Whittaker, 1956]. Here many of the record-size trees of the park are to be found. A considerable variety of herbaceous plants carpets the ground, shrubs and small trees are relatively uncommon, and the main forest species (eastern hemlock, mountain silverbell, yellow buckeye, basswood, sugar maple, yellow birch, yellow-poplar, and American beech) ordinarily grow so tall that the observation of birds is probably more difficult here than in any other type of forest. At this altitudinal range, however, bird study is of considerable interest for it is here that a number of high-mountain species are at their lowest limits (i. e., Black-capped Chickadee, Black-throated Blue Warbler, and Slate-colored Junco) while others (i. e., Tufted Titmouse, Red-eyed Vireo, and Wood Thrush) are at or near their highest penetration. Tanner [1957a] writes that "Altogether about 12 species of birds reach the highest altitude at which they live, and 11 their lowest limit in the cove hardwoods."

Both Shanks [1954a] and Whittaker [1956] * regard the eastern hemlock forest as a vegetation type in the park. Some hemlocks occur as low as 1000 ft. above sea level while the uppermost extension is from 5000 to 5500 ft. Black-throated Green and Parula Warblers, summer residents throughout this wide range, are often to be found associated with stands of these conifers, although these birds are not restricted to hemlocks.

The two remaining vegetation types, according to Shanks [1954a], are dominated by various kinds of oaks. In the closed oak forests where white, chestnut, northern red, and black oaks prevail, the sites occupied are intermediate to dry; the "forest canopy high and continuous; heaths usually present in shrub layer, but not forming a continuous stratum" [ibid.]. In contrast, the open oak and pine stands are dominated by a mixture of four species of oaks (white, scarlet, chestnut, and black) and a similar number of pines (Table-Mountain, pitch, white, and Virginia). The sites these trees occupy are dry, exposed, and often rocky; the trees are short and scattered and "do not form a closed forest canopy; the essentially continuous tall shrub layer, dominated by *Kalmia,* is also the canopy layer of the 'heath balds' " [ibid.]. A

---

* The classification of vegetative types I am following here, and that which I adopted in my *Natural History Handbook* [Stupka, 1960] is based upon the compilation by Shanks [1954a]. The reader is also referred to Whittaker's [1956] comprehensive and detailed report on the "Vegetation of the Great Smoky Mountains" which, in addition to its excellent content, lists well over 200 items of cited literature.

large number of birds are to be found in these forests, including the Whip-poor-will, Downy Woodpecker, Carolina Chickadee, Tufted Titmouse, White-breasted Nuthatch, Yellow-throated Vireo, and warblers such as the Black-and-white, Worm-eating, Yellow-throated, Pine, Prairie, Ovenbird, Yellow-breasted Chat, Hooded, and Redstart.

"Although there is no true timberline in the Southern Appalachians, there are treeless areas on some of the higher mountaintops and ridges. Owing to their lack of forest cover, such places are called balds. That designation, however, is a relative one since other plants form a dense carpet over the balds. If these plants are largely shrubs belonging to the heath family, such balds are known as heath balds; if grasses and sedges prevail, the balds are termed grass balds" [Stupka, 1960]. Whereas the grass balds may number approximately a dozen, the heath balds are much more plentiful. These areas are located at middle or high altitudes; being quite isolated and small in size they have not developed a distinctive bird fauna. This does not mean, however, that the birds one may encounter there are uninteresting. Quite the contrary is true, for to hear the bell-like notes of a raven as the big black bird wings his way over a bald or to come suddenly upon a Turkey and watch it as it takes off from one of these treeless places are among the sounds and sights long to be remembered.

THE NOTES

FAMILY | *GAVIIDAE*

COMMON LOON—*Gavia immer*

There is but one record of this species from within the park. On May 2, 1949, Mrs. Sheril Ogle, of Gatlinburg, caught a mature loon which had been stranded near the 4000 ft. altitude on the Tennessee side of the transmountain road and brought it to the Park Headquarters Building. On May 4 this bird was released on a pond at Elkmont where it remained until May 16. Mack Rauhuff, a member of the park's maintenance force, captured a Common Loon he found stranded December 1, 1961, on the park boundary, at the junction of Route 73 and the Greenbrier entrance. The bird was brought to Park Naturalist Lix for identification before its release in the West Prong of the Little Pigeon River. At Laurel Lake, less than 2 miles north of the park line, single birds have been observed on April 10, 1942 (Manley) ; May 4, 1952 (Stupka) ; October 20, 1950 (Burns) ; December 24, 1960 (Russell) ; and January 1, 1961 (Tanner and party) . One dead specimen was found near Waterrock Knob, on the Blue Ridge Parkway, on May 6, 1961, by Rangers Stark and Atchison; this place, at an elevation of 5600 ft., is approximately 4 miles south of the park.

Common Loons are probably more plentiful transients and winter visitants on the nearby bodies of quiet water than our records would indicate. Lesley [1954] reports a flock of about 50 Common Loons on Lake Junaluska, North Carolina, for the 2 weeks' period beginning December 20, 1953; this body of water is approximately 10 miles southeast of the park.

FAMILY | *PODICIPEDIDAE*

HORNED GREBE—*Podiceps auritus*

The first park record for this grebe came on November 27, 1940, when Manley observed one on a small pond at Elkmont. Since then there have been but 2 additional observations within the area and 3 more on Laurel Lake, nearby. On December 14, 1949, a Horned Grebe, discovered stranded on the parking area just north of the Park Headquarters Building, may have mistaken the wet pavement for a body of water; the nearby mountains were shrouded in heavy fog at the time. On November 24, 1950, Ranger Hannah came upon an injured bird in the Cataloochee section of the park. It died a few days later and was brought to me for examination.

I observed a solitary Horned Grebe on Laurel Lake December 21, 1950. Russell saw one there December 24, 1960. On January 1, 1961, Tanner and party reported 2 of these grebes on the same body of water.

PIED-BILLED GREBE—*Podilymbus podiceps*

There are more records of this little grebe than any other waterbird; but due to the great scarcity of quiet bodies of water, its status in the park is that of a rather uncommon spring and fall transient. Birds have been observed within the park or in adjacent areas each of the months July through November as well as in February, March, and April. Should we add observations made at Laurel Lake, nearby, all months with the exception of May and June would be represented.

Earliest of the so-called "autumn" records was on July 13 (1944), when a Pied-billed Grebe was found dead on the Tennessee side of the transmountain road at an elevation of 3700 ft.; that proved to be the only July occurrence of this species as well as its highest recorded altitude. The latest park record proved to be the dead bird I found at Fighting Creek Gap on April 20 (1940); at Laurel Lake I observed one bird April 30 (1953).

During the 29-year period ending in 1961, Pied-billed Grebes, in numbers ranging from 1 to 25 birds, have been observed in the park and immediate vicinity on 39 days; two-thirds of these observations were made during the three autumn months: September (5), October (15), and November (7). The largest flock, containing 25 birds, was one that Manley saw on a little pond at Elkmont on October 16, 1940. On the 5 Christmas Bird Counts taken in a part of the western portion of Great Smoky Mountains National Park and vicinity, beginning in 1957, the numbers of these grebes observed on Laurel Lake totaled 13, 10, 6, 8, and 2, respectively.

Next to Screech Owls, more dead Pied-billed Grebes have been picked up along park roads than any other bird. Since they appear to migrate at night, it is assumed that these grebes mistake a smooth highway surface for a watercourse, especially after a rain, and thereupon come to grief. Within the park and immediate vicinity, 11 dead and 3 wounded birds were discovered in the roads between 1940 and 1954.

FAMILY | *PELECANIDAE*

WHITE PELICAN—*Pelecanus erythrorhynchos*

There is but one record of this species in the park. On September 21, 1937, while Edward S. Thomas, Curator of Natural History in the Ohio State Museum, and his brother John were viewing the panorama at the Clingmans Dome Parking Area (6311 ft.), 3 White Pelicans came into view. The big birds were flying some 200–400 ft. higher than where their observers were stationed.

Howell and Monroe [1958] give 2 records of White Pelicans for nearby Knox County, Tennessee (May 8, 1935 and September 25, 1949), and Lesley [1953] reports a group of 7 on Lake Junaluska, North Carolina (approximately 10 miles southeast of the park), on May 26, 1953.

FAMILY | *PHALACROCORACIDAE*

DOUBLE-CRESTED CORMORANT—
Phalacrocorax auritus

Manley observed one of these birds on the park boundary at the mouth of Abrams Creek (857 ft.) November 12 and 19, 1942. There are no other records for the park. Manley and I saw a Double-crested Cormorant beside the West Prong of the Little Pigeon River, approximately 10 miles north of Gatlinburg, in late September and early October, 1938.

FAMILY | *ARDEIDAE*

GREAT BLUE HERON—*Ardea herodias*

This large heron, although decidedly uncommon and localized in its occurrence in the park and vicinity, has been observed during every month of the year excepting April. It is not known to breed here. Within the park proper, there have been more records in Cades Cove (9) than any other locality, but it may occur along any of the larger streams at altitudes below 2000 ft. On May 11, 1950, Burns and I saw a Great Blue Heron winging its way over Newfound Gap (5040 ft.), near the center of the park. On November 9, 1956, following a sudden change from mild to cold wet weather, Manley observed 9 of these herons flying over Gatlinburg. There have been a number of observations of this species from Pigeon Forge and vicinity, from Laurel Lake, and from the adjacent large reservoirs south and west of the park.

GREEN HERON—*Butorides virescens*

Since there have been but 32 records of this species in the park or immediate vicinity during the years 1935–61, it is regarded as an uncommon migrant and a rare breeder. There are observations during every month, April through November; earliest, April 8 (1957, Manley); latest, November 4

(1954, Manley) —both of these extremes being from the Gatlinburg area. Of the 8 April records, 5 are between the 8th and 18th; of the 9 September records, 7 are between the 11th and 28th. The highest record is a bird I observed April 17, 1939, at an elevation of 2500 ft. along Little River, above Elkmont.

During some years, the Green Heron has undoubtedly nested in the so-called "Gum Swamp" in Cades Cove, less than one-half mile east of the Cable Mill. I have observed it there May 20 and June 28, 1938; May 17, 1939; and May 6 and 19, 1940. I have also observed it elsewhere in Cades Cove on June 14, 1943, and Manley has reported it from Greenbrier on June 11, 1940. Outside the park, the bird has been observed at Laurel Lake and near Pigeon Forge.

LITTLE BLUE HERON—*Florida caerulea*

Our only record is Manley's observation of one of these birds along the West Prong of the Little Pigeon River, between Gatlinburg and the Park Headquarters area, on November 19, 1939. The bird was an immature in the white plumage. This occurrence is almost 2 months later than the latest record for adjacent Knox County, Tennessee: September 21 (1948) [Howell and Monroe, 1957].

COMMON EGRET—*Casmerodius albus*

On the morning of October 7, 1944, I watched 2 Common Egrets alight in the top of a tall sycamore approximately 150 yards behind the Park Headquarters Building. The birds remained in the vicinity for several hours during which time the late Gerrit S. Miller, Jr., of Washington, D. C., and Koch, both of whom were visiting in Gatlinburg at the time, viewed the birds and agreed with my identification. The heavy intermittent rains at the time may have been a factor in the birds' reluctance to leave, and they permitted fairly close approach. Their large size and white coloration, the long slender necks, yellow bills, and long dark legs were observed to good advantage. A photograph of one of these birds, taken by Koch, is on file. This represents the first record of the Common Egret in Great Smoky Mountains National Park.

On September 2, 1962, an injured bird of this species was captured in Cades Cove by some boys who brought it to District Ranger Royce; color photographs taken before the egret was liberated leave no doubt as to its identification.

AMERICAN BITTERN—*Botaurus lentiginosus*

The first evidence of the occurrence of the American Bittern in the park was on May 17, 1931, when Crouch found 2 left feet of this species among the prey remains at a Peregrine Falcons' eyrie near Alum Cave Bluffs. These feet, along with what proved to be the remains of a Red-breasted Merganser, were sent to H. C. Oberholser who identified them. Since the eyrie is approximately 7 miles inside the park boundary, the falcons must have struck their large victims as the latter were flying over the Great Smoky Mountains at an elevation of more than 5000 ft. [Ganier, 1940].

Mrs. Eugene M. West, President of the Chattanooga Chapter, Tennessee Ornithological Society, kindly informed me [letter] of another high-altitude record for this species in the park: Mr. and Mrs. Jack Wilkinson, members of the Chattanooga Chapter and friends of Mrs. West, while on an extended pack trip along the Appalachian Trail, observed an American Bittern some place between Spence Field and Gregory Bald on September 23, 1954. "The field from which the bird flushed is a grassy opening . . . I believe they stopped nearby and watered their horses at the only source of water they saw all day."

There are 3 additional records of this bird in our area. I observed 1 in Cades Cove November 29, 1938; Ganier and party (Wilson Ornithological Society) reported 1 in the same general area April 27, 1952; and Dr. and Mrs. Baldwin saw 1 along Hills Creek, just inside the park boundary near Emerts Cove, on May 1, 1953.

Manley observed an American Bittern at Walland on October 16, 1939. One of these birds killed at Pigeon Forge, Tennessee, on December 3, 1944, was brought to me for examination shortly thereafter.

FAMILY | *ANATIDAE*

CANADA GOOSE—*Branta canadensis*

The chances of seeing these large spectacular waterfowl winging their way over the Great Smoky Mountains would be best during the latter half of October; approximately one-half of our 59 records (1934–61) are for the period October 16–29. The Canada Goose is an uncommon transient and a rare winter visitor in the park and vicinity. The earliest arrival date is October 2, 1955 (Manley) ; latest departure date is March 28, 1939 (W. Ogle) . Since the type of water these birds prefer is lacking here, they seldom alight within our boundaries; although, occasionally they have come down in places such as Greenbrier, Elkmont, Cades Cove, Gatlinburg, and the Park Headquarters area. Some of these visits were by single off-course birds; confusion resulting from prevailing fog or snow accounted for a number of the records.

Manley, on October 7, 1937, counted 43 geese that had settled near the mouth of Abrams Creek, on the park's western boundary. W. Ogle had a small flock under observation on the Middle Prong of the Little Pigeon River, near Greenbrier, for a few days beginning March 15, 1939. A flock of 73 birds alighted on a large swimming pool in Gatlinburg on November 3, 1951 (Manley) ; Lix reported 35 geese on this same pool on October 12, 1953. One of the Christmas Bird Count parties came upon 22 birds on the Middle Prong, in Greenbrier, January 3, 1954. Condon observed 11 Canada Geese on a temporary pond in Cades Cove on October 15, 1961.

Canada Geese have been recorded flying over the park in November on 13 occasions (1934–52) . Here, as elsewhere, their migrations take place at all hours of the day or night and under a wide variety of climatic conditions. Flocks have been observed flying over Mt. LeConte, the third-highest mountain in the park (6593 ft.) , October 22, 23, and 24, 1939.

We have a few records for Laurel Lake; one of these birds spent most of the winter of 1956–57 at that place [Tanner, 1957b].

BRANT—*Branta bernicla*

On October 22, 1939, a Brant appeared on the little body of water known as the "Murphy Pond" in Elkmont, where it remained for several days associating with a white domestic duck. Manley, who informed me about this rare bird, accompanied me to Elkmont on October 26 where excellent views were had of the Brant at close range. The bird, an immature, was of a rather uniform grayish color with whitish markings on the feathers that covered its back; the tail, legs, and bill were black.

Since this small goose did not take wing when it was closely approached on this little body of water, I suspected that it had been injured, but this could not be proved. The bird was not to be found when I returned to the pond a few days later. This, an accidental occurrence, is the only record for the Brant in Great Smoky Mountains National Park.

SNOW GOOSE—*Chen hyperborea*

A freshly-killed Snow Goose was found along Route 73 in the park November 14, 1948, by Homer E. Smith. The location, about 2 miles west of the Park Headquarters area, coupled with the nature of the bird's injuries (broken right wing and severe neck bruises) appeared to indicate that it had died when it flew into telephone wires which parallel the highway at this place. Parts of the bird were preserved to verify this first record of the species from within Great Smoky Mountains National Park [Stupka, 1948].

Manley observed 3 Snow Geese with a flock of 30 Canada Geese on October 29, 1954; on December 6 of the same year he reported 5 Snow Geese with a flock of 41 Canada Geese. Both observations were made in Gatlinburg.

The occurrence of the Snow Goose in the park is accidental.

BLUE GOOSE—*Chen caerulescens*

On October 30, 1934, Fleetwood observed and photographed a strange goose in Cades Cove. Nine years later (1943) he forwarded the picture and description to the Fish and Wildlife Service requesting the bird's identification.

Thereafter, a note he published [1943] served to establish the first record of the Blue Goose in Great Smoky Mountains National Park.

Tanner [1957b], basing his statement on observations reported to him by Ralph Zaenglein and Mary Enloe, mentioned the occurrence of an immature Blue Goose that was present on Laurel Lake most of the winter of 1956–57.

On October 26, 1960, a freshly-killed specimen of an immature Blue Goose, shot in Emerts Cove about one and one-half miles from the park boundary, was brought in for identification.

Since there are no other records of this species in our area, its status must be regarded as accidental.

MALLARD—*Anas platyrhynchos*

The Mallard has been observed in Cades Cove on 8 occasions, in the Park Headquarters area once, and near the park boundary in Emerts Cove once. Dates of occurrence at these places range from November 14 (1938) to March 9 (1956). A flock of 42 birds, observed in Cades Cove November 16, 1961, represents the largest aggregation of this species (Royce). In the vicinity of the park (Pigeon Forge and Laurel Lake), the Mallard has been reported as early in the autumn as September 16 (1938) and as late in the spring as May 4 (1952). It is an uncommon transient and winter visitor in our area.

BLACK DUCK—*Anas rubripes*

This large duck was observed in the park and vicinity on 10 of the 26 years, 1936–61; the largest flock (Cades Cove, January 3, 1960) was comprised of 15 birds. Black Ducks have been reported from Cades Cove and the adjacent areas on 11 occasions; in Greenbrier, twice; and once from the Park Headquarters area. In addition we have 5 records from Laurel Lake and 3 from Pigeon Forge. Earliest arrival date in the autumn was October 28, 1939 (Manley and King); latest departure date in the spring was April 12, 1951 (Burns). Like the Mallard, the Black Duck is an uncommon transient and winter visitor in these mountains.

PINTAIL—*Anas acuta*

Our only record of the Pintail from within Great Smoky Mountains National Park was on April 14, 1953, when Manley observed a lone drake on the West Prong of the Little Pigeon River, 1 mile south of Gatlinburg. In the vicinity of Pigeon Forge, Tennessee, Manley reported this duck November 23, 1939, while Tanner and other members of the Christmas Bird Count party listed 4 Pintails on Laurel Lake December 21, 1958.

GREEN-WINGED TEAL—*Anas carolinensis*

The first record for this little duck in the park came on October 31, 1938, when I observed a flock of 10 on a quiet stretch of Little River, at Metcalf Bottoms. On November 5, 1950, Price found a freshly-killed Green-winged Teal on the transmountain road at an elevation between 3500 and 4200 ft. (Tennessee side) ; along with a number of other migrants, this bird had been caught in a sudden storm that covered the higher mountains with the first snow of the season [Stupka, 1950]. Another dead specimen was found in Gatlinburg on November 9, 1956, by Manley, Gilbert, and Lix following a sudden change to cold rainy weather.

In the vicinity of the park, one Green-winged Teal was observed on Laurel Lake December 21, 1958, by Tanner and party (Christmas Bird Count).

BLUE-WINGED TEAL—*Anas discors*

During the 26 years ending in 1960 this small duck has been observed and recorded on 43 occasions, making it one of the most common waterbirds in the park and vicinity. As birds go, however, it is an uncommon spring and fall migrant, the fall flights outnumbering those in spring by almost 3 to 1. Whereas only a few birds (1 to 6) comprise the spring flocks, there have been up to 200 individuals making up a flock in the fall (Little River, September 26, 1939—Manley and King).

The earliest record for the spring is March 29 (1935, Cades Cove—Fleetwood) ; latest is April 28 (1953, near Park Headquarters—Manley). Earliest fall record is August 24 (1939, Park Headquarters—Manley) ; latest is November 14 (1938,

Emerts Cove—Manley). On January 13 and 15, 1942, I observed a lone Blue-winged Teal on Laurel Lake; this is our only winter record.

The highest altitude at which one of these ducks has been observed is 3600 ft. This was October 29, 1953, when Manley, Lix, and I saw one stranded on a snow-bank along the transmountain road (Tennessee side) during the first snowfall of the season [Stupka, 1954b].

AMERICAN WIDGEON (BALDPATE) — *Mareca americana*

The first park record for the American Widgeon (formerly known as "Baldpate") came November 13, 1940, when Manley observed 4 of these birds on Little River at Metcalf Bottoms. The only other record was on November 5, 1950, when a freshly-killed specimen, along with several other kinds of birds, was found during the first snowstorm of the season at an elevation between 3500 and 4200 ft., beside the transmountain road, Tennessee side [Stupka, 1950].

Near the park, Manley saw 1 of these ducks on the West Prong of the Little Pigeon River, near Pigeon Forge, November 23, 1939. On Laurel Lake I observed 1 bird March 22, 1951; Burns observed 1 there April 12, 1951.

SHOVELER—*Spatula clypeata*

There is but one park record—Fleetwood's report of 3 Shovelers on Cheoah Lake, near the mouth of Twentymile Creek, on October 8, 1934. This is on the park boundary in the extreme southwestern corner of the area. On April 13, 1952, I observed 4 male Shovelers in full breeding plumage on Laurel Lake.

WOOD DUCK—*Aix sponsa*

On the basis of Stevenson's observation of a female Wood Duck with 8 small young on June 12, 1958, in Cades Cove, this handsome waterfowl is designated as a very rare breeder in our area. No other species of ducks are known to breed in the park. The scarcity of Wood Ducks is revealed by the fact that there are but 10 records, 6 of these being during the month of November. Four birds were noted in Elkmont on

February 29 and March 1, 1944 (H. Smith and Stupka); 6 were in the same area on October 22, 1940 (Manley). On December 6, 1958, Pardue observed 2 birds on Abrams Creek near Happy Valley. All records are below 2200 ft.

RING-NECKED DUCK—*Aythya collaris*

On Laurel Lake this bird is a fairly common winter resident, but within the park and adjacent areas we have but 6 records, all of which are in November. Earliest is November 4, 1950, when a high-altitude snowstorm, the first of the season, grounded a number of migrants including 3 Ring-necked Ducks along the transmountain road; 2 were captured and released while the third was found dead [Stupka, 1950]. Latest is November 23 (1938) when Manley observed a single bird on Little River in Tuckaleechee Cove. Single birds were also reported November 7, 1941, at the Sinks on Little River (Manley); November 8, 1938, at Tremont (Manley); and November 14, 1933, in Greenbrier (E. V. Komarek). On November 17 and 18, 1959, Manley had 2 of these ducks under observation at the north end of Gatlinburg.

SCAUP—*Aythya sp.*

There are 14 records (30 birds) of scaups * from within the park area during the years 1935–59. More than half our records are of birds found dead, wounded, or stunned on or alongside wet or ice-covered highways which the birds may have mistaken for a watercourse. With one exception, each instance involved from 1 to 3 birds. On November 30, 1944, 10 scaups were discovered stranded at an elevation of 3800 ft. along the transmountain road (Tennessee side) that was ice-covered at the time; Assistant Chief Ranger Light captured 1 of the injured birds and placed it on a small pool near his home where it remained for a time. This proved to be the latest fall record for the scaup in our area. The earliest fall appearance, October 29 (1953), involved a lone male that appeared confused very near the aforementioned locality at a time when heavy fog and the first snow of the season en-

---

* Four of these—3 stunned birds and 1 dead bird—were identified as the Lesser Scaup (*Aythya affinis*); most, or all, of the remainder were probably the same species; but in view of the similarity in the appearance of the two scaups, all our records will be referred to simply as "scaup (s)."

veloped the higher mountains [Stupka, 1954b]. The same locality was the scene of a rather similar tragedy for various species of migrating birds on November 4 and 5, 1950; included were 1 dead and 2 stunned scaups [Stupka, 1950]. Ealy discovered a dead scaup near the 4000 ft. altitude on the transmountain road (North Carolina side) November 23, 1949— the coldest day of the month and the highest altitude at which this duck has been recorded here.

In addition 1 or 2 birds have been observed on 6 days in November, ranging from the 7th to the 29th of the month. Our earliest record in the spring is March 17 (1940), when I saw 5 scaups on a small pond in Cades Cove; the only other spring records, all involving single birds, are April 11 (1948), April 21 (1951), and April 28 (1952). On Laurel Lake, near the park, the latest observation of this duck is May 11 (1953).

The occurrence of scaups within the park is more or less accidental, even though the number of records might indicate these birds to be very uncommon spring and fall migrants.

RUDDY DUCK—*Oxyura jamaicensis*

Our only park record is the freshly-killed female bird that Estes found on the transmountain road at 3500 ft. (Tennessee side) November 27, 1951. A few Ruddy Ducks are permanent winter residents on Laurel Lake in Tuckaleechee Cove, where arrival and departure records range from October 14 (1953) to April 30 (1953), respectively.

HOODED MERGANSER—*Lophodytes cucullatus*

This handsome duck is an uncommon winter visitor in the area. From November 6 (1951) through April 14 (1940), 1 to 10 birds have been observed, especially along Little River where 18 of the total of 23 records were located (1936–60). For the 6 months, November through April, the numbers of park records total 6, 7, 3, 1, 3, and 3, respectively. The highest altitude is represented by a female Hooded Merganser that Price picked up during a snowstorm along the transmountain road at 3600 ft. (Tennessee side) on the night of January 15, 1951.

Manley observed a flock of 10 of these ducks on Murphy's Pond in Elkmont November 27, 1940. The remaining 22 park records represent flocks numbering 8 or less birds.

COMMON MERGANSER—*Mergus merganser*

Within the park, this merganser is a rare winter visitant. Manley observed a flock of 8 on the park boundary at the mouth of Abrams Creek February 23, 1940; on December 6, 1940, he reported 1 of these ducks on Little River. Condon, on November 1, 1961, observed a female at close range on the West Prong of the Little Pigeon River, at the 3800 ft. altitude; the stream was at flood stage and the bird appeared incapable of flight. On Laurel Lake I saw a female Common Merganser January 13 and 15, 1942.

RED-BREASTED MERGANSER—*Mergus serrator*

The only record of this rare transient from within the area was established May 17, 1931, when Brockway Crouch discovered the back and feet of a Red-breasted Merganser and two left feet of American Bitterns at a Peregrine Falcons' eyrie near Alum Cave Bluffs [Ganier, 1940]. H. C. Oberholser, to whom these remains were sent, identified them. Manley observed 1 of these mergansers, November 16, 1940, on the West Prong of the Little Pigeon River approximately 2 miles north of Gatlinburg. On December 4, 1942, a wounded female discovered in Gatlinburg was brought to me for identification. Burns has 1 record of this duck from Laurel Lake where, on April 24, 1950, he viewed it at close range.

FAMILY | *CATHARTIDAE*

TURKEY VULTURE—*Cathartes aura*

Throughout the lower altitudes of the park, these large birds are uncommon permanent residents; at high altitudes (above 3500 ft.) Turkey Vultures are uncommon from March through October and rare from November through February. Beginning in March there is a sharp rise in the number of times these birds have been observed, then a gradual tapering off takes place as the spring progresses. There are fewer records for July and August than at any time except the winter season. In September there is evidence of an increase in their numbers that becomes accelerated in October when more of these vultures have been observed than during any other month.

In pre-park days when large numbers of cattle and other livestock grazed on the high-mountain meadows and elsewhere, Turkey Vultures were, in all probability, much more plentiful. At present the scarcity of food available to a large bird of rather specialized feeding habits makes this heavily-forested region unattractive to these carrion-eaters. Animals that are killed in the park by automobiles are mostly of small size and their remains are usually disposed of by crows, ravens, foxes, and other wild life. In Cades Cove, where park regulations permit the grazing of herds of cattle in order to approximate the appearance of that valley as it must have been only a few generations ago, Turkey Vultures are fairly common.

At the higher altitudes, solitary birds are the rule—55 of the 63 records we have for this vulture at elevations above 3500 ft. (1937–53) represent single birds. The largest number of Turkey Vultures observed at one time was on October 19, 1943, when I watched 2 flocks, totaling 85 birds, milling in the air over Brushy Mountain. Flocks of 10 or more vultures are rarely observed; of a total of 328 park records in the 17-year period ending in 1953, there were only 5 flocks with 10 or more individuals.

On June 3, 1925, Ganier [1962] "found a nest containing a young bird nearly as large as its parents" on the steep western face of Greenbrier Pinnacle at the Cat Stairs cliffs. During the Meigs Creek fire, "about 1932," Warden Wesley Ogle found a single egg of this species in a large hollow stump in that part of the park. Mr. Ogle believed that these birds nested regularly in the "Buzzard Rocks" area near Look Rock on Chilhowee Mountain. Having observed Turkey Vultures soaring about the cliffs above the Little Tennessee River, between Calderwood and Chilhowee Dams, on a number of occasions, I suspect that they breed there.

During the 20-year period 1937–56 when the Christmas

Bird Count was taken within a 15 mile diameter area centered on Bull Head (Mt. LeConte), an average of 26 observers recorded the Turkey Vulture on 14 of those years; total number of these vultures listed was 142. In comparison, Black Vultures, observed on but 4 of the 20 years, total 20 birds.

BLACK VULTURE—*Coragyps atratus*

Black Vultures are of rather rare occurrence in Great Smoky Mountains National Park, the ratio of the numbers of these birds as compared to Turkey Vultures being approximately 1 to 11. Winter records are rare—1 in January, 1 in February, and none in December. Absence of any records for the months of April, August, and September reveals the irregularity of the appearances of this species, as does the disclosure that Black Vultures have been observed on but 9 of the 28 years, 1934–61. Of the 16 records we have during that interval, 9 represent single birds.

Only on 3 occasions have I observed more than 4 birds in a flock: March 3, 1938 (12 birds—Cades Cove); October 5, 1938 (10 birds—Rich Mountain); and October 15, 1940 (9 birds—Double Springs Gap).

There is no information pertaining to nesting in the park. There are 3 records for lone birds in May and observations of 2 and 4 birds, respectively, on June 21, 1945 (Gatlinburg) and June 17, 1952 (Tremont).

FAMILY | *ACCIPITRIDAE*

SHARP-SHINNED HAWK—*Accipiter striatus*

There are records in the park for this little hawk every month of the year. For the 28-year period ending in 1961, during which time it was recorded 146 times, almost half these observations were made during the autumn migrations (September–October). Fewest records are for the months of February (3), June (4), and July (4).

Two-thirds of all the higher-elevation records for this uncommon bird are for the September–October period. In these upper regions of the mountains the Sharp-shinned Hawk is rare or absent from November through March and very scarce from April through July.

Of the 146 times this hawk was recorded, 138 represent single birds; once I observed 3 individuals in the air over Mt. LeConte (August 23, 1939), and on 7 occasions 2 birds were observed. The Christmas Bird Count parties listed the Sharp-shinned Hawk on 11 of the 27 years beginning in 1935; altogether 13 of these birds were listed.

In all probability, a few of these small hawks breed here every year. Tanner informed me that on June 2, 1954, while standing on Rocky Spur (Mt. LeConte), at 5000 ft., he watched a Sharp-shinned Hawk carrying food; he believed it was feeding young.

COOPER'S HAWK—*Accipiter cooperii*

Over a period of 29 years (1932–60), available records serve to indicate that the ratio of Sharp-shinned to Cooper's Hawks is approximately 3 to 2. Altogether 106 Cooper's Hawks have been listed on 99 occasions; all but 7 of these have been single birds, there being an observation of 2 of these hawks on 7 days.

Approximately one-third (32) of the 99 records have come during the September–October period when the fall migration is at its height. April, with 11 records, involves the spring migration.

In the higher altitudes, 26 of a total of 40 birds were observed during the August–September period. Throughout the spruce-fir forests where winter birds are scarce, the Cooper's Hawk is rare or absent from November through February.

Although no nests have been discovered, the fact that this uncommon wary hawk occurs here throughout the year would signify that it breeds within the park.

RED-TAILED HAWK—*Buteo jamaicensis*

As far back as 1885, no less an authority than the eminent ornithologist William Brewster [1886] was impressed by the scarcity of all species of hawks in these Southern Appalachian Mountains. Following his visit to a number of western North

Carolina counties, he noted that "The general scarcity—one may almost say absence—of hawks in this region during the breeding season is simply unaccountable. Small birds and mammals, lizards, snakes and other animals upon which the various species subsist are everywhere numerous, the country is wild and heavily-forested and, in short, all the necessary conditions of environment seem to be fulfilled." This condition still prevails, so that when it is stated that the Red-tailed Hawk, based on the number of records, is the most common of the resident species of hawks in Great Smoky Mountains National Park, it does not imply that this is a common bird.

For the 20-year period beginning in 1934, the total number of park records for this large hawk range from a low of 26 for the month of January to 58 for the month of October. April, May, and June, the nesting period, reveal 20-year totals of 39, 28, and 48 records, respectively. Christmas Bird Count parties, during 1937–61, listed Red-tailed Hawks on 23 of the 25 years; the total number of these hawks observed at that time was 65.

Red-tailed Hawks occur at all altitudes in the park, occasionally soaring over some of the highest mountains in the area. Most of our records are of single birds; the largest number observed together was 5 birds, in Cades Cove, on December 8, 1948 (Stupka).

There are a number of reports in our files of the harassment of this large hawk by such birds as Crows and Sharpshinned Hawks. On April 16, 1945, I noted a Red-tailed Hawk pursuing an Osprey.

In October, in the spectacular Charlies Bunion area, I witnessed Red-tailed Hawks capturing the large bird-locusts (*Schistocerca americana*) that are plentiful there in the autumn. These big strong-flying grasshoppers, their wings glistening in the sunlight, fly high over the relatively barren ridges that characterize this part of the park; there the Redtails, perhaps under the influence of Indian Summer weather, appear to pursue them as much for sport as for food.

RED-SHOULDERED HAWK—*Buteo lineatus*

The absence of forested swamps may be the main reason why the Red-shouldered Hawk is a decidedly uncommon bird

—by far the rarest of the three Buteos in this area. In the 28-year period 1934–61, there have been but 18 records for this species, totaling 22 birds. Eight of these records, all at the lower altitudes (below 2000 ft.), are for the 3 winter months beginning with December, and on this basis this hawk might be regarded as an uncommon winter visitor.

Mrs. Eifert's report of a Red-shouldered Hawk in Cades Cove on April 23, 1952, along with my observation of one on Mt. LeConte (May 11, 1942) and of a trio soaring over the mouth of Abrams Creek on May 19, 1944, are designated as irregulars or strays since the prospects of breeding here appear to be somewhat remote. There are 5 late-summer records which may represent casual post-breeding visitants. On July 28, 1941, John L. George observed 2 birds over Mt. Buckley, near Clingmans Dome. Single birds were reported by Wilson on August 22, 1945, between Newfound Gap and Charlies Bunion, and during the last week in August, 1947, at Elkmont. McCamey [1936] and Foster listed 1 on the Meigs Post Prong Trail September 4, 1936, and I examined a Red-shouldered Hawk that had just been shot on the Cherokee Indian Reservation, near the park boundary, September 3, 1943. Single birds that I observed October 11, 1944 (Thunderhead), and October 22, 1940 (Charlies Bunion) may be classed as early autumn migrants.

Christmas Bird Count parties listed a total of 5 Red-shouldered Hawks in the park and vicinity during 1957–60. Three of these birds were observed over Tuckaleechee Cove, bordering the park's northwestern boundary. A freshly-killed specimen was discovered by Johnson and party on December 29, 1946, in Greenbrier.

From near the park there is a record of a Red-shouldered Hawk shot October 26, 1934, near Walland, Tennessee. Another was shot December 5, 1939, in Pigeon Forge.

BROAD-WINGED HAWK—*Buteo platypterus*

From April, when the Broad-wings arrive, through August, the numbers of this hawk in the park are approximately the same as the numbers of Red-tails. For the 20-year period beginning in 1934, the migrant Broad-wings observed here during that five-month period totaled 223; the permanent-resident Red-tails, 249. In September, however, the passage of migrating Broad-wings over the park results in a striking change, their numbers exceeding those of their larger cousins by 10 to 1 (451 to 45) during that month.

The Broad-winged and the Red-tailed are the two most common breeding hawks in the park, the former being a summer resident while the latter resides here throughout the year. Both range throughout all altitudes in our area. Fleetwood's observation of a Broad-winged Hawk on Rich Mountain March 27, 1935, represents our earliest spring record. Most of these hawks arrive during the first half of April, there being 15 occasions during the 21-year period beginning with 1936 when the first arrivals put in their appearance between April 2 and 14.

Flocks of migrating Broad-wings fly over the Great Smoky Mountains every autumn, but no extraordinary concentrations have been noted here. The following have been recorded:

September 24, 1953—Lix and I observed 52 birds in 1 hour passing over Indian Gap; there were up to 10 birds in a flock.

September 25, 1952—Manley observed 112 birds in the Gatlinburg area.

September 26, 1950—Burns and Pfitzer saw 2 flocks over Indian Gap, one numbering 35 and the other 23 birds.*

September 26, 1952—Manley had a flock of 54 birds in view in Gatlinburg.

September 29, 1953—Behrend [letter] reported a total of 84 birds along the 4 miles of the Appalachian Trail between Newfound Gap and Charlies Bunion; the largest group was comprised of 14 birds.

September 30, 1953—Behrend [letter] listed a total of 63 birds along the state-line ridge between Newfound Gap and Clingmans Dome; the largest flock consisted of 8.

October 3, 1934—Fleetwood observed 17 birds in a flock over Welch Ridge.

* Tanner [1950b] makes reference to this same observation but gives the date as September 16, which is a printer's error.

Of 9 October records, 7 represent single birds. Our latest report is my observation of 1 bird over Gatlinburg on October 23, 1944.

GOLDEN EAGLE—*Aquila chrysaëtos*

The Golden Eagle, now rare or absent throughout much of the eastern United States, is an infrequent and irregular visitor to the park and vicinity. Between 1924 and 1961 there are 12 records of this bird in our area, as follows:

1924—On June 1, Mayfield and Ganier observed 2 birds over Mt. LeConte; on June 3, Ganier [1926] reported 2 birds at 4500 ft. near the summit of Greenbrier Pinnacle.

1934—On November 3, one bird was shot along Cataloochee Creek, just outside the park boundary above Walters Dam. The specimen was mounted and, at a later date, acquired for the park.

1936—Along the main crest of the Smokies, near Inadu Knob, I observed one of these birds August 14.

1937—Keating reported an immature Golden Eagle that flew low over Andrews Bald while he was on that high-mountain meadow on June 13.

1938—On June 16, as members of the Tennessee Ornithological Society were hiking on Spence Field Bald, elevation 4886 ft., "they had the pleasure of flushing two Golden Eagles from the ground, the spot being marked by the bones and fur of a fox. The eagles arose, when surprised at close range, and majestically soared away. We were told later, by Miss Agnes Milger of Cleveland, who with her father had been on this 'bald' on June 12, that on that day they had found the torn body of a fox lying on the ground and that a large bird was seen circling overhead—doubtless the same scene that our party was to come upon four days later." [Ganier and Clebsch, 1938.]

On December 18, near the junction of the Boulevard Trail with the state-line ridge (6000 ft.), Ogden and a party participating in the Christmas Bird Count noted a Golden Eagle.

1943—I observed an immature bird on September 28 as it soared over Brushy Mountain (4911 ft.).

1944—On September 21, while in the main parking area at the eastern end of Cades Cove, I observed an immature Golden Eagle soaring overhead.

1948—Tanner [1948] reported one adult bird on the wing over Newfound Gap on July 18.

1950—On June 14, members of the Greeneville Chapter, Tennessee Ornithological Society, observed a Golden Eagle "immediately below Newfound Gap" [Nevius, 1950].

1961—Reid observed one of these birds soaring over the Sugarlands Visitor Center (Headquarters area) September 12.

Between December 1933 and July 1939 a total of 9 Golden and 2 Bald Eagles, captured mostly in middle Tennessee, were shipped to Great Smoky Mountains National Park by the Tennessee Department of Game and Fish. These birds had either been confiscated by the Department or had been delivered there by persons interested in the welfare of these eagles. Arrangements had been made with park officials who agreed to receive the birds, acclimatize them for a time in an aviary, and then release them in the hope that they might have a new lease on life. Most of these eagles arrived at the park in poor physical condition; 2 (1 Golden and 1 Bald) died from wounds they had received when captured. Eight Golden Eagles and 1 immature Bald Eagle were released by August 1939, at which time it was decided to abandon the plan. One of these Golden Eagles, banded and released here on February 26, 1936, was killed at Head Waters, Highland County, Virginia, on March 10, 1938 [Laskey, 1938].

Normally, neither the Golden nor the Bald Eagle breeds in the type of environment which prevails in the park, even though some of the early writers published comments to the contrary. The guide who directed Charles Lanman [1849] to Alum Cave Bluffs in 1848 stated that the first time he came to this place he decided to climb a steep face at the north end of the formation, "opposite to an eagles nest, where the creatures were screaming at a fearful rate." In spite of the considerable difference between the size of an eagle and of a Peregrine Falcon, the writer is of the opinion that the latter, and not the former, bird was encountered there. Lemoyne [1886] purloined the journal of a friend in which there is an account of the killing of a pair of Golden Eagles at their eyrie in Blount County and the collecting of 2 eggs. This report is referred to by Rhoads [1895] and Ganier [1926], but the latter, in his correspondence with me (1943), had serious doubts regarding Lemoyne's narrative. Cairns [1902] and Brimley [1940] state that these birds breed on the cliffs of the higher mountains in western North Carolina, but they give no particulars and it is assumed that the information is second-hand.

BALD EAGLE—*Haliaeetus leucocephalus*

From July 1934 to January 1961 there are 14 records for this bird from the park or adjacent areas, as follows:

July 25, 1934—Adult; Big Cove, Cherokee Indian Reservation (Fleetwood).

June 26, 1938—Adult; Camp No. 2 Bridge, Little River (Walker).

October 6, 1944—Immature; Newfound Gap (Koch).

June 12, 1945—Immature; Smokemont [Hawkins, 1946].

August 30, 1947—Adult; Andrews Bald (Stupka).

September 17, 1947—Adult; Andrews Bald (McCamey).

October 1, 1947—Immature; Collins Gap (Stimson and McCamey).

October 11, 1950—One immature and 1 adult; Appalachian Trail near Laurel Top (Dr. and Mrs. Baldwin).

December 31, 1950—Adult; Park Headquarters (Stupka).

April 27, 1952—Adult; Gatlinburg (Saunders).

January 3, 1954—Adult; Greenbrier (Tanner and party).

January 19, 1955—Adult; Gatlinburg (Manley).

March 19, 1956—Adult; Gatlinburg (Manley). Both this and the preceding observation were made during a snowfall.

January 1, 1961—Adult; Little River, at Metcalf Bottoms (Mrs. Monroe and party).

Over the 28-year period, there has been an average of 1 record every 2 years. Like the Golden Eagle, the visits of the Bald Eagle are infrequent and irregular. The presence of extensive water impoundments along, or near, the park boundary does not appear to have influenced the status of this very uncommon species within this area.

MARSH HAWK—*Circus cyaneus*

The Marsh Hawk, an uncommon spring and fall migrant, may spend a portion of some winters in Cades Cove and in the coves and relatively flat farmlands to the north. Approximately half (16) of the 33 records of this bird in the park are in October (9) and April (7). Earliest record is the bird I saw August 14, 1938, near Clingmans Dome, at an altitude of 6000 ft.; latest is Tanner's report of this species over Andrews Bald (5800 ft.) on May 4, 1957. Between those extreme dates are 17 records for Cades Cove ranging between October 23 (1934) and April 25 (1944), 10 records at high altitudes (5000–6600 ft.), and 4 at the 2000–2400 ft. altitude. All the winter observations were made in Cades Cove.

A female Marsh Hawk, with a snake in its talons, was observed over the state-line ridge, near Charlies Bunion, by M. Brooks and party on April 12, 1952.

This hawk has been observed near the park at Walland, Tennessee (December 19, 1943), and there are 10 records for the Pigeon Forge area, September 14 (1953) —April 17 (1940).

FAMILY | *PANDIONIDAE*

OSPREY—*Pandion haliaetus*

The Osprey, an uncommon spring and fall migrant, has been reported 75 times in the 20 years beginning with 1934. It has been observed most often in April (34 times) and September (16 times), those 2 months accounting for two-thirds of all the records. There have also been 9 records in May, 7 in October, 4 in August, 2 each in March and June, and 1 in July (July 4, 1942, in Greenbrier).

Earliest spring record was on March 23, 1937, along Little River (Gordon); Manley reported 1 in the Cosby area March 31, 1941. Latest spring record was my observation of 1 bird at Fontana Dam on May 28, 1949. The above-mentioned record in July and two more in June (June 18, 1940, and June 20, 1942—both along Little River) may represent wanderers from the large reservoirs to the north of the park where the species is known to breed. The fall migration begins in August, our earliest record coming on the 13th (1934) when Fleetwood observed 1 along the Oconaluftee River, at Ravensford. Latest of the fall records came on October 25 (1940, Little River—Manley; 1941, mouth of Abrams Creek —Stupka).

With but one exception, all our records for the Osprey are at elevations below 2500 ft. On April 29, 1950, Burns observed 1 of these hawks flying over the parking area near Clingmans Dome, at an elevation of approximately 6400 ft.

FAMILY | *FALCONIDAE*

PEREGRINE FALCON—*Falco peregrinus*

As long as the spectacular eyrie near Alum Cave Bluffs was being used as a nesting site by these handsome hawks, the Peregrine Falcon was regarded as a permanent resident in Great Smoky Mountains National Park. Ganier [1931] discovered the site on May 31, 1925,* and returned to it accompanied by Crouch on April 7, 1929, at which time he collected the 3 well-incubated eggs. On May 17, 1931, when Crouch returned to the site, he found that the young birds

---

* In 1848, in one of his "Letters from the Alleghany Mountains," Charles Lanman [1849] describes his visit to Alum Cave, "a very narrow and ragged ridge, which is without a particle of vegetation . . . holes leading like windows entirely through it." His guide informed him that the first time he came to this place, with two Indians, he decided to climb a steep face at the north end of the formation "opposite to an eagles nest, where the creatures were screaming at a fearful rate." In view of what is known about eagles supposedly breeding in these mountains, I am inclined to believe that this eyrie was already being used not by eagles but by nesting Peregrine Falcons at the time of Lanman's visit.

were almost ready to take wing; of the 3 that comprised the brood, he captured 1 which he brought to his home in Knoxville [Ganier, 1940]. By the following year the area was well on its way to becoming part of a full-fledged National Park, the nucleus of a ranger force had been realized, and protection was given to all its animal and plant life.

In view of the frequency of the observations of these falcons at this place in subsequent years, it is believed they continued to use the Peregrine Ridge site through 1942. On June 9, 1941, while on the trail near Alum Cave Bluffs, I watched an adult peregrine attending 2 noisy immature birds that were walking along the crest of Peregrine Ridge fanning the air with their wings. On April 30, 1942, I could hear young birds crying for food at this same site. In April 1943, Koch discovered that the falcons had deserted the Peregrine Ridge site for one just above the Alum Cave Bluffs overhang; on April 27 of that year he pointed out an adult to me that appeared to be incubating eggs, but the location was such that we could not be certain of its nesting. In his examination of the Peregrine Ridge eyrie in 1944, Spofford [letter] could determine no recent nesting evidence, and although these hawks have been observed there and in the vicinity many times since, actual nesting evidence is lacking.

Ijams [1933] and a group of Tennessee Ornithological Society members reported hearing young Peregrine Falcons on the cliff below the Jump Off, on Mt. Kephart, in June 1932. A year later this same party again reported these hawks from that area. In June 1934, King and Fleetwood reported that their observations pointed to the nesting of these falcons in the vicinity of Charlies Bunion; and Keating, as a result of his visit to that location in June 1937, came to the same conclusion. Peregrines have been observed in the Great Smoky Mountains every month of the year, although records in January (1), February (2), and November (3) are scarce due, perhaps, to scarcity of qualified observers at those times of year.* If the progressive increase in the reported number of these falcons from March through June (7, 9, 15, 31) is

---

* The month of December would also show a paucity of records if it were not for the annual Christmas Bird Count parties in the field at that time.

to be correlated with the normal increase in park visitors, the drop to but 7 reports in July (a month of greater visitation than June) cannot be accounted for unless we assume that a period of molt takes place at that time. However, Bent [1938] states that "Signs of molting may be found during almost any month." The sharp increase in numbers of recorded observations during August (20), September (28), and October (27) reveals no post-breeding exodus by these birds.

These hawks are birds of the high altitudes, my only exceptions being one at Park Headquarters in September 1939, and another in Emerts Cove in October 1939. By far the bulk of our records come from the Canadian zone areas of the park (Clingmans Dome and eastward to Mt. Guyot) ; in fact, other records are quite scarce. Based on 159 observations of peregrines during a 20-year period beginning in 1934, by far the greatest number have been concentrated in the Alum Cave-Mt. LeConte area, site of the aforementioned eyrie; next would be the Charlies Bunion–Mt. Kephart area; then Clingmans Dome and vicinity.

Ganier [1931], when he visited the eyrie near Alum Cave Bluffs on April 7, 1929, reported that the first egg had evidently been laid about March 20. Dixon [1933], who had been guided to the site by Crouch, found 3 recently-hatched young and 1 chipped egg there on April 10 (1932) ; since the incubation period has been determined as 33 to 35 days [Bent, 1938], this would indicate that egg-laying was completed March 6–8.

Numerous feathers of robins, thrushes, jays, and juncos were found by Ganier [1931] at the Alum Cave nesting site on April 7, 1929. There also he found the vertebrae of a small snake. On May 17, 1931, Crouch found 3 young birds about ready to fly and "the remains of some quarries that were of unusual interest. These consisted of a back and attached feet of a Red-breasted Merganser and 2 left feet of American Bitterns, all of which were identified by the U. S. Biological Survey" [Ganier, 1940].* Dixon [1933] was interested in the food remains he found at this same site which he visited

* The receipt and identification of these items was verified in correspondence that I had with H. C. Oberholser (1940) .

April 10, 1932: "Dozens of wings and legs of bluejays were found strewn about the nest . . . a few flicker feathers were also found."

Within Great Smoky Mountains National Park are a number of sites where Peregrine Falcons might breed, and it is hoped that here, where full protection is given all wild life, one or more pairs of these splendid birds will continue to reside.

PIGEON HAWK—*Falco columbarius*

There is but one record of this little falcon in the park. On September 23, 1940, at the Clingmans Dome Parking Area (6311 ft.), Amadon [letter] observed two Pigeon Hawks as they were "chasing each other with great speed through the tree tops . . . in what appeared like a game of tag. One of them perched for some minutes in a dead tree remarkably close to the crowded parking area. . . ." Amadon had these birds in view for about twenty minutes.

Although Sprunt [1933b] regards it as occurring regularly in parts of western North Carolina in late summer, this small hawk is mostly an uncommon to rare transient in the Southern Appalachian region. Spring records in particular are scarce. The only Knox County, Tennessee, record was on May 13, 1957 [Howell and Monroe, 1958].

SPARROW HAWK—*Falco sparverius*

The Sparrow Hawk, along with the Bobwhite, was probably much more common throughout the lower altitudes in pre-park days than it is today. Being a bird of the open country, this pretty little falcon is much more prevalent in the cultivated coves to the north of the park than on the forested mountainsides within our area. In all probability it breeds in Cades Cove and in Cataloochee where it may be regarded as a permanent resident, but over most of the remainder of the park its occurrence is rather irregular. Our records of this species cover every month of the year, but during the breeding season (April and May) most of these small hawks leave our area.

A review of observations of Sparrow Hawks for the 20-year period beginning with 1934 reveals a peak of 30 records in

October followed by 25 in February, the former representing fall migration while the latter may, perhaps, be attributed to the appreciable increase in the winter population as noted by Burleigh in Georgia [1958] and Sprunt and Chamberlain in South Carolina [1949]. Although there are more records of these hawks during the summer months than during the breeding season, it remains an uncommon bird throughout June, July, and August. For the six months' period beginning in October, we have over three and one-half times more records of Sparrow Hawks than for the remaining six months.

There are no high-altitude records of this falcon in the park during the spring months, nor during November, but at other times of year it has been observed along the main crest of the Smokies and in a few other places at or above 5000 ft. as follows: Newfound Gap—December 20, 1942 (Goddard), and January 2, 1955 (Stupka); Collins Gap—January 5, 1948 (McCamey); Rocky Spur—June 2, 1954 (Tanner); Ledge Bald—June 19, 1935, and July 23, 1934 (Fleetwood); Thunderhead—August 20, 1936 (Stupka); Andrews Bald—August 31, 1961 (T. Savage); Mt. Kephart—September 1, 1941 (George and Quay); Charlies Bunion—September 4 and 18, 1941 (Quay); and Pecks Corner—September 8, 1961 (T. Savage).

Fleetwood observed a pair of these hawks mating on March 15, 1935, along the Blanket Mountain Trail, and on March 26, 1935, near Deals Gap on the park boundary.

In the great majority of cases our records of this species represent single birds. On August 20, 1936, I observed 3 Sparrow Hawks maneuvering over the main divide near Thunderhead.

FAMILY | *TETRAONIDAE*

RUFFED GROUSE—*Bonasa umbellus*

The Ruffed Grouse, usually referred to as "pheasant" by the local people, is a fairly common permanent resident here where it occurs at all altitudes and in all types of forests. Although a bird of the woodlands, it "does not attain its greatest numbers in unbroken forest," as pointed out by Traut-man [1940], and since heavily-forested mountainsides prevail over most of the park, the prospects for any improvement in its status here are unfavorable. While it is protected from man, such protection is also accorded all its natural enemies within the park, the latter preying at will upon grown birds as well as upon the eggs and young. In addition to the diseases and parasites to which grouse are subject, weather conditions remain, and in a region such as this where there is considerable rainfall, this can be critical for the downy chicks.

In the following tabulation, the relative scarcity of records of Ruffed Grouse during July and August is of interest and may be caused, in part, by the infrequency of drumming by the cocks and, to some extent, perhaps, by inactivity correlated with the molting period. The annual Christmas Bird Count is a factor in the relatively high number of December records. The total number of records for October has, of course, been influenced by the high incidence of drumming during that month. If, as Bent [1932] has stated, drumming is a "challenge to other males to keep out of the drummer's territory," why should the number of October drumming records be almost double the number for April? Are the young cocks practicing this performance during October? Ordinarily, as stated by Forbush [1929], drumming "is less common in autumn than in spring."

TOTAL NUMBER OF RECORDS, NUMBER OF DAYS WHEN
DRUMMING WAS HEARD, AND NUMBER OF BROODS OF
RUFFED GROUSE OBSERVED FOR THE
20-YEAR PERIOD, 1934–53.

Month	Total Number of Records	Number of Days Drumming Was Heard	Number of Broods Observed
January	58	1	
February	56	7	
March	74	16	
April	107	22	
May	77	14	31
June	101	5	56
July	36	3	8
August	26	4	1
September	49	18	
October	108	42	
November	47	14	
December	92	2	

The courtship performance involving strutting and spreading of tail has been observed on a number of days in April, the earliest of which is April 4 (1946); it was also witnessed May 11 (1948, Fawver), and October 17 (1941).

Ruffed Grouse may nest at any altitude in the park. Ganier [1926] reports a nest at 6500 ft. on Mt. LeConte. Our earliest egg-laying date is April 12 (1948) near Smokemont, when Hadley flushed a hen from a nest containing a single egg. Since, ordinarily, one egg is laid each day [Bent, 1932], my discovery of a nest with 10 eggs on April 20, 1949, along upper Little River (2500 ft.) is comparable. On April 28, 1957, R. Maher came upon a hen sitting on 8 eggs on the slope of Wooly Tops, at 3500–4000 ft. Near Indian Gap (5266 ft.), May 1, 1948, Tanner came upon a nest with 11 eggs; this, along with another similar-size clutch which Rolen discovered on Deep Creek (2000 ft.) on May 5, 1950, represent the largest sets. Our latest egg record is June 5, 1947, at Cherokee Orchard (2600 ft.) when Hester flushed a hen from a nest containing 3 eggs. Ganier [1926] discovered a nest with 7 fresh eggs on Silers Bald (5620 ft.) June 1, 1924.

Over a period of 27 years, beginning in 1934, there are records of 96 broods of young grouse. The earliest of these was my observation of very small chicks on May 10, 1948, along Collins Creek (3100 ft.). However, on May 14, 1948, Grossman reported seeing chicks along Roaring Fork that were already able to make short flights, indicating that the first eggs had probably been laid by late March or early April —abnormally warm weather prevailed beginning in middle March that year. Total number of records of chicks, usually accompanied by the hen, are as follows: May 10–14 (5), May 16–29 (26), June 1–15 (36), June 18–30 (20), July 2–9 (8). The latest record is for half-grown birds on July 9, 1953, at 6000 ft., near the Clingmans Dome Parking Area. Fleetwood, who spent a full year in the park (June 1934–June 1935) during which time he was in the field most of the days observing wild life, came upon 20 groups of Ruffed Grouse chicks.

There are but few recorded observations of groups of adult-sized birds. King reported a flock of 12 to 14 Ruffed Grouse along Little River, near Elkmont, January 23, 1935. Near Elkmont, on March 1, 1944, I came upon a group of 5.

On July 25, 1954, approximately a mile south of Gatlinburg, Gilbert observed a group of 8; these may have been young of the year. At dawn, during the second week of August, 1960, Shields watched 15 grown birds feeding on corn (bait) within a large wire trap set for feral hogs near the summit of Gregory Bald.

Fleetwood observed Ruffed Grouse feeding on huckleberries in August and September and on the buds of the sweet birch in November. Pardue reported these birds feeding on seeds of yellow-poplar in January.

There are a number of instances of dead birds having been found along park roads. On September 8, 1947, near the Alum Cave Parking Area, the windshield of a car was splintered when a grouse flew into it. One dead bird that I examined after it struck a car April 19 (1948) in the Sugarlands had well-developed fringes on its toes. On January 28, 1946, Owenby found a Ruffed Grouse that had perished after becoming entangled in a growth of smilax.

Aldrich and Goodrum [1946] found one pair of these birds in the 23-acre virgin hardwood forest area they censused June 23–28, 1946, in Porters Flat. During 20 consecutive Christmas Bird Counts (1937–56) the average number of Ruffed Grouse per count is almost 9, the figures ranging from 1 to 25 birds. There have been times when observers regarded these birds as scarce and, at other times, as very common, but no study of cyclic fluctuations (if any) has been made.

FAMILY | *PHASIANIDAE*

BOBWHITE—*Colinus virginianus*

The Bobwhite, an uncommon permanent resident in the park, is more plentiful in clearings and somewhat open areas than in the prevailing heavy forests. Over the park as a whole, with most of the regions that had been cleared by lumbering and farming operations reverting to forest, this bird is becoming less common as the years go by. Not only is the habitat becoming less suited to it but the many natural enemies of the Bobwhite now enjoy year around protection from hunting and trapping. Furthermore, dogs and cats find their way into the park and, in recent years, the appearance of feral hogs has presented an additional hazard to all ground-nesting birds. In places like Cades Cove where agricultural practices serve to maintain the open meadowlands, the Bobwhite may continue to persist in fair numbers.

Based on a total of 416 records for this bird for the 20-year period beginning with 1934, the ratio of low- to high-altitude observations is approximately 9 to 1, respectively. Bob-whites may occur in the high mountains (above 3500 ft.) in late May and through June and July when they frequent the grass balds and other forest openings, but from September through the following April this bird is scarce or absent in those places. Winter conditions, which determine the north-ward range of this species [Todd, 1940], likewise appear to limit its occupancy of the high-altitude retreats in the Southern Appalachian Region. This results in a limited or localized type of vertical "migration" performed by some of the population. Bent [1932] remarks that "In some sections they are said to make seasonal migrations from one type of country to another." Ordinarily, Bobwhites are non-migratory.

On May 19, 1949, four "quail" appeared near the lodge close to the summit of Mt. LeConte where they remained until early July of that year; it was the first time in many years these birds had been observed there (J. Huff).

On the Christmas Bird Counts for the 27-year period beginning with 1935, field parties listed a total of 265 Bob-whites; these were observed on 18 of the 27 years, the totals ranging up to 55 birds (4 coveys) per count.

From the high altitudes (3500–6500 ft.) there are, altogether, 6 records of Bobwhites in May (1 to 4 birds); 20, in June (1 to 6 birds); 10, in July (1 or 2 birds); 3, in August (1 to 5 birds); and 1 each in September, January, and February. Only on two occasions were coveys of more than 6 Bobwhites observed in these higher reaches—on Welch Bald, January 25, 1944, 20 birds (W. Savage) and on Gregory Bald, September 3, 1936, 12 birds (McCamey).

The largest covey, consisting of 25 birds, was reported by

King on September 24, 1934, from near Roundbottom (2860 ft.).

There are but three records of nests and eggs, as follows:

June 15, 1939—Park Headquarters area (1460 ft.), nest with 14 eggs (Stupka).

June 20, 1950—Cherokee Orchard (2600 ft.), nest with 18 eggs (M. M. Whittle).

September 2, 1936—Sugarlands (1700 ft.), nest with 11 eggs (Stupka).

Records of chicks are as follows:

July 20, 1934—Caldwell Fork, Cataloochee (3100 ft.), brood of 14 newly-hatched young still in the nest (Fleetwood).

July 28, 1951—Park boundary just south of Gatlinburg, brood of 7 young approximately a day or two old (Stupka).

July 29, 1951—Buckhorn Creek, Emerts Cove, less than one-half mile north of park line (1700 ft.), a hen with chicks that were 6–8 weeks old (Stupka).

August 24–25, 1951—Andrews Bald (5800 ft.), a hen with 4 half-grown chicks reported by Burns on August 24; on the following day I observed 2 adult birds with 3 half-grown chicks at the same place.

Beginning in 1936, the Tennessee State Game and Fish Commission began releasing considerable numbers of Bobwhites on lands in Cocke, Sevier, Blount, and Monroe Counties. Of the tens of thousands of these birds, some have undoubtedly made their way into the park, but whether they have interbred with the native quail and left any impression on the local birds is not known.

FAMILY | *MELEAGRIDIDAE*

TURKEY—*Meleagris gallopavo*

This, the largest bird in Great Smoky Mountains National Park, is an uncommon permanent resident occurring at all altitudes in the area. In 1885 Brewster [1886], who made a careful survey of the birds in some counties adjacent to those in which the park is located, regarded the Turkey as "Abundant everywhere, ranging, according to the hunters, over the highest mountains and breeding quite as numerously throughout the black growth [spruce and fir] above 5000 feet as in the hardwood forests below." Three years later, in May 1888, Jeffries and Jeffries [1889] from their base of operations at Dillsboro, in Jackson County, North Carolina, concluded that the bird was "now certainly rare." Cairns [1902], in his report on the birds of Buncombe County, North Carolina, in 1891, predicted that the Turkey "will soon be extinct" as the result of relentless hunting.

The loss of one of its favorite foods, the fruit of the American chestnut, represented an additional hazard for the Turkey. Observers report that the fatal chestnut-blight disease reached its peak in the late 1920's in the Southern Appalachian region. This left the acorn as the most important plant food item, and although oaks are abundant in numbers and in kinds, lean harvests have occurred at unpredictable intervals. The American beech, also important, is not as prevalent and its fruiting is irregular.

The realization of Great Smoky Mountains National Park made a sanctuary of some 800 square miles of mountainous terrain where the remnants of the Turkey population were henceforth accorded protection from all hunting. But protection was likewise given to the natural predators of the Turkey, its eggs, and poults (i. e., skunks, opossums, foxes, bobcats, crows, hawks, owls, snakes, and others). The activities of stray domestic cats and dogs and, in later years, feral hogs are inimical to the Turkey. Perhaps most important are weather conditions, it being well known that heavy losses may be inflicted upon the young by storms; wetting or chilling during the first two weeks in the lives of the chicks is often fatal [Bent, 1932]. Considering also the parasites and diseases which plague the Turkey, it is rather remarkable that this splendid bird has survived.

Fleetwood, who, in June 1935, had completed a full year of bird observations in the park, recorded the Turkey on 27 occasions, the total number of birds being 58. Twenty of the

27 records were from altitudes above 3500 ft. while 7 were below that elevation. The largest number of birds he came upon in one day was 7; the month with the largest number of records of Turkeys was August (9 records totaling 12 birds). Only in February did Fleetwood fail to observe this species.

When King, in 1939, after a stay of five years in the park, estimated the total Turkey population at 150, he regarded that figure as "probably a very low estimate." Parties engaged in taking the Christmas Bird Count for the 27-year period beginning in 1935, observed a total of 50 birds; these were listed on 11 of the 27 years, the maximum number counted in one day being 11 (December 31, 1961).

Although the Turkey occurs throughout the park, it prefers forest clearings, open woodlands and borders of open fields. Cades Cove is the most favored region in spite of the birds' tendency to avoid areas used regularly by man. It has not always been that way, however. Fleetwood, who spent many a day in Cades Cove in 1934–35, observed no Turkeys there, and it is well known that a more or less intensive pursuit of these birds by some of the residents of the Cove, prior to the creation of the park, decimated the flocks and caused the remnants to resort to the higher altitudes. Our records of observations of Turkeys in Cades Cove reveal a gradual increase in numbers during 1939–43, culminating in a total of 61 in the five-year period 1944 to 1948, inclusive. During 1949–53, the number of records dropped to 35, possibly due to a heavy increase in tourist visitation with the opening of a new road into that area. Thereafter, as if inured to the ever-increasing flow of visitors, Turkeys have been on the increase in Cades Cove where their presence adds greatly to the attractiveness of that part of the park.

Based on a total of 327 records of Turkeys for the 20-year period beginning with 1934, the ratio of high to low altitude occurrence is approximately as 1 is to $2\frac{1}{2}$ (91:236). However, a marked decrease in the number of records of Turkeys from the higher altitudes is revealed when the decade beginning in 1934 is contrasted with the one that followed it (beginning in 1944). During the former 10-year period there were 75 records of these birds from along the main crest of the park and some of the tributary ridges (Hughes Ridge,

Thomas Ridge, Andrews Bald) as contrasted to 19 records for the 1944–53 period, a ratio of approximately 4 to 1. Cessation of practically all hunting, beginning in the early 30's, may have been an important factor in these birds' gradually filtering down from the uplands to which they were forced to resort in pre-park years.

Also, as revealed by records obtained during the 20-year period beginning in 1934, the 4-months' period of June–September, inclusive, finds practically the same number at the high elevations (63) as at the low altitudes (62). However, for the 4-months' period prior to that (February–May) the ratio is as 1 is to $6\frac{1}{2}$ while for the 4-months' period which follows (October–January) the ratio is as 1 is to 5, respectively. Even when allowing for the greater number of hikers (observers) in summer as contrasted to winter, one is inclined to conclude that during the warmest one-third of the year (June–September) the higher altitudes appear to be just as attractive to Turkeys as the low elevations, but that at other times these birds are most likely to be encountered below 3500 ft.

Turkeys were relatively uncommon in the Greenbrier area from the time this became a part of the park until the mid-40's. During the 1946–50 interval, however, this species was observed on a number of occasions, including a record of a hen with 15 chicks on June 8, 1949 (E. Ogle). Thereafter, these birds again became scarce, possibly due to the unhampered invasion of old clearings by the forest.

The occurrence of these birds near the summit of Mt. LeConte on May 3, 1943 (1 bird, J. Huff) and September 19, 1944 (4 birds, J. Huff) reveals an occasional tendency to make fairly long journeys. In these instances it involved traveling through dense forests of spruce and fir for a considerable distance.

At high altitudes, flocks of Turkeys are uncommon at all times. In lowland areas the flocks begin forming in September and start breaking up the following April, just prior to the breeding season. The exceptionally cold and wet early spring of 1961 may have delayed the breaking up of a flock of 15 Turkeys that Davis observed in Cades Cove on April 19. Flocks of 12 to 17 birds have been reported from Cades Cove on a number of occasions; on December 9, 1961, Davis and Earnst counted 42 birds there in one flock—the largest group reported. On March 14, 1938, Manley came upon a flock of at least 30 birds feeding in a beech woods near Greenbrier Ridge.

Most of the gobbling is to be heard from late March until some time in May. Fleetwood, however, reported hearing the sound on December 4, 1934, on Newton Bald, at 5100 ft. I have witnessed the cock spread his tail and strut before the hen on March 30, 1946, in Cades Cove, and on May 26, 1949, along Laurel Creek.

Late in the morning of January 18, 1946, Cades Cove residents Clyde Smith, his wife, and Labe Myers came upon an unusual encounter between two gobblers. These birds coiled their necks one around the other, during a kind of conflict that was being watched by six other gobblers. Finally one bird was routed and the winner strutted about with tail spread. Neither Smith nor Myers, who witnessed the scuffle from their car at a distance of approximately 50 yards and who were familiar with the habits of these birds, had ever observed the neck-entwining episode. Unseasonably warm weather may have prompted this unusually early sparring demonstration.

The earliest of 8 recorded nests and eggs was discovered by R. G. Wilson on Fish Camp Prong, at 2900 ft., April 28 (1956); the 12 eggs comprising the clutch would indicate that egg-laying had begun in mid-April, or earlier. Seven additional records of nests and eggs are as follows:

> May 4, 1953—13 eggs, Pinnacle Creek (approx. 2000 ft.); Rogers.
> May 15, 1944—9 eggs, Crib Gap (2100 ft.); L. Myers.
> May 31, 1952—7 eggs, Brier Knob (5200 ft.); E. Miller.
> May 1934—14 eggs, Deep Creek (2400 ft.); Kirkland.
> June 2, 1938—9 eggs, Bote Mt. (4800 ft.); Stupka.
> June 5, 1939—10 eggs, Spence Field Bald (5000 ft.); W. Myers.
> June 15, 1953—9 eggs, Parson Bald (4730 ft.); Oliver.

During the 27-year period 1934–60, there are 25 records of hen Turkeys accompanied by young birds, the latter ranging from newly-hatched chicks to poults that were two-thirds grown. These denote a span of up to two months in the time when the chicks are hatched. Some of these records are as follows:

May 24, 1944—E. Moore came upon a hen leading 9 newly-hatched chicks in the spruce forest near the summit of Mt. Mingus (5800 ft.). Presumably this hen had laid the first egg about mid-April, following a period of over a week of unusually mild weather. This, along with an Andrews Bald (5800 ft.) record of 2 adults with 3 young poults on June 12, 1936 (King and Stupka), represent our highest-altitude breeding sites for the Turkey.

May 29, 1938—Frizzell flushed a hen leading 12 or 13 quail-size chicks on the Appalachian Trail at Sugartree Gap (4435 ft.). This like the preceding represents a very early nesting and may possibly be correlated with the abnormally early spring of 1938.

June 3, 1945—Forrer and Kent encountered a hen with 6 poults, the latter about grouse size, along the Appalachian Trail two miles west of Silers Bald.

July 22, 1946—A brood of 7 or 8 poults, presumed to be approximately 4 days old, were observed along Laurel Creek, near Cades Cove (C. Smith).

July 24, 1941—At Double Spring Gap (5590 ft.) along the state line ridge, Quay and party came upon a hen with about 8 chicks, the latter being 2 to 4 days old. He reported the poults as being wet and appearing quite weak. This and the preceding represent late breeding records.

August 6, 1947—On this date, and again on June 8, 1949, E. Ogle reported a hen and 15 poults in the Greenbrier area; these represent the largest broods of young birds.

October 14, 1946—Another late record is my observation of 9 poults, approximately half-grown, along the Middle Prong of Little River (2500 ft.).

It has been reported that approximately 80 Turkeys of unknown pedigree were liberated on Hazel Creek about 1930; this has not been verified. Releases of game-farm Turkeys have been made near Newport and Tellico Plains, Tennessee, in the 40's [Schultz, 1955] and at Harmon Den, near Davenport Gap, in 1959 and 1961 [letter, T. S. Critcher]. Whether any of these birds ever made their way into the park is unknown.

FAMILY | *RALLIDAE*

KING RAIL—*Rallus elegans*

There are but two records of this large rail. On October 28, 1947, McCamey and I observed a King Rail at the edge of the lawn near the Park Headquarters Building. On August 9, 1959, Superintendent Overly brought in a live rail of this species that had just been captured near the park boundary, in Gatlinburg.

VIRGINIA RAIL—*Rallus limicola*

There were no records for this rail in the park until November 5, 1950, when Pfitzer and I found 3 dead birds near the 4000 ft. elevation along the transmountain road (Tennessee side). A sudden change from unseasonally warm to very cold weather, accompanied by the first snow of the autumn, precipitated a flight of various birds, mostly shore and water inhabitants, that became enveloped in a storm over the Smokies; the 3 Virginia Rails were among these southward-moving migrants [Stupka, 1950].

The only other record for this rail came on October 16, 1952, when a dead bird was picked up in the Sugarlands just outside the park garage building, by S. Henry. My examination of the specimen revealed it had died very recently.

SORA—*Porzana carolina*

This rail is an uncommon and irregular fall migrant through the park. Six of the 7 Soras represent wounded or dead birds. Five came into our area following storms or sudden changes in the weather. The earliest record, September 2, 1955, is represented by a dead bird I picked up at the rear of a garage in the Park Headquarters area where it had crashed against a window. On November 5, 1950, one of the victims of a high-altitude snowstorm was a Sora; this, representing our latest record, was discovered along the transmountain road (Tennessee side) near the 4000 ft. altitude [Stupka, 1950]. In addition there are 5 records of single birds from the Gatlinburg–Park Headquarters–Sugarlands vicinities between September 14 and October 30.

COMMON GALLINULE—*Gallinula chloropus*

There is but one record of this gallinule in the park. On April 28, 1955, Williams [1955] discovered a freshly-killed specimen in the transmountain road (North Carolina side) at an altitude of approximately 4500 ft.

AMERICAN COOT—*Fulica americana*

Although considerable numbers of American Coots winter on Laurel Lake, within two miles of the park boundary, their appearance within the park area is accidental. On November 9, 1935, one of these birds appeared at the Clingmans Dome Parking Area (6311 ft.) which was then under construction. Injured and incapable of flight, the bird was captured and photographed—this being the first record of a coot in the park. Fifteen years later, on November 4–5, 1950, the bodies of 12 coots were picked up and 7 additional birds (including some injured individuals) were observed in the immediate vicinity of the transmountain road (Tennessee side) at 3500–4200 ft. following a sharp change from mild to cold and snowy weather [Stupka, 1950]. Again on November 8, 1956, during a rain and snowstorm that brought an end to a protracted period of warm weather, over two dozen coots were killed when they crashed into buildings, signs, and wet pavements, in Gatlinburg.

A coot was killed when it flew against the window of a house near the park boundary, approximately one mile west of Emerts Cove, on November 4, 1953. The only other record refers to a dead bird picked up November 9, 1961, along the Little River Road, approximately two miles below the Sinks, by Royce.

FAMILY | *CHARADRIIDAE*

KILLDEER—*Charadrius vociferus*

Park records for this bird are rare during August and September (1, each), and uncommon during February, June, and July (5, each); otherwise, with the exception of Cades Cove where most of the records are concentrated and where it may breed during certain years, the appearance of Killdeer is often associated with storms and sudden changes in the weather.

Although he made no mention of activities which would indicate its breeding there, Fleetwood recorded this species in Cades Cove 33 times during March–April–May, 1935, the total number of birds being 107.

Killdeer have occurred most frequently in the park during October–November–December (69 records) and again during March–April–May (58 records). Eighteen of the 19 records along the transmountain road were associated with storms. On a number of occasions the first snowstorm of the season would bring some Killdeer into the area, and particularly heavy snowfalls or periods of exceptional cold sometimes had a similar effect. The following are examples:

March 25, 1940—temperature 11° above zero at Park Headquarters this morning following yesterday's heavy snowfall. A flock of 11 Killdeer were reported in the Sugarlands and I observed single birds at the 2700 and 4600 ft. altitudes along the transmountain road (Tennessee side).

January 24, 1948—Snow fell throughout the park; at Newfound Gap it totaled about 14 inches. One Killdeer appeared at Park Headquarters; 3 in Gatlinburg; and 10 to 12 along the transmountain road.

November 22, 1949—About 50 Killdeer were reported between 2000 and 3500 ft. along the transmountain road following the first low-altitude snowstorm of the season.

November 26, 1949—Three Killdeer were found smashed by cars on the transmountain road following yesterday's snowfall.

November 24, 1950—Snow fell throughout the morning, accompanied by a sharp drop in the temperature. The small flock of Killdeer that appeared on the lawn near Park Headquarters Building was gradually augmented as the storm progressed until finally it consisted of 56 birds. They waited out the storm, motionless on the ground. By mid-afternoon, when the storm abated, the birds had left for parts unknown.

November 21, 1952—A flock of about 15 Killdeer reported in Gatlinburg (Manley) during the first snow of the season.

November 9, 1956—A flock of over 100 Killdeer appeared in Gatlinburg following a sudden change to cold weather. One dead bird was brought in. Snowing in the mountains.

December 12, 1957—Over a dozen Killdeer were in Gatlinburg two days ago, just before the change to snow and bitter cold weather. Today, with record-breaking low temperatures (10° below zero, Park Headquarters), groups of 4 and 12 birds were observed at high altitudes along the transmountain road; one injured and one dead Killdeer were brought in. A large flock appeared in the Floyd-Enloe Bottoms, along the transmountain road, near Cherokee, North Carolina.

For the period 1935–61, parties engaged in the Christmas Bird Count observed Killdeer on 19 of the 27 years. Total number of birds was 347; largest number listed in one day was 40. Most of these were located outside the park boundaries (Pigeon Forge, Tuckaleechee Cove) with some in Cades Cove.

AMERICAN GOLDEN PLOVER—*Pluvialis dominica*

There is but one record for this bird in the park. On October 29, 1953, following the first snowfall of the season in the higher elevations, Manley, Lix, and I discovered two American Golden Plovers beside the transmountain road at an altitude of approximately 4000 ft. (Tennessee side). One of the birds was dead, the other died later of its injuries. A considerable amount of fog enveloped the area where these plovers were found. Several Killdeer and two or three kinds of ducks had also been grounded in the vicinity at that time. This proved to be the first recorded occurrence of the American Golden Plover in East Tennessee [Stupka, 1954b].

FAMILY | *SCOLOPACIDAE*

AMERICAN WOODCOCK—*Philohela minor*

This secretive bird of the twilight is an uncommon spring and fall migrant and a very uncommon summer resident. Weather conditions appear to play an important part in the times of its arrival and departure, the earliest arrival dates—January 20 (1951) and February 3 (1957)—coming during periods of mild weather, while the latest departure dates—November 24 (1950) and November 25 (1958)—coincided with an onset of wintry conditions.

There are a number of low-altitude arrival records from February 17 to 28, but during the spring months, and again from August until its departure in November, reports of the American Woodcock are scarce. Manley's observation of one of these birds on December 9 (1961), in Gatlinburg, is the only December record.

Although no nests or eggs have been reported from within the park, evidence of the woodcock breeding here rests on the presence of these birds in June (8 records) and July (10 records) and in my observation of a female with at least 2 young not yet able to fly on June 4, 1940, along the Middle Prong of Little River, at approximately 2000 ft.

A few middle- and high-altitude records are the following:

April 8, 1951—4850 ft., transmountain road, Carolina side (Ealy).

June 12, 1935—5150 ft., Heintooga Bald, Fleetwood [1937].

June 19, 1937—5000 ft., Cosby Knob, Wetmore [1939].

July 15, 1944—5400 ft., Clingmans Dome Road. A freshly-killed bird found and brought in by Morrell.

July 29, 1953—3900 ft., Rainbow Falls Trail (Tanner).

August 11, 1941—3800 ft., Alum Cave Parking Area (Quay).

Singing dates range from February 3 to April 11. Although most singing is done at dusk, it has also been heard as late as 10:30 P.M. on a clear moonlit night and at dawn.

COMMON SNIPE—*Capella gallinago*

This bird occurs in Cades Cove as an uncommon winter resident; elsewhere it is mostly an uncommon or rare winter resident. For the period 1934–61, there are 61 records, all but June, July, and August being represented. The earliest fall record is my discovery of a Common Snipe at the Bryson Place, on Deep Creek (2400 ft.), September 2 (1938); the latest spring record, also on Deep Creek, came May 11 (1950, Stupka). Fleetwood observed from 1 to 13 snipe in Cades Cove on 20 days between March 18 and May 4, 1935. On January 3, 1960, P. Huff and I flushed a total of 13 snipe along a meadow brook in Cades Cove.

Bellrose [1938], in a list of birds he observed in the park August 31–September 7, 1937, mentions the discovery of a Common Snipe: "It is a mystery what this bird was doing on Mt. LeConte at an elevation of 4,250 feet, but nevertheless one was positively identified there on September 6." This is the only high-altitude record we have for this species.

SPOTTED SANDPIPER—*Actitis macularia*

The Spotted Sandpiper, an uncommon spring and fall migrant, has appeared in our area as early as April 1 (1957, Manley). Next is E. V. Komarek's record of April 15 (1932), followed by 13 records between April 21 and May 2. Latest spring date is May 30 (1950, Chiles). Earliest of the fall arrival dates is July 25 (1955, Tanner) followed by one on July 26 (1939, Manley). Latest fall record is October 8 (1940, Manley). Total number of records is 24 for spring and 10 for fall.

The highest altitude this bird has been noted is 3500–4000 ft. along the transmountain road (North Carolina side) —

H. C. Land and H. K. Land [letter] observed it "feeding in the gravel beside the highway" April 26, 1952.

SOLITARY SANDPIPER—*Tringa solitaria*

The earliest of 14 spring records for this scarce transient is April 18 (1935, Fleetwood); the latest spring departure is May 22 (1935, Fleetwood). In the fall the earliest bird was noted August 23 (1934, Fleetwood); the latest departure date is October 8 (1940, Manley).

Fleetwood observed this sandpiper on 4 days in April and 6 days in May 1935, all of these records being in Cades Cove. There are but 8 additional records including 2 birds at an altitude of 4202 ft. at Three Forks (junction of the Left, Middle, and Right Forks of Raven Fork) on August 23, 1934 (Fleetwood). Other than Fleetwood's records, the Solitary Sandpiper has been observed by Manley at Tremont (April 24, 1940) and Elkmont (October 8, 1940); by Stupka at Park Headquarters (May 13, 1938, and September 23, 1947) and Cades Cove (October 5, 1938); by Burns in Cataloochee (April 21, 1951); and by Saunders in Gatlinburg (April 27, 1952).

On April 22, 1935, following heavy rains, Fleetwood observed a total of 18 Solitary Sandpipers along Rowans Creek and in the vicinity of a small body of water in Cades Cove.

GREATER YELLOWLEGS—*Totanus melanoleucus*

The Greater Yellowlegs is a rare spring and fall migrant in the park. Fleetwood observed single birds in Cades Cove April 3 and 18, 1935. On October 18, 1948, a specimen that had just been shot in Gatlinburg was brought to me for examination. Manley reported one from Laurel Lake May 1, 1942.

LESSER YELLOWLEGS—*Totanus flavipes*

There are but two records of the Lesser Yellowlegs, both from Cades Cove. The first was collected by E. V. Komarek on May 6, 1933, while the second was observed by Fleetwood on April 29, 1935.

FAMILY | *PHALAROPODIDAE*

RED PHALAROPE—*Phalaropus fulicarius*

On December 17, 1944, while Mrs. Leonhard and party were engaged in the annual Christmas Bird Count in the vicinity of Park Headquarters Building, they discovered a partly decomposed Red Phalarope. According to Walker [1946] who examined it and who recorded this unusual find, the bird had evidently been run over by a car some days before. The specimen was cleaned and made into a study skin for the park collection. How this maritime species came to a place so far removed from its normal habitat is a matter for speculation.

A Red Phalarope in the fall plumage was observed at close range on Fontana Reservoir, a few hundred yards from the park boundary, October 1, 1949. Several members of the Carolina Bird Club, including Chamberlain and me, viewed the bird from the dock; later, as we pursued the phalarope in a boat, we came within a few feet of it [Green, 1949].*

FAMILY | *LARIDAE*

HERRING GULL—*Larus argentatus*

Although there are a few records of this gull in the park, its occurrence here is purely accidental. On January 6, 1936, an injured immature bird was found along the road between Gatlinburg and Fighting Creek Gap. A two-year old Herring Gull was discovered at the entrance to Chimneys Campground on February 9, 1948, by McCamey; the bird flew off when approached closely. In Gatlinburg, on the night of December 26, 1950, Curtis McCarter captured an immature bird that had been struck and stunned by a car; next day,

* On November 29, 1959, a freshly-killed Red Phalarope was found below high tension power lines leading into the Aluminum Company, 2 miles west of Maryville, Tennessee, and approximately 10 miles from the northwestern edge of Great Smoky Mountains National Park [Monroe, 1959].

when I liberated it, the gull flew off on strong wings. Mrs. Eifert reported this species from near Fighting Creek Gap April 26, 1952; the next day a Herring Gull that appeared to be lost in the fog was observed on Gatlinburg's main street by Hebard, Gunn, and D. S. Miller.

RING-BILLED GULL—*Larus delawarensis*

Records of the Ring-billed Gull in the park and immediate vicinity are as follows:

November 24, 1950—One found dead in Gatlinburg by Jack Reagan who brought it to me for identification. Snow and extremely cold weather prevailed at the time.

December 26, 1950—Price picked up one dead and one injured bird along the transmountain road (Tennessee side) and brought them in for identification. Heavy fog shrouded the mountains at the time. The dead gull, an immature in the first winter plumage, appeared to have been struck by a car near the 3800 ft. altitude. The injured bird was in the road near the entrance to the Chimneys Campground, at 2700 ft.

April 27, 1952—Ganier and party, while motoring in Cades Cove, observed an immature bird that rose from a field and accepted biscuits that were thrown to it. "The quickness with which the bird accepted food from people probably came from its having received food from groups of people wherever it had spent the winter." [Ganier, 1952.]

January 3, 1960—Tanner and party, while taking the Christmas Bird Count in Tuckaleechee Cove, discovered one of these gulls along Little River.

The appearance of any species of gull in the park area is purely accidental.

LAUGHING GULL—*Larus atricilla*

When Roger Tory Peterson walked into my office on April 30, 1953, accompanied by James Fisher, one of his first questions was, "What is the status of the Laughing Gull in the park?" As far as I knew, that bird had no "status" here, and I so informed these gentlemen. But, to my surprise, Peterson retorted that he and Fisher had just observed one of these gulls between Smokemont and Kephart Prong, along the transmountain road (2700 ft.) . The bird was standing close to the road. Its accidental appearance there cannot be accounted for.

SOOTY TERN—*Sterna fuscata*

There is one record of an injured bird discovered by Elizabeth Ijams and Mary Ruth Chiles, July 30, 1926, on Lynn Camp Prong, above Tremont, near an elevation of 2000 ft.* The accidental occurrence of this tern is attributed to the severe tropical hurricane that originated near Martinique, lashed the Bahama Islands with winds up to 130 miles per hour (July 26–27), and struck the South Carolina coast (July 28). In the wake of this storm the discovery of Sooty Terns in South Carolina [Wayne, 1926] and West Virginia [Johnson, I. H., 1926] established initial records for those states; the second North Carolina record of this species [Brimley, H. H., 1926] and the first record for inland Georgia [Burleigh, 1958] were likewise established.

FAMILY | *COLUMBIDAE*

MOURNING DOVE—*Zenaidura macroura*

On lands adjacent to or in the vicinity of the park, especially in cornfields and cultivated areas, Mourning Doves are common permanent residents. At the lower altitudes these birds are to be found in fair numbers the year around, but there is a rapid decrease in the population on the heavily forested mountainsides above 2000 ft. Their appearance at the middle or high altitudes is more or less accidental. Fleetwood reported hearing the notes of this bird near Black Camp Gap (4522 ft.) on June 13, 1935, and I observed one flying through Indian Gap (5266 ft.) on March 14, 1944. Near a house high up on the slopes above Indian Creek, at about 3000 ft., Fleetwood discovered a flock of about 50 birds December 7, 1934.

* Not 3300 ft., as stated by Ganier [1929].

I have heard these doves cooing as early as January 29 (1962) and as late as October 9 (1954). Billing and mating activities were observed February 16, 1961, near Emerts Cove.

FAMILY | *CUCULIDAE*

YELLOW-BILLED CUCKOO—*Coccyzus americanus*

Both species of cuckoos are fairly common summer residents in the park where they occur in approximately equal numbers; for the years 1933–61, there are 45 records of the Yellow-billed and 38 of the Black-billed Cuckoo. But whereas the ratio of Yellow-billed occurrences at low altitudes in contrast to their presence at high elevations (above 3500 ft.) is approximately 10 to 1 (41:4), that of the Black-billed Cuckoo is but 2 to 1 (25:13). This coincides with what is known concerning the breeding ranges of these two species, the Yellow-billed being less common in the north. Fleetwood, who recorded the Yellow-billed Cuckoo on 12 occasions, observed it but once at a high altitude.

The earliest arrival date is April 25 (1933, E. V. Komarek); Watkins' record of April 28 (1958) is the only other April record. The latest departure in the fall is November 5 (1950) when Pfitzer discovered one live and one dead bird near the 4000 ft. altitude on the transmountain road (Tennessee side) following a sudden change to snow and cold weather [Stupka, 1950].

On June 18, 1940, during the course of a day's birding in Cades Cove and vicinity, Trautman [letter] counted 9 Yellow-billed Cuckoos.

BLACK-BILLED CUCKOO—*Coccyzus erythropthalmus*

As stated above, this fairly common summer resident is present in approximately the same numbers as its yellow-billed cousin. During April and May, all 18 records are for lowland areas, but beginning in June and continuing through

September, 13 of the 19 Black-billed Cuckoos observed were in the higher mountains.*

The earliest arrival date is April 26 (1935, Fleetwood); my record of April 29, 1942, represents the only other April observation of this species. In May, 11 of the 16 earliest arrival records range between May 1 and 10. Latest departure date in the fall is October 13 (1938, Manley).

FAMILY | *TYTONIDAE*

BARN OWL—*Tyto alba*

On April 23, 1932, one of these owls, killed somewhere in Sevier County, Tennessee, was brought to Ogden [1933] to be prepared as a mounted specimen. Ogden also prepared a study skin of one of these birds taken October 22, 1934, near Walland, in Blount County, Tennessee; at a later date, he donated the specimen to the park. Among a collection of birds from Cocke County, Tennessee, Walker [1935] includes a Barn Owl.

One of these owls, shot September 24, 1947, in Fontana Village, North Carolina, was brought to me for identification; this is practically on the southwestern boundary of the park.

FAMILY | *STRIGIDAE*

SCREECH OWL—*Otus asio*

This owl ** is a fairly common permanent resident, especially along the periphery of the park and throughout the lower altitudes. It becomes progressively less plentiful with

* In Knox County, Tennessee, near the park, the Black-billed Cuckoo is a spring and fall migrant whereas the Yellow-billed is a summer resident [Howell and Monroe, 1957].

** Four Screech Owls which members of the Chicago Academy of Sciences collected in this area in 1931 and 1933 were examined by Wetmore who, in January 1943, informed me they represented the southern race (*Otus asio asio*).

increased elevation, and in the spruce-fir forests it is very rare or absent. It has been observed on 3 or 4 occasions at an elevation of approximately 4000 ft. on the North Carolina side of the transmountain road. On August 27, 1945, Dr. and Mrs. Baldwin discovered a disintegrated pellet containing the remains of a Screech Owl at Ramsey Cascades (4200 ft.); these consisted of part of the skull, the feet, and miscellaneous bones and feathers.

SCREECH OWLS—MISCELLANEOUS DATA

Month	Total number of records 1931–61	Singing records 1934–54	Numbers found dead along roads 1936–61
January	34	5	12
February	12	2	3
March	24	20	2
April	7	1	4
May	6	4	0
June	10	7	0
July	27	20	2
August	37	30	2
September	58	39	5
October	73	37	17
November	25	8	8
December	29	9	6
TOTALS	342	182	61

The tabulation reveals how relatively few records there are for this owl during April, May, and June. Singing is likewise at a low ebb, and the number of birds found dead along roads is then at a minimum. Apparently these owls are most retiring during the breeding season.

Our statistics reveal an appreciable amount of singing in March just prior to the breeding season, almost no singing in April, very little in May and June, and heaviest singing during the summer and early autumn. This is in agreement with Saunders' [1935] remarks but not with Bent [1938] and Todd [1940] who regard early spring as the time of most frequent singing.

There are but two records of eggs or young birds. On June 30, 1950, a young Screech Owl only recently out of the nest was captured just south of the park at Cherokee, North Carolina, and brought to our Oconaluftee Visitor Center where it was liberated in a large log barn nearby. It remained there for several days during which time it would accept grasshoppers from the hand. On July 4, 1950, when I paid it a visit, the owl held a small brown bat in its talons. An adult bird, along with 2 eggs and 2 fledglings that appeared to be 7 or 8 days old, was brought to the school in Gatlinburg on April 24, 1953. These had been discovered near that city.

Within the park and vicinity, it appears as though cars kill more Screech Owls than any other kind of bird. The owls are killed not by any tendency to be drawn to the glare of oncoming headlights but by being struck while occupied in feeding upon prey they find on the highways [Stupka, 1953]. A glance at the last column in the tabulation shows that highest mortality comes not in the summer when traffic is heaviest but in the fall when the owls are lured by large orthopterous insects that appear on the macadam roads. Occasionally the birds are merely stunned, and we have discovered such individuals a few times, but usually they are killed either by the impact or under the wheels of the vehicle. In a one-half mile stretch of road, located approximately halfway between Gatlinburg and the Park Headquarters Building, I have known 4 Screech Owls to be killed by cars within a period of less than four months (December 14, 1948—April 3, 1949). Crows and various mammals may find and feed upon these carcasses; in the stomach of an opossum I examined in November, 1938, were the remains of one of these little owls.

Screech Owls feed upon such animals as are easily secured, and the matter of chance plays a very important part in what is taken. Consequently their food habits vary considerably from place to place. Mention has already been made of a small bat one of these owls had secured. On the night of January 6, 1950, Ranger Ealy drove so close to a Screech Owl on the transmountain road near Mingus Creek that he could readily identify a wood frog (*Rana sylvatica*) the bird held in its talons and with which it promptly flew off (an abnormally warm spell of weather was responsible for the emergence of these amphibians).

Between the years 1936–54 I examined 53 dead Screech Owls in order to learn something about their food habits. These were birds found along the park roads and along roads in the immediate vicinity of the park. Fifty-one of the fifty-three birds had items in their stomachs which I identified as follows: Insects in 43 stomachs, spiders in 14, myriapods in 8, crayfish in 7, small mammals in 6, salamanders in 2, and bird, earthworm, or snail in 1 each.

Altogether 104 of the 343 Screech Owls that have been recorded were observed sufficiently well to determine the color phase; of these, 84 were red and 20, gray—a ratio of more than four red to one gray.

GREAT HORNED OWL—*Bubo virginianus*

Ganier [1926] regarded this as a bird of the high and middle altitudes, but by far the greatest number of our records are from the lower elevations, mostly near the park boundary, where the species is an uncommon permanent resident. Our only high-altitude record was made along the Appalachian Trail between Clingmans Dome and Silers Bald on December 18, 1938, by E. O. Henry and a Christmas Bird Count party who observed this big owl at a distance of 70 ft.

Unlike the Barred Owl, the Great Horned is almost entirely nocturnal in its activities. Occasionally, crows will discover and harass one of these big owls during the daytime, as Fleetwood observed in Cades Cove (May 24, 1935) and as I [Stupka, 1943] reported in the Sugarlands (March 4, 1938). Otherwise, unless these birds have been found dead, injured, or in a weakened condition,* the Great Horned Owl is rarely discovered. As with all our owls, one is much more likely to hear than to see this bird, there being 86 sound to but 12 sight records.

The deep-throated hooting of this bird has been heard in the park and vicinity every month of the year. Only rarely does it call in the daytime. The early hours of the night ap-

---

* Five such records, as follows:
(1) August 31, 1936—One captured along transmountain road, near Smokemont; this weak bird died the following day.
(2) March 29, 1937—One was caught in a steel trap, in Cades Cove; the trap had been set for a "chicken thief."
(3) March 12, 1940—An incubating female (underparts bare of feathers) was killed when struck by a car, at Elkmont.
(4) September 1, 1943—One bird wounded by a hunter in Emerts Cove, close to the park line.
(5) April 4, 1949—W. Ogle found a small and very weak adult bird near Tremont; it weighed one pound twelve ounces.

pear to be favored, although it may call at any time from dusk to dawn. December and January are the months when most hooting has been recorded; April, May, and June are the months with fewest such records.

BARRED OWL—*Strix varia*

The Barred Owl,* like the Great Horned, is an uncommon permanent resident in the park; but whereas the latter species is rare at the higher altitudes, the Barred Owl, on the basis of more than 100 reports, is somewat more prevalent in the higher than in the lower elevations. Especially is this true during the seven months April–October, inclusive, when 60 percent of the records (53) are for elevations above 3500 ft. Since our information points to a scarcity of these owls in the higher elevations during the five coldest months of the year (November–March, inclusive), due, in part, to a lack of qualified observers during that period, there is the possibility that an insufficiency of food during periods when the snowcover is deep may result in a movement to the lower elevations— but this is merely conjectural.

I have heard the Barred Owl hooting on Mt. LeConte at an elevation of 6300 ft. (July 15, 1936), at Tricorner Knob near 5800 ft. (August 12, 1936), at Collins Gap, 5720 ft. (February 7, 1939), at Newfound Gap, 5040 ft., on a number of occasions, and elsewhere at high altitudes. Ganier [1938] reports it from 6300 to 6600 ft. on Clingmans Dome (June 13, 1938); Keating notified me of having observed it on Andrews Bald (June 12, 1937); and Wetmore [1939] makes mention of it in late June 1937, at Cosby Knob and Inadu Knob. White and Worthington observed a Barred Owl at close range at 5900 ft. on the slopes of Mt. Collins on January 24, 1962.

Barred Owls have been heard hooting in 10 of the 12 months of the year—there are no records for January and November. Unlike the Great Horned which does most of its

---

* Wetmore [1939], whose party collected a female Barred Owl in late June 1937, at an elevation of 3500 ft. on Snake Den Mountain, states that the feathering on the toes of this specimen extended "down past the middle of the final joint, as is characteristic of the northern race [*Strix varia varia*]. It is supposed that others heard or seen . . . on Cosby Knob (5,000 feet), Inadu Knob (5,700 feet), and near Cosby (2,700 feet) between June 19 and June 29 were of this same race."

hooting in early winter, the Barred Owl has been heard most often during the spring and summer. There are very few records of hooting by Barred Owls from November through March. Also unlike its larger relative, the Barred Owl is not averse to uttering its notes at any time of the day or night; there are at least 18 recorded daytime hootings, 3 of these at noon and some during periods of bright sunshine.

There are two records of young birds. On June 18, 1934, Fleetwood released a young Barred Owl that had been discovered and brought in by one of the enrollees at the C.C.C. Camp in Greenbrier; the bird, described as having down on its head, had been found near Porters Flat (2200 ft.). On July 6, 1960, two adult Barred Owls were observed feeding a young bird that had left the nest; Shields witnessed the incident about two miles northeast of Crib Gap, near Laurel Creek (1600 ft.).*

On January 3, 1943, while walking along the Thomas Ridge Trail, I came upon a place (4900 ft.) where tragedy had recently overtaken a Barred Owl. Feathers from the bird's wings, tail, and breast lay strewn about, an owl's pellet containing the remains of a short-tailed shrew was on the ground nearby, and a fairly strong scent of skunk hovered over the scene. Lack of additional clues prevents one from reconstructing what happened there.

On April 8, 1944, at 2:30 P.M., I viewed a Barred Owl at such close range that the small prey it carried in its talons (a short-tailed shrew) could be identified. The incident happened on an overcast day at approximately 2600 ft., along Little River (above Elkmont). On July 14, 1952, an adult Barred Owl, found dead along the transmountain road (4600 ft., North Carolina side) had the remains of one camel cricket and one common black cricket in its stomach.

SAW-WHET OWL—*Aegolius acadicus*

On June 21, 1941, at about 9 P.M., Norman P. Hill and Richard Bowen, two Harvard University students who were

---

* Bent [1938] says: "I have evidence to indicate that young barred owls are attended, and probably fed, by their parents during their first summer and perhaps much longer."

studying birds in the Great Smoky Mountains National Park, heard the notes of a Saw-whet Owl at the Clingmans Dome Parking Area. Their list of birds including this record, with which they favored me a day or two later, was our first evidence of the occurrence of the Saw-whet Owl in the Southern Appalachian Mountains during the breeding season.* Later events substantiated this interesting report and these served to extend the breeding range of our smallest and most boreal owl some 250 miles southwest of West Virginia's Cranberry Glades—heretofore the southernmost known breeding locality in the eastern United States [A. B. Brooks, 1933].

Koch and I heard the notes of this bird at about 9 P.M. on May 26, 1944, from the Clingmans Dome Parking Area. We then drove to Newfound Gap where the monotonous cooing notes of another were heard; upon stepping out of our car and imitating the notes, we were surprised by what we assumed was one of these little owls hovering over our heads as though attempting to alight—against the night sky it was seen only in silhouette.** Two nights later, Koch and I again heard this bird at Newfound Gap and also at Indian Gap [Stupka, 1946a]. Since then the notes of this owl have been heard between Newfound Gap and Clingmans Dome by a number of persons interested in birds [Lewy, 1945; Castles, 1957].

With but one exception, all singing records are at high altitudes in spruce-fir forests—1 in March, 9 in April, 7 in May, and 1 in June. On March 15, 1955, beginning about 9:30 P.M., I listened for over 20 minutes to the monotonous cooing notes of a Saw-whet Owl that appeared to be coming from near the western edge of Emerts Cove, close to the park line. The sound carried quite clearly to where I stood, near

---

* Ganier [1946] mentions the observation of what he believed to be this owl near the summit of Mt. LeConte at dusk on June 20, 1933. He did not publish this, however, until after I recorded the Hill-Bowen report [Stupka, 1946.]

** It was not until later that I came upon Major Bendire's [1892] account of a similar incident as related by Dr. William L. Ralph: "Just before and during the mating season these little owls [Saw-whet] are quite lively; their peculiar whistle can be heard in almost any suitable wood, and one may by imitating it often decoy them within reach of the hand. Upon one occasion, when my assistant was imitating one, it alighted on the fur cap of a friend that stood near him."

my residence, at an altitude of 1600–1700 ft. The night was clear and mild.

On February 3, 1954, Manley observed one of these owls alight in a holly tree near his home, in Gatlinburg; he approached to within about 10 ft. of the bird before it flew off. Tanner [1957c], who on May 29, 1957, heard and saw an adult Saw-whet Owl at 5400 ft. on Mt. LeConte, is the first to have had a good view of one of these birds within the park area. The incident took place between 10 and 11 A.M., the observer approaching the owl closely enough to observe the ripple of its throat feathers when it called.

In view of the foregoing records, the Saw-whet Owl is regarded as an uncommon permanent resident in the spruce-fir forests of Great Smoky Mountains National Park. So far (1962), no nest, eggs, or young birds have been observed here.

FAMILY | *CAPRIMULGIDAE*

CHUCK-WILL'S-WIDOW—*Caprimulgus carolinensis*

The Great Smoky Mountains are somewhat out-of-bounds for the three members of the Goatsucker family of birds. The Chuck-will's-widow is a very uncommon spring migrant, the Whip-poor-will is a summer resident only in the lower altitudes, while the Nighthawk mostly avoids the mountains except when migrating southward in late summer.

The Chuck-will's-widow was first reported from Gatlinburg by Saunders [letter] on April 24, 1952, when he heard one bird from the hotel where he was staying. That is also our earliest spring record. It was heard again in Gatlinburg on May 1, 1953, by Mrs. Hadley, and on May 25, 1957, by Lix. Herndon notified me that he and Mrs. Dunbar heard the notes of a Chuck-will's-widow at about 10 A.M. on May 5, 1957, in Cades Cove. Russell reported hearing this species in the Park Headquarters area at 8:30 P.M. on May 27, 1960. On May 16, 1961, one of these birds announced its presence near my home (1700 ft.), close to the park boundary, about a mile west of Emerts Cove; after a stay of 9 days, during which time it called daily mostly at dawn and at dusk, the bird disappeared.

Although there are no records which would lead one to believe this species nests in the park, further investigations, particularly in Tuckaleechee Cove and Happy Valley, may reveal its presence in the immediate vicinity.

WHIP-POOR-WILL—*Caprimulgus vociferus*

This loud-voiced bird of the night is a fairly common summer resident below the 3000 ft. altitude. Wetmore [1939] reports it from four miles southeast of Cosby at 2700 ft.; Tanner from Cherokee Orchard (near Gatlinburg) at 2600 ft.; and Hadley from Cataloochee at 2600 ft.—all during the breeding season. With the natural reforestation of numerous low-altitude areas that had been cleared or under cultivation, this bird, in all probability, is less plentiful than it was in pre-park days.

The earliest arrival date is March 30 (1949, Deep Creek—Hadley; 1962, The Glades—Snowden). Fleetwood reported one from Cades Cove on March 31, 1935. There are 6 years when the earliest birds arrived between April 1 and 3, inclusive, and 13 years when first arrivals were recorded April 10 to 18.

Whip-poor-wills call very infrequently in late summer. Of 11 September records, the latest is on the 29th (1939, Manley), in Gatlinburg.

Only rarely does this species sing in the daytime. On May 17, 1943, the familiar notes were given at 2 P.M. and, two days later, at 11 A.M. Since both were heard in the Park Headquarters area, it is possible the same individual was responsible.

Mrs. Allen [1946] had the good fortune to observe the remarkable courtship dance of this nocturnal species on June 15, 1946, near her home in the Glades, approximately one mile west of Emerts Cove and one mile north of the park boundary. While the male strutted back and forth before the object of his affections he uttered guttural "chucks" each time his head bobbed up and down.

COMMON NIGHTHAWK—*Chordeiles minor*

Fairly large flocks of southward-moving nighthawks pass over our area in the late summer, but in the spring these birds are quite scarce. Trautman observed a lone bird in Cades Cove on June 18 (1940) and I have seen single birds on the park's boundary in Tuckaleechee Cove on June 12 (1938) ; in Gatlinburg on June 5 (1939) ; and in Bryson City, North Carolina, on June 24 (1941). No eggs or young of this species have been discovered here. Fleetwood observed 1 or 2 birds in Cades Cove on 11 days during May 1935, and it appears significant that he noted none during the 8 days he spent there the following month.

A bird heard in Gatlinburg by Mrs. Eifert on April 22 (1952) proved to be our earliest record in the spring; the latest spring record was June 24 (1941—the Bryson City, North Carolina, observation given above). Earliest fall appearance was August 12 (1944, Cades Cove). Fifty or more birds were reported August 14, 1950, by Burns, and August 14, 1960, by Lix—both from near Emerts Cove. Our only October records came in 1957 in Gatlinburg; I observed 2 birds on the 4th and Manley saw 3 on the 9th.

Flocks numbering from 100 to 500 birds were reported on 5 occasions between August 15 and 29 (1941–52). Early September is the time when most of the large flights of nighthawks occur over the lower altitudes in and near the park, there being records of 14 flights numbering from 100 to 861 birds between September 2 and 11 (1936–56). A heavy flight of nighthawks passed SSE. over Gatlinburg between 5:35 and 7:05 P.M., September 8, 1948; of the 861 I counted, the greatest concentration came between 6:50 and 7 P.M. when 385 high-flying birds passed over. This flight came immediately following 4 days of rain. Two years later, the heavy flight of September 4, 1950, was followed by a sudden change to much cooler temperatures.

FAMILY | *APODIDAE*

CHIMNEY SWIFT—*Chaetura pelagica*

Irrespective of altitudes, or types of forests, or mankind's influence upon the landscape, Chimney Swifts are common summer residents throughout Great Smoky Mountains National Park. Their tireless wings carry them over the highest mountains and into the lowest valleys. Probably no other bird in our area is so truly at home on the wing. Two birds I observed in Gatlinburg on March 31 (1957) and one reported from the park area by E. V. Komarek on April 1 (1933) represent our earliest records. During 1933–60 there were 12 years when the earliest swift arrivals appeared April 6 to 14; on 6 years the dates ranged from April 16 to 19.

In most years, the last of these birds leave the park during the first week in October. Our latest record is of a flock of approximately 1,500 swifts observed over the Deep Creek Campground, two miles north of Bryson City, North Carolina, on October 17 (1959) by Pardue and Overton [letter]. This also happened to be the largest flock reported.

Our information relating to nesting consists of the following:

July 4, 1936—A nest containing 4 young that were almost ready for flight fell from its attachment inside a fireplace chimney in a building in the Sugarlands.

June 17, 1938—On the park boundary at Black Camp Gap, 4522 ft., I observed a Chimney Swift incubating 4 eggs in a nest attached to a bare wooden wall within a building where tools were stored. The nest was near the ceiling, approximately 10 feet from the floor.

July 4, 1944—A nest with 1 egg and 1 naked fledgling fell from inside the fireplace chimney of a house, in Gatlinburg.

August 5, 1951—A nest with 2 half-grown young fell from inside the above-mentioned chimney (Gatlinburg). The fledglings were placed on the top of a stick of cordwood that was set on end in a corner of the fireplace, and there they continued to be fed by the adults until August 14, at which time the young birds, now well feathered, disappeared.

July 1–17, 1952—From the above-mentioned chimney (Gatlinburg), the loud chattering made by the young birds while being fed could be heard daily during this interval.

Ganier [1962] writes that on May 30, 1925 "one of a pair was seen flying in and out of a hollow tree near the top of Silers Bald and it is logical to assume that it was prospecting for a nest site in the absence of chimneys." Wetmore [1939] writes that "In the wilder sections of the Great Smoky Mountains from June 19 to 30 [1937] chimney swifts were found nesting in hollow trees on Mount Guyot, Inadu Knob, and Old Black Mountain." It is unfortunate that additional particulars are not mentioned. There are a number of statements made by ornithologists [Brewster, 1886; Cairns, 1889; Ganier and Mayfield, 1946] who reported that these birds were using hollow trees as nesting sites in the nearby mountains, but details are fragmentary or are lacking.

Chimney Swifts, like swallows and certain other birds, capture their insect prey while skimming through the air. But in the Sugarlands on August 10, 1941, George observed a flock of perhaps 100 swifts that appeared to be feeding in the top of a tall yellow-poplar where a swarm of insects had congregated, the birds barely touching the topmost leaves in a kind of fluttering flight that gave the impression that they were on the verge of alighting there.

A Chimney Swift banded by H. Meyer at Knoxville, Tennessee, on September 1, 1941, was captured in the home of Mrs. Harry A. Gervin, in Gatlinburg, on July 23, 1945, where it was rearing young. After the number on the band was recorded, the bird was released.

FAMILY | *TROCHILIDAE*

RUBY-THROATED HUMMINGBIRD—
Archilochus colubris

This, the smallest bird in Eastern United States, is a common summer resident in the park where it occurs at all altitudes. The earliest hummingbirds were noted during the last 10 days of April on more than half the years from 1935 to 1960. An unusually early arrival was a male bird observed by Mrs. Stupka in her garden near Emerts Cove on April 7 (1954) following two weeks of abnormally warm weather. Manley reported an early arrival on April 14 (1953) in Gatlinburg, and there were two years when I observed the vanguards of this northward migration on April 18—once in Cades Cove (1948) and once at Black Camp Gap, 4522 ft., (1939). Latest departure date was October 12 (1947, Gatlinburg—Stupka).

On May 21, 1938, while at Indian Gap (5266 ft.), I watched a Ruby-throated Hummingbird gathering the pappus from a dandelion that had gone to seed. In the Park Headquarters area, the gathering of willow pappus was noted May 12, 1958.

Fleetwood observed the building of a nest by a female hummingbird May 8, 1935, in Cades Cove; the structure was in a sourwood tree about 25 ft. from the ground. On May 22, 1937, a nest perched on a slender hemlock branch approximately 8 ft. above the ground in the Park Headquarters area was pointed out to me. In Gatlinburg, on April 25, 1952, a nest was being built on a tree limb that hung over the West Prong of the Little Pigeon River.

Since there appear to be no published reports of more than 2 eggs in the nest of a Ruby-throated Hummingbird [Bent, 1940],* the following account of a nest reported to contain 3 fledglings is given: The nest, saddled on a small branch of a *Rhododendron maximum* approximately 8 ft. above the

---

* According to Bent [1940], the Black-chinned Hummingbird (*Archilochus alexandri*) of our western states, may, on occasion, lay 3 eggs. This is the nearest relative of the Ruby-throated Hummingbird (*A. colubris*).

ground, was within 10 ft. of the corner of a summer cottage owned by Rush Rawlings, of Gatlinburg. The cottage is located close to the park boundary at the southern edge of Gatlinburg. Mr. and Mrs. Rawlings, along with their guests Mr. and Mrs. Carlyle C. Potter and Mr. and Mrs. Ralph Arnold, had the nest and 3 fledglings under observation for some hours on June 11, 1961, during which time an adult bird visited and fed the young on several occasions. The birds were seen at very close range by this group of watchers, some of whom climbed into the rhododendron which supported the nest in order to observe the young to better advantage, and I was assured that there could be no question that the brood consisted of 3, not 2, fledglings. The consensus of opinion was that one of the trio appeared somewhat smaller than the other two. Unfortunately I was not apprised of this incident until three days later (June 14, 1961) at which time I accompanied Mr. Rawlings and Assistant Park Superintendent David deL. Condon to the site. The nest now contained 2 well-developed fledglings. After an interval of 15–20 minutes, during which Mr. Condon took a number of photographs of the nest and its occupants, one of the birds flew off into the nearby tangle of rhododendrons on what appeared to be its initial flight. We heard but did not see an adult hummingbird in the immediate area. On the following day the nest was empty.

FAMILY | *ALCEDINIDAE*

BELTED KINGFISHER—*Megaceryle alcyon*

The kingfisher is a fairly common permanent resident along the lower-altitude watercourses. It may extend upward to approximately 3000 ft. along most of the larger streams, but it is most frequently encountered well below that elevation. Fleetwood observed it at Three Forks (junction of the Left, Middle, and Right Forks on Raven Fork, elevation 4202 ft.) on August 13 and 22, 1934, and I have also observed it there (November 4, 1935). On July 31, 1934, Fleetwood reported one of these birds in flight over Black Camp

Gap, 4522 ft., and I have noted the species along the West Fork of the Little Pigeon River up to the Alum Cave Parking Area at 3800 ft. It is unlikely that kingfishers nest at these higher altitudes, there being no record of a nest burrow above 3000 ft. in the area [Ganier, 1926].

These birds become quite noisy during their courtship in March. A nest was reported by Fleetwood on April 25, 1935, near Elkmont.

There has been a total of 111 Belted Kingfishers observed by groups participating in the annual one-day count of winter birds for the 27-year period beginning in 1935—an average of approximately 4 per count. Many of these were observed along Little River and the West Fork of the Little Pigeon River.

FAMILY | *PICIDAE*

YELLOW-SHAFTED FLICKER—*Colaptes auratus*

A few flickers * winter in Cades Cove and elsewhere at the lower elevations but most of these birds leave the park in October. From middle March, when they return, until some time in October flickers are common birds occurring throughout the area. Ordinarily, dense stands of spruce and fir are avoided, but the birds may be found in the vicinity of openings in this forest and along its fringes. In these high-altitude forests, flickers are rare or absent in winter.

Large numbers of these woodpeckers arrive in the park during the latter half of March and in early April, and then their loud singing may be heard over wide areas. During the fall migration (October) it is not unusual to come upon loose flocks of 10–15 flickers.

* Wetmore [letter, 1943] identified a flicker taken April 12, 1931, in Greenbrier (2000 ft.), as belonging to the northern subspecies (*Colaptes auratus luteus*). Another bird, collected June 19, 1937, on Cosby Knob (5000 ft.) was determined as a representative of the southern race (*C. a. auratus*) [Wetmore, 1939]. As he states in his report [1939], "More specimens are needed from the Great Smoky Mountain area to determine the status of the bird in that section."

Trees at the margins of high-altitude grass balds appear to be favored as nesting sites. I have observed flickers in the forest opening near Mt. LeConte Lodge (6300 ft.) in April, September, and October, but it is unlikely that nesting takes place there. In Cades Cove on June 6, 1935, Fleetwood observed a sycamore within which were the nests of a Yellow-shafted Flicker and a Pileated Woodpecker, spaced approximately 5 ft. apart and about 25–30 ft. from the ground. Fleetwood also reported young flickers in a nest on Hemphill Bald (5573 ft.) on June 11, 1935. On May 1, 1954, I watched a pair of these birds excavating for a nest in a tree at Newfound Gap (5040 ft.).

Two pairs of flickers were listed by Aldrich and Goodrum [1946] in the breeding bird census they conducted June 23–28, 1946, in a 23-acre virgin hardwood forest area in Porters Flat (2950–3200 ft.).

Over a period of 27 years (beginning in 1935), Christmas Bird Count parties reported a total of 93 flickers, mostly observed in the coves along the park's northern boundary. Twelve of the 15 birds counted December 28, 1952, were in the vicinity of Pigeon Forge.

In addition to ants, which appear to be their favorite food item, I have observed flickers feeding on the fruit of the flowering dogwood and American holly.

Dixon [1933] reported the discovery of a few Yellow-shafted Flicker feathers while examining the nesting site of Peregrine Falcons near Alum Cave Bluffs in April 1932.

PILEATED WOODPECKER—*Dryocopus pileatus*

This large woodpecker * is a common permanent resident throughout most of the area. Although less plentiful in spruce and fir forests, it may occur there at all seasons of the year. I have observed this bird at Indian Gap, 5266 ft., in late November (1946); at Newfound Gap, 5040 ft., in December (1949) and January (1950); and elsewhere at the higher elevations on at least 5 occasions during the winter months.

* A bird taken in the Greenbrier area on November 1, 1932 [letter], and another collected near Cosby on June 30, 1937, have been referred to the southern race (*Dryocopus p. pileatus*) by Wetmore [1939].

In 1940, Trautman observed it on Clingmans Dome, 6643 ft., on June 17 and on Andrews Bald, 5800 ft., on June 22. In addition there are a dozen or more records for this species at altitudes ranging from 4000 to 5300 ft. during the breeding season. Fleetwood reported young birds in the nest of a Pileated Woodpecker he had under observation in Cades Cove on June 6, 1935; the nest cavity, approximately 30 ft. from the ground, was within 5 ft. of a nest occupied by a family of Yellow-shafted Flickers.

For the 27 years beginning in 1935, parties engaged in the annual one-day count of winter birds listed a total of 289 Pileated Woodpeckers over that period, an average of approximately 10 per count. Larger numbers have been reported from near the western part of the park (Cades Cove and vicinity) than from the central portion (Mt. LeConte and vicinity).

In addition to unidentified grubs, this woodpecker has been observed feeding on pokeberries (Fleetwood) and on the fruits of poison-ivy (Manley) and American holly (Stupka).

RED-BELLIED WOODPECKER—*Centurus carolinus*

Even though I find no records of this woodpecker in the park during the 3 summer months (June–August), I am inclined to regard it as an uncommon permanent resident here. I have observed it in Cades Cove March 24 (1939) and 27 (1951), and on April 13 (1939). Walker reported it from the Little River Gorge May 22 (1938) and from Cades Cove May 31 (1937). Fleetwood observed it at Cherokee Orchard, near Gatlinburg, May 27 (1934).

The numbers of records per month, beginning in September and on through February are 5, 8, 4, 10, 6, and 2, respectively. A number of these represent records of birds observed in open stands of mature trees on fairly dry middle-altitude ridges, such as Thomas, Sunkota, Jenkins, Hughes, and Welch. I have noted this species every month from September through March near the park boundary in Emerts Cove where, in recent years, a single bird has been visiting my feeding station a number of times each day. Christmas Bird

Count parties listed single birds on but 5 of the 26 years, 1935–60; three were counted December 31, 1961.

The lack of summer records cannot be accounted for. Fleetwood, who was studying the birds of the park and who was in the field almost daily during all of June, July, and August, 1934, and most of June, 1935, failed to observe a Red-bellied Woodpecker at that season of year. His total of 9 records for September and October, 1934, may include birds that moved in from areas to the north of the park, as mentioned by Bent [1939].

RED-HEADED WOODPECKER—*Melanerpes erythrocephalus*

Langdon [1887], who spent August 11–21, 1886, studying the birds of the Chilhowee Mountains and of the coves just to the northwest of the park, regarded the Red-headed Woodpecker as a common low-altitude species. Since then this strikingly-marked bird has decreased in numbers over much of its former range to such an extent that now (1963) it is quite an event to discover one of them in our area. It is considered a very uncommon to rare permanent resident in some years and may be absent during others.

Since 1934 there are 33 records of this woodpecker in the park, all months excepting February and November being represented. However there is but one record for January, July, August, and December, and but two records for March and June. April (5), May (6), September (7), and October (7), together account for 25 of the 33 records. Christmas Bird Count parties listed this woodpecker on but 2 occasions in 27 years: December 18, 1938 (4 birds), and January 2, 1949 (1 bird) —both observations being made near Emerts Cove, close to the park line.

Our only record of a nest with young birds was on June 11, 1935, when Fleetwood came upon such a nest in a dead oak tree on Hemphill Bald, at the extreme southeastern boundary of the park. On April 29, 1938, I had 2 adult birds under observation in a grove containing a number of dead or hollow trees at the edge of Spence Field Bald, but no nesting evidences were noted. Fleetwood observed 2 of these woodpeckers in Cades Cove on May 25, 1935.

High altitude records, in addition to the above at Hemphill Bald (5573 ft.) and Spence Field Bald (approx. 5000 ft.), are as follows:

Ekaneetlee Gap (3800 ft.), May 3, 1935—1 bird (Fleetwood).

Thomas Ridge (approx. 5000 ft.), July 4, 1934—1 bird (W. King).

Clingmans Dome (approx. 6000 ft.), August 26–27, 1937—1 bird [Metcalf, 1938].

Charlies Bunion (5375 ft.), September 30, 1938—1 bird (Stupka).

Andrews Bald (5800 ft.), September 30, 1940—1 bird (Stupka).

Indian Gap (5266 ft.), September 12, 1942—1 bird (Stupka).

Mt. LeConte (approx. 6300 ft.), October 4, 1944—1 bird (Stupka).

Newfound Gap (5040 ft.), October 6, 1950—2 birds (Burns).

YELLOW-BELLIED SAPSUCKER—
Sphyrapicus varius

Two races of this bird are represented in the area. The resident race, rather uncommon and localized, breeds in the higher elevations (above 3500 ft.); Ganier [1954], who described it, calls it the Appalachian Yellow-bellied Sapsucker,* and it is assumed that this bird has a vertical migration in the park and vicinity. In October the Eastern Yellow-bellied Sapsuckers ** arrive from the north, remaining mostly at the lower altitudes until some time in April. Therefore, any sapsucker found in the park from late spring through to late summer should belong to the Appalachian race, but from October through to the following early spring both races may be present and, in view of their similarity, it would be unwise to attempt to distinguish one from the other in the field. The following tabulation gives the num-

* *Sphyrapicus varius appalachiensis*
** *S. v. varius*

bers of records of Yellow-bellied Sapsuckers, by months, for the years 1934–61:

RECORDS OF YELLOW-BELLIED SAPSUCKERS, 1934–61

Month	Above 3500 feet	Below 3500 feet	Total
January	2	34	36
February	0	16	16
March	1	31	32
April	2	29	31
May	10	1	11
June	29	0	29
July	7	1	8
August	2	1	3
September	3	7	10
October	11	35	46
November	0	22	22
December	8	28	36
Total	75	205	280

The spring departure of the non-breeding birds is reflected in the sharp drop between April and May (below 3500 ft.) ; their return is denoted by the sudden rise in the figures from September to October. The single low-altitude record for May was on May 1 (1952) in the Park Headquarters area. The lone July record was on the 26th (1938) at Mingus Creek, 2200 ft., when I observed an adult being followed by 2 noisy young, in all probability the vanguard of the local race that bred in the higher altitudes. As revealed by the foregoing tabulation, some sapsuckers are to be found in the higher elevations during the winter months, but the majority of these birds spend the winter in the lower altitudes.

Although sapsuckers breed in these mountains only at elevations in excess of 3500 ft., their nesting, ordinarily, is not in stands of coniferous forests but in deciduous groves of mature trees where openings have been brought about by such destructive forces as lumbering, fire, windthrow, chestnut blight, etc. In June 1935, Fleetwood discovered nests with young on the 10th at Brushy Gap (4750 ft.) , on the 11th at Deep Gap (5200 ft.) , and on the 13th at Black Camp Gap (4550 ft.) . On June 17, 1936, I observed an adult feeding young in the cavity of an old yellow birch, about 40 ft. from the ground, along Flat Creek (4000 ft.). On June 16, 1938, members of the Tennessee Ornithological Society reported young sapsuckers being fed in a nest near Spence Field Bald (5000 ft.) [Ganier and Clebsch, 1938]. I have come upon noisy young birds following one of the parents on June 20, 1942, along the Gregory Ridge Trail (4100 ft.), and June 16, 1945, along the Hannah Mountain Trail (4300 ft.).

In the park, sapsuckers have been known to feed upon the fruits of black gum, flowering dogwood, American holly, and pokeberry. It is unlikely that any species of tree is immune to drilling by this bird.

HAIRY WOODPECKER—*Dendrocopos villosus*

Both the Hairy * and the Downy Woodpeckers are common permanent residents occurring throughout the year at all altitudes and in practically all types of forests. Above the 3500 ft. altitude, our records reveal that the Hairy outnumbers the Downy approximately 4 to 1; below that altitude, Downys outnumber Hairys about 6 to 1. Five times as many Hairys have been reported above 3500 ft. as have been observed below that altitude, while Downys show exactly the opposite ratio, there being 5 times more Downys than Hairys at the lower altitudes. These statistics, based on a tabulation of over 1,000 birds for the period 1934–61, do not reveal the actual state of affairs since no attempt was made at a population study and since factors such as the greater wariness of the Hairy Woodpecker, as contrasted with the Downy, are not taken into consideration. However, the generalization can be made that the larger bird (Hairy) appears to outnumber the smaller (Downy) in the higher altitudes and that this situation is reversed below 3500 ft.

On June 2, 1934, while hiking to Mt. Guyot, Fleetwood came upon a Hairy Woodpecker in a dead tree containing a nest with young. Near Bunches Bald on May 25, 1945, I ob-

* In January 1943, Wetmore [letter] identified two Hairy Woodpeckers that had been collected in the park August 22 and December 15, 1932, as belonging to the eastern race (*D. v. villosus*). That is also the name he placed on a small series of specimens collected in the park in June 1937 [Wetmore, 1939], by representatives of the U. S. National Museum.

served an adult with food in its bill; another adult appeared and the two birds complained against my intrusion. On June 23–24, 1937, Wetmore [1939] reports birds of the year, fully grown, at an elevation of 2700 ft. near Cosby, at 5700 ft. on Inadu Knob, and at 6000 ft. on Old Black Mountain.

DOWNY WOODPECKER—*Dendrocopos pubescens*

The Downy Woodpecker * is a common permanent resident throughout the park. Although found in the higher altitudes at all times of year, it occurs in appreciably greater numbers at the lower elevations. Whereas it appears to be outnumbered by the Hairy Woodpecker above 3500 ft., the reverse is true below that altitude. (See Hairy Woodpecker).

Aldrich and Goodrum [1946] found one pair of Downy Woodpeckers in the 23-acre virgin hardwood forest area they censused June 23–28, 1946, in Porters Flat (elevation 2950–3200 ft.). Christmas Bird Count parties, for the period 1935–61, averaged approximately 19 Downy Woodpeckers per count in contrast to 6 Hairys.

On March 25, 1935, in Cades Cove, Fleetwood observed a male and a female Downy Woodpecker drilling a cavity that, in all probability, was intended for a nest. In Gatlinburg, on March 30, 1938, I witnessed the mating of a pair of these birds. A young bird away from the nest was observed being fed by an adult in Cades Cove on May 20, 1938, while in Tuckaleechee Cove on June 4, 1942, I watched a parent bird feeding young in a nest cavity.

RED-COCKADED WOODPECKER— *Dendrocopos borealis*

Fleetwood [1936] reported the discovery of one of these birds on April 16, 1935, at the extreme western end of the park near Revenue Hill, approximately 3 miles east of Calderwood. On the following day, upon returning to this place, he observed 2 of these woodpeckers; these he believed to be a

---

* Eight Downy Woodpeckers collected in Greenbrier in 1932–33 were identified by Wetmore in January 1943, as belonging to the northern race (*D. p. medianus*). He placed similar determinations on specimens taken in June 1937, on Old Black Mountain and on Inadu Knob [Wetmore, 1939].

mated pair. At Cane Gap, near the park line, approximately 10 miles north of Revenue Hill, Fleetwood reported another of these birds on April 19, 1935. Still another he observed on Andy McCully Ridge, near Rabbit Creek, April 29, 1935. These localities are in extensive stands of pines at fairly low altitudes.

Our only other record of this bird was by James E. Liles on March 17, 1953, along Tabcat Creek near the park boundary. Liles reported 3 birds in a pine forest less than 3 miles from where Fleetwood's initial observation was made.

The need of considerable field work in the pine forests of the western part of the park is evident in order to determine the status of the Red-cockaded Woodpecker. It has been reported as nesting near Athens, Tennessee [Ijams and Hofferbert, 1934], and specimens were taken at Rockwood, Tennessee [Fox, 1886]—approximately 40 miles west and northwest of the park, respectively.

FAMILY | *TYRANNIDAE*

EASTERN KINGBIRD—*Tyrannus tyrannus*

This flycatcher is an uncommon spring and fall transient and a scarce summer resident in the park. Of a total of 80 records (1935–61), 42 occurred in April–May, 7 in June–July, and 31 in August–September. The earliest arrival date is April 9 (1942, Gatlinburg—Manley) ; latest date of departure is September 21 (1940, Gatlinburg—Manley).

The Eastern Kingbird was observed in the park June 27, 1940, by Manley (Sugarlands) and June 7, 1958, by Stimson (Cades Cove). There are June records for adjacent localities such as Tuckaleechee Cove (June 18, 1940—Trautman), Happy Valley (June 29, 1942—Manley), and Gatlinburg (1955, Manley). Wetmore [1939] reports it from near Cosby on July 5, 1937, and I observed it July 15, 1953, in Gatlinburg.

The largest number of these flycatchers to be listed in one day was 30–40, on September 3, 1940, near Gatlinburg (Manley). Fleetwood recorded 18 birds in Cades Cove on May 3, 1935.

During the summer, this species is more likely to be encountered just outside the park in the more open coves and cultivated areas.

WESTERN KINGBIRD—*Tyrannus verticalis*

On October 1, 1957, Manley notified me that he had one of these flycatchers under observation in Gatlinburg, within 100 yards of the park boundary. A few minutes later we were both watching this bird. For a time it fed on pokeberries; later it perched on some telephone wires where it was in excellent view. On the following day, in the same area, Manley saw a Western Kingbird that in all probability was the same individual.

This is the only record of a species that appears to be extending its range eastward.

GREAT CRESTED FLYCATCHER— *Myiarchus crinitus*

At low and middle altitudes, this handsome flycatcher is a fairly common summer resident over much of the park. Metcalf [1938] reported one from near the Clingmans Dome Parking Area on August 27, 1937—the only record from the spruce-fir zone. In 1935, Fleetwood listed this bird from Russell Field (May 18) and from Parson Bald (May 23), both on the state-line ridge.

The earliest spring record is April 18 (1948, Cades Cove—Stupka); 12 other earliest-arrival dates range from April 24 through 30. The August 27 (1937) report mentioned above is the latest as well as the highest record.

Fleetwood reported that the pair of Great Crested Flycatchers he observed near Parson Bald on May 23, 1935, acted as though they were nesting there in a tree. I noted a group of at least 4 of these birds on June 21, 1952, near Emerts Cove; these may have been a family that had nested in the vicinity.

EASTERN PHOEBE—*Sayornis phoebe*

The phoebe, a common permanent resident at the low and middle altitudes, is our only overwintering flycatcher. Although the majority of these birds leave us in the fall, a number will remain in the lower elevations. Christmas Bird Count parties listed a total of 15 phoebes on December 28, 1947, and again on January 3, 1954; a total of 14 were counted on December 21, 1958, and again on January 3, 1960.

The number of these flycatchers decreases at a rapid rate at altitudes above 3000 ft., due largely to the scarcity of desirable habitats, and in spruce-fir forests they are absent or rare. Trautman [letter] observed 2 phoebes along the high-altitude road between Indian Gap and the Clingmans Dome Parking Area on June 19, 1940. Ganier and Clebsch [1938] report 2 birds along the Appalachian Trail between Clingmans Dome and Silers Bald on June 18, 1938. Burns observed a phoebe at Alum Cave Bluffs (4900 ft.) on May 30, 1950. Tanner (May 19, 1957) and I (June 10, 1950) recorded the species at an elevation of 4800 ft. along the transmountain road (Tennessee side).

Johnson informed me of finding a phoebe's nest with 3 eggs at Lickstone Fire Tower (4500 ft.) in the Cherokee Indian Reservation, June 11, 1950. These birds breed regularly at Cataloochee Ranch (4888 ft.) near the southeastern boundary of the park; there, on May 28, 1952, I found young about ready to leave one nest while eggs in another nest were being incubated. On October 12, 1943, I observed one of these birds at Newfound Gap (5040 ft.) while on October 11, 1950, Pfitzer and I saw a phoebe at the Ice Water Spring Shelter on the Appalachian Trail (5600 ft.).

Two broods may be the normal quota for this species, although my observation of adults feeding young birds out of the nest in the vicinity of the Sinks on Little River on July 8, 1937, leads one to suspect an occasional third brood. Fleetwood, in 1935, records the discovery of two exceptionally early nests and eggs in Cades Cove—one March 9 in an old house (4 eggs) and one March 14 on a rock ledge (5 eggs). Additional records (Stupka) of nests are as follows:

April 7 (1949) —Headquarters area, 4 eggs. (On April 25 this nest held 1 egg and 3 very small fledglings).
April 17 (1948) —Bradley Fork (2400 ft.), 5 eggs.
April 18 (1948) —Cades Cove, 5 eggs.

May 19 (1954) —Vicinity of Emerts Cove, 5 fledglings left
their nest.

May 29 (1936) —Cades Cove, a second brood hatched in a
nest on ledge above entrance to Gregorys Cave.

A recurrence of the familiar "phoebe" notes begins in late
summer and may continue throughout the fall and winter, especially when the weather is mild. This becomes intensified
during February and March.

ACADIAN FLYCATCHER—*Empidonax virescens*

This little flycatcher is a common summer resident at the
low and middle altitudes where rhododendron-bordered
streams are a favorite habitat. During the years 1935–60, the
earliest spring arrivals were noted between April 24 and 30
on 17 occasions; the earliest is April 20 (1938, Gatlinburg—
Stupka). The latest departure date is October 2 (1934, Forney
Creek—Fleetwood).

There are very few reports of the Acadian Flycatcher occurring above 3500 ft. in these mountains. Tanner [1955]
noted it up to 3700 ft. in the valley of LeConte Creek and
Trautman [letter] observed what was probably a stray individual between Newfound and Indian Gaps on June 22, 1940.
Stevenson and Stupka [1948] recorded this bird to 3800 ft.
at Highlands, North Carolina.

Fleetwood makes mention of a nest of this species in Cataloochee, June 18, 1935. It was constructed of *Usnea* lichens in
a hemlock tree, about 10 ft. from the ground.

TRAILL'S FLYCATCHER—*Empidonax traillii*

The first record of Traill's Flycatcher in this area came on
May 2, 1962, when Dr. John O. Watkins reported this species along the Laurel Creek Road, approximately one and
one-half miles east of Cades Cove. A month later (June 2,
1962) Drs. Joseph C. Howell and Samuel R. Tipton heard
the "fitsbew" notes of this bird approximately 300 yards beyond Wilson's Restaurant, in Tuckaleechee Cove, along the
road to Laurel Lake; good views were had at a distance of 50
ft. as the bird sang repeatedly from the top of a willow tree
beside a stream.

Herndon's [1958] discovery of breeding birds in the northeast corner of Tennessee (Elizabethton) in June 1958, represents the first record of the nesting of this little flycatcher in Tennessee and serves to extend the breeding range southward from West Virginia, Maryland, and eastern Pennsylvania [A.O.U. *Check-list of North American Birds*, 1957]. This species was reported breeding in that same area in 1959, 1960, and 1961 Herndon. "Strong circumstantial evidence now exists that this species breeds in Kentucky, Virginia and North Carolina" [Herndon, 1958].

Although predictions may result in future embarrassment,* the writer is inclined to believe that Traill's Flycatcher is one of the birds whose breeding range may extend to include the Great Smoky Mountains National Park and vicinity.

LEAST FLYCATCHER—*Empidonax minimus*

On the basis of more than 100 records of this little flycatcher, it is considered a somewhat uncommon transient and summer resident in the eastern half of the park. West of Gatlinburg and the Park Headquarters area it appears to have been overlooked as there is but one record at Elkmont (April 25, 1935—Fleetwood) and two in Fontana Village (May 28, 1949, and June 4–5, 1952—Stupka). Over the 18-year period 1936–53, I have heard its vigorous "chebec, chebec" notes in Gatlinburg during the month of May in every year except one (1938). This bird nested in Gatlinburg in an open grove of Virginia pines near the southern end of the city for a number of years (1950–53); there I heard its emphatic notes almost daily throughout June, but the cutting of those trees forced it to move elsewhere. Another pair probably nested in or near the mature stand of beech trees close to the Mountain View Hotel. Other low-altitude localities where Least Flycatchers have been observed in June include the Park Headquarters area (1460 ft.) 4 records; Mt. Sterling, North Carolina (1557 ft.) 3 records; Cosby and vicinity

---

* In their predictions concerning this flycatcher, Pearson, Brimley, and Brimley [1959] make the statement that "It is unlikely that it will ever be found breeding in North Carolina, unless perchance in some of the higher mountains."

(1700 ft.) 2 records; and Cherokee, North Carolina (1900 ft.) 2 records.

These birds are also known to breed in fairly open high-altitude localities in the vicinity of the southeastern boundary of the park. I have observed them in June at Soco Gap, 4300 ft. (4 records); in the vicinity of Black Camp Gap, 4522 ft. (3 records); along Flat Creek, 5000 ft. (2 records); and at Cataloochee Ranch, 4888 ft. (1 record). They do not occur in spruce forests at comparable elevations.

This flycatcher arrives during the latter part of April; there are 7 earliest-arrival dates from April 22 through 24, and 8 between April 27 and 30. The earliest is a bird I saw and heard in Gatlinburg on April 20 (1946). The species is very quiet in late summer; however, on September 7 and 8, 1953, Lix heard the notes repeatedly near his home, in Gatlinburg. Those are also the last dates of its occurrence in our area.

EASTERN WOOD PEWEE—*Contopus virens*

This flycatcher is a common summer resident throughout the park. While it occurs at all altitudes, it is not nearly as prevalent in the spruce-fir forests as at low and middle elevations. Trautman [letter] observed it on Clingmans Dome June 22, 1940, and Stimson records it from Mt. LeConte October 5, 1947. I have a record from 6000 ft. on Mt. LeConte August 27, 1942. In addition there are numerous records of this bird above the 3500 ft. altitude. Records for the period 1935 to 1960 reveal that the earliest spring arrivals were noted between April 26 and May 1 on 17 years; the earliest record is April 20 (1941, Stupka). The latest departure date in the fall is October 25 (1961, Stupka).

On June 7, 1949, I observed a pewee completing its nest about 20 ft. from the ground in the Park Headquarters area. Young birds were discovered in a nest near Fontana Village on June 25, 1953 (Stupka). Ganier and Clebsch [1938] report that on June 16, 1938, two of the four pewees they saw on Spence Field Bald were young birds.

Aldrich and Goodrum [1946] found one pair of Eastern Wood Pewees in the 23-acre virgin hardwood forest area they censused June 23–28, 1946, in Porters Flat.

OLIVE-SIDED FLYCATCHER—*Nuttallornis borealis*

This boreal species is near the southernmost extension of its breeding range in Great Smoky Mountains National Park [A.O.U. *Check-list of North American Birds,* 1957] where it is an uncommon summer resident in the high-altitude spruce-fir forests. Of the 148 records of this bird, all but 4 are at elevations in excess of 3500 ft. It is one of the latest migrants to arrive—on 6 years the vanguard of these flycatchers appeared between April 26 and May 2; on 12 years the earliest arrivals were noted between May 11 and 21. The earliest record is April 26 (1952) —Sutton and party at 4600 ft. along the trans-mountain road (Tennessee side), and my record in the Park Headquarters area on the same day in 1961. My observation of one of these birds on September 19 (1940) on Mt. Kephart (6150 ft.) proved to be our latest record for the fall migration.

The numbers of records of this flycatcher during the years 1934–61 reveal that it is by no means a rare breeder in the park: 5 records in April, 46 in May, 49 in June, 37 in July, 7 in August, and 4 in September. The sharp drop from July to August coincides with the cessation of song; rarely, in the late summer, do we hear the emphatic "What peeves you?"—a reiterated question so characteristic of this high-mountain bird.

The vicinity of Newfound Gap has long been a favored resort of this species. Along the Appalachian Trail in the region of the Sawteeth, and between Arch Rock and Alum Cave Bluffs are other locations where the Olive-sided Flycatcher has been noted on a number of occasions.

FAMILY | *ALAUDIDAE*

HORNED LARK—*Eremophila alpestris*

This bird is a very uncommon winter resident and a rare summer resident in the Cades Cove area. Elsewhere within the park its occurrences have been scarce, irregular, and fleeting. There are the following 6 records from Cades Cove:

January 5, 1946—14 birds (Stupka).

April 27, 1952—1 singing (Howell and party).

May 31, 1953—Upon being notified by Mrs. Weig and Mrs. Appleby (Morristown, Virginia) that they had observed young birds in Cades Cove, these ladies and I drove to that area where 2 adults and a fledgling were discovered. This served to establish the first breeding record for the Horned Lark in the park.

December 4, 1953—A flock of approximately 50 birds was flushed in the open meadowlands (Stupka).

December 22, 1957—The party listing birds on the Christmas Bird Count observed a flock of 18 Horned Larks.

June 7, 1958—3 birds (Stimson).

Elsewhere the records are few and widely scattered, as follows:

December 2, 1934—1 bird on Silers Bald (Fleetwood).

December 12, 1936—2 birds along Laurel Creek (Stupka).

November 15, 1944—4 birds along the transmountain road, one-half mile below Newfound Gap, on the North Carolina side (Stupka).

February 1, 1951—a flock of 22 birds appeared on the lawn in the Park Headquarters area during a sharp drop in the temperature and just prior to a storm (Stupka).

May 8, 1960—1 bird observed at the Clingmans Dome Parking Area (Hebard).

Foster [letter] reported a flock of 30 birds in Gatlinburg on December 30, 1935, and I have records from Emerts Cove, Wears Cove, and Pigeon Forge—all in December or January. During the 20-year period 1937–56, when Christmas Bird Count parties included the Pigeon Forge area in their territory, a total of 225 Horned Larks was counted; the species was observed there on 12 of the 20 years. On March 31, 1956, Manley observed 2 young birds on the golf course at Pigeon Forge that appeared to be fledged but were not yet able to fly.

FAMILY | *HIRUNDINIDAE*

TREE SWALLOW—*Iridoprocne bicolor*

Apparently Tree Swallows avoid the mountain ranges for they are very scarce spring and fall transients in our area. I observed one of these swallows in Wears Cove April 13 (1939); in Tuckaleechee Cove, I noted 10 birds April 21 (1949) and 1 bird April 30 (1953). At Laurel Lake, within 2 miles of the park line, Manley counted approximately 75 on April 10 (1942) and Burns reported 20 on April 13 (1950).

Our only fall record represents a late flight of this species. On October 26, 1957, the day following a sudden drop in the temperature, Manley counted 19 Tree Swallows on wires in Gatlinburg; some were still present when I came to view them later in the day. Two days later (October 28) a few of these birds were still in the area.

BANK SWALLOW—*Riparia riparia*

The only Bank Swallow record I am recognizing is one furnished by Saunders [letter] who observed 4 of these birds in Gatlinburg on April 25, 1952. Since this rare transient resembles the Rough-winged Swallow (*Stelgidopteryx ruficollis*), it may have been overlooked.

ROUGH-WINGED SWALLOW— *Stelgidopteryx ruficollis*

This bird is a fairly common summer resident. On 10 of the years between 1935 and 1956, the vanguards of the spring arrivals put in their appearance between March 28 and 31; the earliest is a bird I observed in Elkmont March 19 (1945). The latest fall record is represented by Foster's and Mc-Camey's report [letter] of 4 Rough-winged Swallows on Parson Bald on September 3 (1936).

Although this swallow does not appear to breed at altitudes above 2500 ft. (Elkmont vicinity), it occurs above the main crest of the Smokies during the summer months. Seibert [letter] observed it over Silers Bald and Andrews Bald in late July 1936, and I have August records of birds over Mt. Guyot, Double Springs Gap, and Andrews Bald.

A bird carrying what appeared to be nesting material was seen May 16, 1939, in the Sugarlands (Stupka). Fleetwood reports the discovery of a nest and eggs in Greenbrier on June 4, 1934. Two adult Rough-winged Swallows were feeding 5 young out of the nest, June 12, 1946, in Gatlinburg (Stupka).

Normally the spring arrivals consist of from 1 to 4 birds, but on March 27, 1953, Liles reported a flock of 15 over Laurel Lake. Larger flocks are not uncommon after the nesting cares are over; on August 27 (1944) I observed a few hundred birds on wires or milling about in the air near Laurel Lake. A flock of 15 birds was in the air over Andrews Bald on August 28, 1947, and a large flock was noted along the main divide between Double Springs Gap and Silers Bald on August 29, 1938 (Stupka).

BARN SWALLOW—*Hirundo rustica*

This swallow is an uncommon spring and fall migrant and may be a rare summer resident in the park. In 1935, Fleetwood reported this species from Cades Cove on May 4 (2 birds), May 8 (1 bird), May 18 (9 birds), and May 20 (4 birds), but he made no mention of their nesting. Stimson observed 2 Barn Swallows in Cades Cove on June 7, 1958. In all probability, these birds have bred in Cades Cove in recent years. The earliest of 10 April records (1934–61) was on April 4 (1960, Gatlinburg—Manley); latest fall departure date was September 14 (1941, Tuckaleechee Cove—Stupka).

Manley observed 3 or 4 pairs nesting under the Greystone Hotel bridge, in Gatlinburg, on May 9, 1960; he informed me that these swallows had also nested there during the previous year. On June 25, 1960, at least 4 nests were being visited at frequent intervals by adult birds (Stupka).

At Cataloochee Ranch (4888 ft.), approximately one mile southeast of the park line, I observed a nesting pair of these birds June 4 and 5, 1961. The nest, placed against the side of a rafter in the horse barn, was called to my attention by Tom Alexander, proprietor of Cataloochee Ranch, who also informed me that a single pair of Barn Swallows had nested in that building during each of the past 5 years. This appears to be the highest elevation for the breeding of this bird [Stevenson and Stupka, 1948; Stevenson, 1957] and one of the few records in western North Carolina [Pearson, Brimley, and Brimley, 1959].

Barn Swallows have been reported from near Cosby on July 10, 1934 (Fleetwood), and from Tuckaleechee Cove on June 17 and 29, 1942 (Manley). The largest flock observed, approximately 30 birds, was in Gatlinburg on April 14, 1961 (Manley).

CLIFF SWALLOW—*Petrochelidon pyrrhonota*

This swallow is a very uncommon fall migrant in the vicinity of the park and a very rare fall migrant within the area. Only in the years 1937, 1941, and 1942 has this bird been reported. On July 23, 1937, I observed between 300 and 400 Cliff Swallows resting on telephone wires in Bryson City, North Carolina, approximately one mile from the park line; this represents our earliest fall record and the only July record. Manley observed a few of these birds August 11, 1942, in Tuckaleechee Cove, and August 15, 1942, in Gatlinburg. George estimated there were 150 Cliff Swallows in a flock he saw in Tuckaleechee Cove August 15, 1942. Bellrose [1938] noted a mixed flock of Cliff and Barn Swallows flying over fields near Gatlinburg on August 30, 1937.

Quay, on September 7, 1941, estimated that the large flock of Cliff Swallows he had under observation in Tuckaleechee Cove, near the park line, totaled more than 1,500 birds. Three days later (September 10, 1941) Manley brought in a dead bird he had discovered at Metcalf Bottoms, along the Little River road.

PURPLE MARTIN—*Progne subis*

Now that almost all the people who lived in what is now Great Smoky Mountains National Park have moved elsewhere, the martin houses have disappeared and with them the breeding martins. Here as elsewhere in the southern states, poles with crossarms were erected and from the crossarms gourds were suspended. This was done to encourage martins to rear a brood of young, these large swallows being so fearless in the defense of their territory that any hawk with designs on poultry would be attacked and routed. Along the periphery of the park some of these gourd houses continue to be available for these birds, so that martins are uncommon summer residents in the immediate vicinity. Within the park they are uncommon spring and fall transients and summer visitants. The earliest spring arrival date is March 15 (1952, Gatlinburg—Stupka); in the fall the latest record is September 10 (1938, Gatlinburg—Stupka).

Kincaid [letter] reported 2 Purple Martins from Cades Cove between May 7 and 11, 1958, and Ganier and Clebsch [1938] observed 4 birds in that area on June 16, 1938. Records above 4700 ft. include the following:

Andrews Bald—May 4, 1957 (6 birds, Tanner).
Spence Field Bald—June 16, 1938 (2 birds) [Ganier and Clebsch, 1938].
Newfound Gap—July 13, 1938 (1 bird, Stupka).
Double Springs Gap—July 28, 1939 (1 bird, Stupka).
Newton Bald—August 3 and 6, 1934 (1 bird, Fleetwood).
Parson Bald—September 3, 1936 (12 birds) [McCamey, letter].
Clingmans Dome—September 5, 1936 (1 bird) [McCamey, letter].

FAMILY | *CORVIDAE*

BLUE JAY—*Cyanocitta cristata*

This familiar bird* is a common permanent resident throughout the park. Although a few are to be found in the higher altitudes during the winter months, Blue Jays are relatively scarce there from November on into early spring. Breeding takes place from the lowest to the highest elevations. In Cades Cove (1800 ft.) I observed a bird sitting on a nest May 4, 1948, and Fleetwood reported young capable of

* A specimen collected in the Greenbrier area on April 8, 1931, was determined by Wetmore [letter] as belonging to the northern race (*Cyanocitta cristata bromia*). According to the distribution of the eastern Blue Jays as given in the A.O.U. Check-list [1957], both the northern and the southern (*C. c. cristata*) subspecies may occur in the park.

flight May 15, 1935. At Dry Sluice Gap (5375 ft.) on the main ridge of the Smokies, McCamey watched a parent Blue Jay feeding young July 10, 1947.

The largest flock on record, comprised of about 100 birds, was observed by Gilbert at Fighting Creek Gap on October 6, 1957. The average number of Blue Jays listed in one day by Christmas Bird Count parties (1935–60) is 16, but as many as 93 were counted (January 3, 1960) when the area worked included Tuckaleechee Cove and Cades Cove.

COMMON RAVEN—*Corvus corax*

In the higher and more remote regions of the Great Smokies, where mankind has wrought but little change in the prevailing wilderness, the raven is an uncommon permanent resident. In these heavily-forested mountains no bird is as symbolic of wildness and of solitude. If we are to believe the accounts of various people who resided here in pre-park days, ravens were more plentiful then than now. Hundreds of cattle, hogs, and sheep roamed the high-altitude forests and "balds" for many months of the year, and their presence, directly and indirectly, made possible a larger population of ravens. The conversion of 800 square miles of the Great Smoky Mountains into a sanctuary, thereby removing all live-stock from the higher altitudes, proved to be a mixed blessing for the raven.*

During the warmer months of the year ravens occur but rarely at the lower altitudes. In fact there are but 4 records of these birds below the 3500 ft. elevation during the 5 consecutive months beginning with May (1934–61). On May 28, 1949, Manley saw and heard a group of 6 ravens calling as they flew over the Little Pigeon River, in Gatlin-burg (1300 ft.). There are many low-altitude records of these birds from October through April, but even then they are much more likely to occur in the higher mountains.

* Bent [1946], on the authority of Mrs. Nice, tells us that "the raven was formerly an abundant resident in Oklahoma in the days of the buffalo, but that with the disappearance of the bison the ravens have gone." To some degree, this state of affairs was attributed to the eating of poisoned baits and the viscera of wolves that had been poisoned, but even without the poisoning, the chances are that both the ravens and the wolves would have disappeared with the passing of the bison.

Kephart [1921] calls attention to a "Ravens Cliff" * on Locust Ridge, west of Hazel Creek, "where they winter and breed." Campbell [1936] describes an attempt by Crouch to reach a raven's nest situated in a crevice half-way up a perpendicular 100-foot cliff above Roaring Fork. Trail Foreman Wear notified me that on May 10, 1943, near Dry Sluice Gap, he observed 2 ravens and heard what he took to be the cries of their young—the sounds resembling the crying of young crows. Koch, on May 21, 1944, reported 2 pairs of ravens in the vicinity of Alum Cave Bluffs where he also heard young birds crying for food. Ganier [1962] describes the finding of a nest on the steep face of Peregrine Ridge (near Alum Cave Bluffs) on May 4, 1960, that held 3 well-feathered young; one of these young ravens was seen to leave the nest on the following day.

This shy bird is of a rather solitary nature, but small groups are not unusual. On October 7, 1936, a group consisting of 9 ravens and 2 Cooper's Hawks soared over Pin Oak Gap (Stupka). Behrend [letter] observed 10 ravens at the Clingmans Dome Parking Area September 30, 1953. The foreman of a work crew, stationed near Newfound Gap, notified me that on December 19, 1936, shortly after a heavy snowstorm, a group of 14 ravens put in their appearance and fed upon pieces of bread and other scraps scattered for their benefit. We have three reports of groups of 8 ravens, three reports of groups of 7, and nine reports of groups of 6 of these birds. Since such gatherings usually take place from August through December, a good proportion of them probably represent family groups.

Being a bird of mostly high altitudes, the raven encounters his relative, the crow, rather infrequently. In the Park Headquarters area I witnessed the bigger bird being harassed by 4 crows on October 28 and again on December 8, 1937. A Cooper's Hawk was observed diving at a raven near Newfound Gap on October 20, 1937, and a Broad-winged Hawk was in pursuit of a raven above Indian Gap on May 2, 1942 (Stupka).

* Designated as "Raven Den" on the U.S.G.S. Topographic Map, Great Smoky Mountains National Park (West half), Scale 1:62 500, Surveyed in 1927–31.

While 12 Turkey Vultures and 5 ravens were circling together over the summit of Cove Mountain on October 21, 1953, I observed that the ravens would make occasional dives at the vultures.

During the 20-year period beginning in 1937 when the annual one-day count of winter birds was conducted in an area centering on Mt. LeConte, a total of 94 ravens was listed. Between 1 and 10 ravens were observed on 19 of the 20 years.

Along park roads, at the higher altitudes, ravens have been seen in the vicinity of garbage cans and at picnic sites on numerous occasions. They glean scraps of food from along the highways and feed upon the carcasses of animals killed by cars. Ordinarily such activity takes place in the early morning hours before there is much traffic on the roads.

COMMON CROW—*Corvus brachyrhynchos*

In the lower altitudes of the park, where it occurs throughout the year, the crow * is a fairly common bird. In most of the watersheds it seldom breeds above the 3000 ft. altitude, but the high divide along the southeastern boundary of the park appears to be an exception where some crows may nest well above 3000 ft. I observed parent crows feeding young out of the nest on April 18, 1950, in the Park Headquarters area and on June 28, 1953, near Emerts Cove.

Mr. Alexander, proprietor of Cataloochee Ranch (4888 ft.), informs me that up to 60 crows may winter in his immediate area, close to the park. Ordinarily these birds avoid the high altitudes at all times of year, but this is particularly true in winter. During the warmer months a few crows make infrequent visits to Newfound Gap (5040 ft.), Indian Gap (5266 ft.), Heintooga Ridge (5325 ft.), and perhaps elsewhere to check on the garbage cans at such places.

What appeared to be a migrating flock of 200–300 crows was observed November 9, 1938, at about 8 A.M. over the Park Headquarters area. The birds, flying high and rapidly

* Based on the examination of 37 crows shot in January 1938, near Maryville, Tennessee, about 10 miles northwest of the park, Wing [1940] reveals the presence of two subspecies (*Corvus b. brachyrhynchos* and *C. b. paulus*). In all probability, this situation prevails in the wintering crow populations within the park as well.

in a southwesterly direction, were in close formation. A few of the familiar cawing notes were uttered. There had been a sudden change in the weather just prior to this flight. Again on the late afternoon of October 28, 1955, in the same area, a flock of 30 crows was seen flying in the same direction. A flock of approximately 250 birds was noted milling over the Park Headquarters Building at 6 P.M. February 8, 1962 (Cole and Whaley).

There is no record of a winter roost of any sizable proportions within the park.* Up to a few hundred crows frequent Cades Cove, and in the Cherokee Indian Reservation there may be an even greater population, some of which invades the Oconaluftee meadows near the southern terminus of the Blue Ridge Parkway.

For the 20-year period 1937–56 when the annual one-day count of winter birds was made in the north-central part of the park (including the Pigeon Forge area), the average number of crows per count was approximately 248. The greatest number reported, an estimation of 1,000 birds, was on January 2, 1949.

FAMILY | *PARIDAE*

BLACK-CAPPED CHICKADEE—*Parus atricapillus*

William Brewster [1886] appears to have been the first to reveal the presence of the Black-capped Chickadee south of Virginia and, on the basis of two pairs of breeding birds he collected in western North Carolina, to suspect that it might merit recognition as a new subspecies. More than a half-century later this was finally accomplished by Oberholser [1937] who, basing his description on a bird collected at 6500 ft. on Mt. Guyot (by Thomas D. Burleigh, April 15, 1932) went on record to describe the new race. This, *Parus atricapillus practicus,* is the only bird originally described from Great Smoky Mountains National Park. Here it is at the southern limit of its range.

* Wing [1940] writes of a roost of approximately 5,000 birds near Maryville, Tennessee (Blount County), about 10 miles northwest of the park boundary.

The Black-capped Chickadee is a fairly common permanent resident in the park where, during the breeding season, it occurs mostly at altitudes above 3000 ft. The similar-appearing Carolina Chickadee (*P. carolinensis*) frequents the lower elevations but on occasion may range to 5000 ft. or even higher [Cairns, 1889; Burleigh, 1941; Tanner, 1952]. Brewster [1886] reported that Black-capped and Carolina Chickadees mingled along the lower borders of the former's range, but according to Tanner [1952] the occasional overlapping takes place only in the non-breeding season.

All who are interested in the chickadees of the Southern Appalachian Mountains should read Tanner's report * on a study of these birds which he conducted mostly in Great Smoky Mountains National Park. From his summary, I quote, in part, as follows:

"The Black-capped and Carolina chickadees are closely related species that are similar in appearance and habits but which have fairly constant differences in measurements, plumage, and voice. Hybridization, if such actually occurs, is so rare as to have little effect on the characteristics of either species except for small, isolated populations . . .

". . . Black-capped Chickadees are found . . . in the Great Smoky Mountains . . . nesting mostly above 4000 feet. They are more abundant at higher elevations, apparently being better adapted to conditions found there. Carolina Chickadees are found at lower elevations; they do not nest at higher elevations wherever Black-capped Chickadees are present; but where the latter are absent, Carolinas nest sparsely as high as 5000 feet. In the Great Smoky Mountains there is a gap between the nesting range of the two species, wherein neither one nests. In the spring, this gap is occupied by Black-capped Chickadees which behave as if they are going to nest, but which disappear from these areas about the time that Carolina Chickadees begin incubation. These facts indicate: 1) that there is some form of competition between the two species, that operates during the early nesting season; and 2) that the presence of Black-capped Chickadees prevents

---

* *The Auk,* 69:407–424, October, 1952.

the Carolinas from inhabiting the higher parts of the mountains."

In a table in which he designates the comparative abundance of Black-capped Chickadees in three major forest types in the Great Smoky Mountains (from high to low altitudes), Tanner [1952] found that during the nesting season 64 percent inhabited spruce-fir, 29 percent were found in northern hardwoods, and 7 percent dropped down into the southern hardwoods; during the winter season these percentages were 28, 56, and 16, respectively.

All four of the Black-capped Chickadee nests which Tanner [1952] discovered were from 5 to 60 ft. above ground in dead trunks of yellow birch trees. Consequently he infers "that the Black-capped Chickadees of this part of the Appalachians require yellow birch trees for nesting sites and are found only where mature trees of this species are abundant." He observed the digging of nests in late April and early May, two or three weeks later than nesting activities by Carolina Chickadees.

Except during the breeding season, Black-capped Chickadees in the Great Smoky Mountains are prone to associate with Golden-crowned Kinglets, Red-breasted Nuthatches, and Brown Creepers.

CAROLINA CHICKADEE—*Parus carolinensis*

This chickadee is a common permanent resident throughout the lower and middle elevations. Occasionally it is to be found at altitudes above 4000 ft. [Brewster, 1886; Lemoyne, 1886; Ganier and Clebsch, 1944; Tanner, 1952] where it may be associated with the Black-capped Chickadee. Brewster [1886] found Carolina Chickadees "breeding sparingly along the lower edge of the balsam belt" in the Black Mountains of western North Carolina. "In one place a male of each species was singing in the same tree." Cairns [1889] stated that this species was abundant up to 6000 ft. in the Craggy Mountains. Tanner [1952] calls attention to Burleigh's collection of one of these birds near Indian Gap, at 5500 ft., on November 30, 1930.

Carolina Chickadees have been mistaken for Black-caps, and vice versa. In the field, correct determination is often difficult. "To most observers the difference in song has appeared to be the best way to distinguish between the two species in the field. The song of the Black-capped Chickadee is usually a clear, whistled *'phee-bee-ee,'* or less often, *'phee-bee.'* The typical song of the Carolina is a thinner, higher-pitched, four-noted *'se-fee-se-fu'* . . ." [Tanner, 1952]. In addition, the Carolina Chickadee is slightly smaller and tends to be less curious and more timid than its Black-capped relative; plumage differences are slight, but in the Carolina Chickadees the edging to the secondaries is not as wide nor as white as it is in the Black-caps [ibid.].

In view of the similarity between these two species, no distinction has been made during the annual one-day count of winter birds conducted in the park and vicinity since 1935. Through 1961, the average number of chickadees is 167 per count.

The following observations relate to the nesting activities of Carolina Chickadees in the Gatlinburg–Park Headquarters area:

April 2 (1946) —Five eggs in a nest in a fence post.
April 18 (1948) —Seven eggs in a nest in a fence post.
April 18 (1950) —Six eggs in a nest in a fence post. (All 6 had hatched by May 3 and the 6 fledglings left the nest May 18.)
May 17 (1942) —An adult feeding young in a bird box.
May 20 (1953) —Young almost ready to leave their nest in a metal post.

All 6 nests of Carolina Chickadees which Tanner [1952] found during the course of his study in the park were in dead trunks of silverbell trees. "Nest digging began by April 1 or earlier. Incubation began between April 20 and May 6. At one nest the incubation period was apparently 12 days (May 6 to 18). One nest contained five eggs, another seven, and a third held six young."

Although Carolina Chickadees may be found at high altitudes, they seldom invade the spruce-fir forests. Tanner [1952] found 93 percent of these birds in the southern hardwood forest, 7 percent in northern hardwoods, and none in spruce-fir.

TUFTED TITMOUSE—*Parus bicolor*

At altitudes up to 5000 ft., this bird is a common permanent resident. It may occur along the lower fringe of the spruce-fir zone, but favors mature stands of deciduous trees. Occasionally some of these birds wander from their usual haunts; this may explain Metcalf's [1938] observation of one at the Clingmans Dome Parking Area in late August 1937, and my record of one at 6000 ft. on Mt. Kephart on October 4, 1944.

On June 2, 1953, near Emerts Cove, close to the park line, a pair of Tufted Titmice were found nesting in a bird box only recently vacated by bluebirds; the young titmice left this nest July 1. Fleetwood reported hearing fledglings on June 6, 1934, in Greenbrier.

Over a period of 27 years (1935–61) the Christmas Bird Count parties listed an average of 37 Tufted Titmice per count in the park and vicinity.

FAMILY | *SITTIDAE*

WHITE-BREASTED NUTHATCH—*Sitta carolinensis*

This bird, a permanent resident in the park, frequents forests dominated by mature deciduous trees; it is scarce or absent in spruce-fir. From the lowest altitudes it occurs to the upper limits of oak forests (5000–5500 ft.) where, in the latter environment, it is usually a fairly common species. It may be expected in Cades Cove, along most of the drier ridges not dominated by pines, and in open forests in the vicinity of some of the high-altitude grass balds. At Cataloochee Ranch, Hemphill Bald, and the high divide along the southeastern boundary of the park it is fairly common. Walker counted 10 birds in Cades Cove on May 31, 1937, and Crouch and party listed 11 on December 31, 1950, along the Laurel Falls Trail to Cove Mountain.

On August 26, 1937, the Metcalfs [1938] observed a White-breasted Nuthatch along the trail from the parking area (6311 ft.) to the summit of Clingmans Dome (6643 ft.).

This and the lone birds Stimson [letter] reported from above 6000 ft. on Mt. LeConte October 4 and 5, 1947, were probably wanderers. There are 3 records for the Indian Gap area (5266 ft.), 2 in May and 1 in July.

Fleetwood reported both parents feeding young birds in a dead tree at Bunches Bald (5250 ft.) on June 13, 1935. Aldrich and Goodrum [1946] found one pair in the 23-acre virgin hardwood forest area they censused June 23-28, 1946, in Porters Flat (2950-3200 ft.).

Over a period of 27 years (1935-61), Christmas Bird Count parties listed an average of 3 White-breasted Nuthatches per count; 14 birds, observed on December 31, 1961, is the largest number recorded in one day.

RED-BREASTED NUTHATCH—*Sitta canadensis*

Ordinarily, this bird is a permanent resident in the spruce-fir forests of the park, but its numbers fluctuate considerably and unpredictably. Only during very infrequent winters, such as that of 1939-40, does this species appear to forsake these mountains completely, and this, as suggested by Burleigh [1941] and Bent [1948], may have been brought about by the scarcity of spruce and fir seed. Large numbers of Red-breasted Nuthatches were present during the winters of 1937-38, 1940-41, 1949-50, 1953-54, and 1955-56. Christmas Bird Count parties listed this bird on 25 of the 27 years, 1935-61, in numbers ranging up to 175 (1949). During the summer months the breeding population does not appear to undergo this erratic fluctuation in numbers.

In 1940, the earliest reappearance in the spring, following their unusual absence during the winter of 1939-40, was April 16, when I observed a lone bird on Mt. LeConte. The latest low-altitude record in the spring is April 27 (1952) when Howell reported a bird in Cades Cove. Tanner's record of one at 2400 ft. near Cherokee Orchard on September 16, 1949, was probably a bird that had only recently moved down from the nearby mountains. My earliest fall record near Emerts Cove (1600 ft.) is October 9 (1954).

Ganier [1926], on June 2, 1925, noted two pairs building their nests in spruce-fir forests; 12 days later he found one of these nests to contain 6 fresh eggs. Grimes [1952], while attempting to photograph this species at its nest near Newfound Gap, in June (1949–52), observed a red squirrel raid the nest and make off with a young bird almost fully feathered. Edwards reported a pair of Red-breasted Nuthatches feeding young in a nest near Rocky Spring Gap (5500 ft.) on June 26, 1952. During the breeding season, the lowest altitude at which this bird has been noted is approximately 2900 ft.—one record on June 12, 1958, above Cades Cove, by Stevenson [letter].

These birds often associate with Golden-crowned Kinglets, Brown Creepers, and Black-capped Chickadees except during the nesting period.

FAMILY | *CERTHIIDAE*

BROWN CREEPER—*Certhia familiaris*

This bird is a fairly common permanent resident in the park where it breeds in the higher altitudes. Brown Creepers * winter throughout the area. Burleigh [1941] reported that on Mt. Mitchell, less than 50 miles east of Great Smoky Mountains National Park, this species did not occur above 4500 ft. in the winter, but this does not apply here where 19 December and 21 January records are for localities above that altitude.

My observation of a Brown Creeper in the vicinity of Emerts Cove (1600 ft.) on April 10, 1955, appears to be the latest record at a low altitude. Fleetwood reported one April 17, 1935, on Bunker Hill Lead (2500 ft.). On October 10, 1953, the Brown Creeper I noted near Emerts Cove represents the earliest low-altitude record in the fall.

The singing of this bird is largely confined to the period from late March through June. I have heard its rather weak but very pleasing song as early as February 14 (1949, New-

---

* Two subspecies may winter in the park—the northern race, *Certhia familiaris americana*, whose southernmost breeding limits are in Ohio, Pennsylvania, and Maryland [A.O.U. Check-list, 1957], and the darker-colored resident race, *C. f. nigrescens* [Burleigh, 1935], known to breed as far south as Highlands, North Carolina [Odum, 1949].

found Gap), March 3 (1948, Park Headquarters), and March 14 (1953, Emerts Cove), but all of these early efforts were squeaky, fuzzy, or incomplete. From late April through June the birds are in song on their high-altitude breeding grounds, mostly in forests of spruce and fir. I have but 2 singing records for each of the months July, August, and October; 6 records for September; and none for November, December, and January.

Lemoyne [1886] appears to have been the first to observe and record the nesting of this species in the Great Smoky Mountains. On May 15, 1885 [1886 ?] he watched a pair of Brown Creepers constructing a nest under the loose bark of a spruce. Ten days later he returned to the nest which "was a medley of lichens, *usnea,* moss, feathers, grass and a few rootlets, in which was placed five eggs." Ganier and Clebsch [1938] describe the discovery of 3 nests at high altitudes between June 14 and 19, 1938; 2 were in the process of construction while the third contained 5 eggs (June 19) nearly fresh. On May 14, 1940, I observed 2 creepers gathering spiderwebs under the rocky overhang at Alum Cave Bluffs (4900 ft.). Tanner on April 27, 1949, watched this species building a nest at 5300 ft. along the Rainbow Falls Trail on Mt. LeConte. Edwards, on June 27, 1952, reported 3 young birds accompanied by 2 adults along the Appalachian Trail. On July 31, 1952, Tanner reported young out of the nest at 6000 ft. on Mt. LeConte.

Before and after the breeding season, Brown Creepers are often to be found associated with chickadees, Golden-crowned Kinglets, and Red-breasted Nuthatches.

Christmas Bird Count parties listed 164 Brown Creepers during the 20-year period 1937–56, an average of approximately 8 per count.

FAMILY | *TROGLODYTIDAE*

HOUSE WREN—*Troglodytes aedon*

In recent years, this wren has been extending its breeding range southward [Burleigh, 1958; Howell and Monroe, 1957; Pearson, Brimley, and Brimley, 1959]. Records of its occurrence in the park and in the immediate vicinity are quite irregular, but it has been noted during all but three months (February, March, and August), and it is possible that nesting has taken place on rare occasions.

In the spring, the earliest record is April 22 (1935, Cades Cove—Fleetwood). Mrs. Eifert [letter] includes this species in a list of birds from Gatlinburg, and vicinity, April 23, 1952. At Park Headquarters I observed a singing House Wren on April 26, 1958, and Watkins reported one there April 27, 1955. On May 30, 1924, Mayfield included one of these birds in a list he compiled at Elkmont [letter from Ganier]. On May 23 and 28, 1953, and again on July 15 and 17 of that year I heard the repeated song of this species in the same yard along the main street in Gatlinburg, but could not determine whether more than one bird was present. In June 1937, Keating [letter] observed one in Elkmont on the 9th and another in Cades Cove between the 9th and 11th. In July 1955, I heard the song of this bird along Deep Creek on the 19th, and at Bryson City, approximately a mile away, on the 29th. On a number of days in July 1956, a lone House Wren was heard singing near Emerts Cove. In the Park Headquarters area I observed one bird September 23, 1943.

There are 9 records during October, 7 of which are for the Park Headquarters–Sugarlands–Gatlinburg region. On October 23, 1934, Fleetwood listed two birds in Cades Cove; on October 15, 1949, I heard one singing near Emerts Cove. In the Sugarlands on October 28, 1947, I heard the charming whisper song which Todd [1940] describes as "strangely faint, soft, and low."

There are 3 records of single birds in November, 1 on December 20–21, 1942, and 1 on January 5, 1951 (Burns) — all in the Park Headquarters–Gatlinburg region.

WINTER WREN—*Troglodytes troglodytes*

This bird,* like a few other Canadian zone species with which it associates on its breeding grounds (e. g., Golden-

---

* Burleigh [1935], on the basis of a series of specimens he collected here, on Mt. Mitchell, and elsewhere in western North Carolina, described this as a distinct race, *T. t. pullus;* it not only winters at the foot of the mountains whereon it breeds, but may travel as far as the Gulf Coast of Mississippi [Bur-

crowned Kinglet, Brown Creeper, and Red-breasted Nut-hatch), is a fairly common permanent resident in the park, nesting at the highest altitudes and wintering mostly in the lowlands.

It is in April that the latest of the Winter Wrens leave the low altitudes for either their high-elevation, or their more northerly breeding grounds. Our latest report is of a bird observed by Lix near Emerts Cove (1700 ft.) April 27, 1958. I have noted it in the Park Headquarters area (1460 ft.) as late as April 18, 1952, and April 22, 1944.

The fall migration is under way throughout October; at elevations below 2000 ft. (Gatlinburg, Sugarlands, Emerts Cove) there are 5 first-arrival records between October 6 and 9, and 9 such records between October 14 and 17. The earliest is October 6 (1945, Gatlinburg—Stupka). A few birds remain in the high mountains during the winter, there being 3 records of Winter Wrens in November, 9 in December, 3 in January, and 1 in February—all above 4300 ft. One cannot help but wonder how these midgets survive the rigorous conditions which often prevail in our higher mountains. Bent [1948] is of the opinion that many perish from hunger and cold, "especially if their meager food supply is buried under deep snow." After the record-breaking cold and snow of the 1939–40 winter, Winter Wrens were unusually scarce throughout the following months; not until May 3, 1940, was one heard singing on its breeding grounds. Again in 1955, when extremely low temperatures prevailed late in March, Winter Wrens were at a low population level. Three years later, following one of the coldest winters on record, these birds were uncommon.

Few who are familiar with the song of the Winter Wren will deny that it is one of the finest musical performances among our eastern birds. An unusually long-continued melodious trill, it has a rapid warbling quality, sparkling and rippling, as charming and delightful to the ear as its evergreen setting is pleasing to the eye. There are singing records dur-

leigh, 1944] and the North Carolina coast [Wetmore, 1941] to spend the winter months. On October 31, 1933, a specimen of the eastern race, *T. t. hiemalis,* was collected in Greenbrier (1800 ft.); Wetmore made the determination in January 1943.

ing every month of the year, but it is in the high-altitude Canadian zone forests of the park from late April until middle July that the song is at its best. On rare occasions the listener may be favored by antiphonal singing, when the refrain is carried on by two or more musicians—as soon as one utters his last note another begins, round after tuneful round, so charmingly synchronized that the performance becomes a never-to-be-forgotten experience [Stupkia, 1943]. Skutch [1940] informs us of such singing on the part of Central American wrens, but in that part of the world both sexes are good singers and the antiphonal vocalization appears to be harmonized between male and female. Fleetwood reported hearing this responsive singing but once— along Forney Creek, December 14, 1934. I have recorded it at Tricorner Knob (5900 ft.) June 28, 1936; in Gatlinburg, on the early mornings of November 9, 1937, and December 5, 1946; and near Emerts Cove, November 6, 1956.

During the latter half of the summer some birds continue to sing, but then the song is uttered less frequently. My records reveal that more than half the songs delivered in August and September are incomplete, scratchy, or irregular.

Bent [1948] and Burleigh [1958] state that the Winter Wren sings but rarely in the fall migration or in winter. In the Great Smoky Mountains those birds that are to be found at high altitudes from October on through February sing rarely or not at all, but the Winter Wrens that arrive in the lowlands in October sing occasionally during that month. In November there is a considerable amount of singing, some of which is reminiscent of the performance on the breeding grounds; in Gatlinburg, often at dawn, I have listened to the song dozens of times. Less, but still a fair amount of singing, takes place in December, and I have heard it a few times in January and February. The soft whisper song to which Forbush [1929] refers was heard August 25, 1943, on Mt. LeConte and September 10, 1943, on Mt. Kephart (Stupka).

Ganier and Mayfield [1946], during the course of a hiking trip from Newfound Gap to Mt. LeConte, June 20–21, 1933, reported finding a nest from which 5 young birds took wing. Fleetwood observed an adult and two young June 10, 1935, at 4000 ft., near Heintooga Ridge; the young birds were able to fly. Keating [letter], on June 12, 1937, observed young, recently out of the nest, on Andrews Bald (5800 ft.). Wetmore [1939] mentions juvenile birds at high altitudes in late June 1937.

An average of approximately 8 Winter Wrens per count were reported by Christmas Bird Count parties, 1935–61.

BEWICK'S WREN—*Thryomanes bewickii*

This wren is a very uncommon summer resident and a rare winter visitor in the park. It is of somewhat more frequent occurrence at low altitudes just outside the area (Emerts Cove, Gatlinburg, Pigeon Forge, Tuckaleechee Cove, Fontana Dam, Bryson City) where a more favorable habitat prevails. Competition with the aggressive House Wren would not be a factor in limiting the local population of the Bewick's Wren * since the former species is scarce in our region, but if, as Sutton has pointed out [Bent, 1948], Bewick's and Carolina Wrens do not occupy the same area without friction, the prevalent and larger Carolina Wren may be partly responsible for the uncommon status of Bewick's.

Fleetwood reported from 1 to 4 of these wrens in Cades Cove on a number of days in March (earliest, March 2), April, and May 1935, during which time nesting probably took place. In addition there are from 10 to 14 records each month, March through June (1933–60)—all from low-altitude locations with the exception of 4 that are on or near the park boundary in the extreme southeastern region (Hemphill Bald, Cataloochee Ranch, and Black Camp Gap). The only July records are Fleetwood's (1934)—2 from Black Camp Gap (4522 ft.) and 1 from Hemphill Bald (5573 ft.). There are no August records. The 11 September records, of which September 3 (1937) is earliest, and 16 October records are mostly from the Sugarlands–Park Headquarters area. The only high-altitude observation during the fall season was a single bird at The Narrows, near Silers Bald, on October 1, 1934 (Fleetwood). Two records each in November, December, and January complete the list—all from

* Replacement of the Bewick's by the House Wren was predicted at Johnson City, Tennessee, by Tyler and Lyle [1947] and in Shenandoah National Park, Virginia, by Wetmore [1950].

low altitudes. There are no February records and no records from the spruce-fir zone.

On June 19, 1943, I listened to the repeated singing of 2 Bewick's Wrens at Black Camp Gap (4522 ft.) where I suspected the species was nesting. Fleetwood, in 1934, observed 2 fledglings at this locality on July 28. On May 28, 1952, at Cataloochee Ranch (4888 ft.), I heard the song of this wren and watched one fly off with food in its bill.

Christmas Bird Count parties listed a total of 13 Bewick's Wrens during the years 1937–61 in numbers ranging up to 3 birds per count; 9 of the birds were from Pigeon Forge, 2 from Tuckaleechee Cove, 1 from Greenbrier, and 1 from Elkmont.

CAROLINA WREN—*Thryothorus ludovicianus*

This bird is a common permanent resident throughout the lower altitudes where it favors the margins of watercourses and the proximity of human habitations. Although it is quite sedentary, a few are known to wander, particularly in late summer and fall, appearing in rather unexpected areas where mostly single birds may remain for many weeks. One Carolina Wren appeared near Mt. LeConte Lodge (6300 ft.) on August 31, 1939, and was observed there throughout the following September and October. Another, heard singing at Newfound Gap (5040 ft.) September 8, 1944, was joined by a second individual some days later and these remained at that place at least through the 26th of that month. Again, two months later (November 28, 1944), I heard a Carolina Wren singing at Newfound Gap.

At Arch Rock (4200 ft.), along Alum Cave Creek, one of these wrens was heard singing March 29, 1939, and again on May 11 and December 4 of that year. Whether it nested there is not known, but if it wintered there the consequences, in all probability, were disastrous since the winter of 1939–40 was exceptionally severe. Griscom's [1945] statements are pertinent:

"The Carolina wren of the eastern United States is a bird which is constantly pushing northward from Washington, D. C., as far as Massachusetts. At the end of a ten-

or fifteen-year period, the bird is a general summer resident or rather a permanent resident throughout this area, with scattered pairs nesting in Massachusetts. All of this is apparently in vain, because sooner or later a winter comes along with a particularly heavy snowfall. The Carolina wrens starve to death, and they are exterminated back to the southern limits of this heavy snowfall."

It is reasonable to assume that in a mountainous region this die-off functions vertically as well as horizontally, and that those individuals that move to the high altitudes to spend the winter are in real danger—the higher they go the greater the peril.

Additional casual occurrences of this bird, well above its normal range, are as follows: Pretty Hollow Gap, 5280 ft.—January 26, 1935 (Fleetwood); Clingmans Dome Parking Area, 6311 ft.—June 8, 1944 (Hyder); slope of Mt. Kephart, 5800 ft.—August 15, 1944 (Stupka); Indian Gap, 5266 ft.—August 17, 1951 (Burns); Newfound Gap, 5040 ft.—September 14, 1943 (Stupka); vicinity of Alum Cave Bluffs, 4600 ft.—October 3 and 17, 1944 (Stupka); and Charlies Bunion, 5375 ft.—October 27, 1939 (Stupka).

This, the largest and most common of our wrens, has been heard singing every month of the year. On the morning of January 30, 1952, in the Park Headquarters area, a Carolina Wren was heard singing when the temperature read 6° above zero.

Manley observed the construction of a nest in the Sugarlands March 22, 1941. Fleetwood reported 5 eggs in a nest in Greenbrier June 14, 1934; on June 28 of that year he examined a nest along Big Creek that contained 4 eggs. On April 22, 1937, I watched a pair feeding their young in a birdbox, in Gatlinburg. Cairns [1889] who lived near Asheville, North Carolina, remarked that "the birds are very prolific. A pair have nested in our barn the past three summers. In 1886 they raised fifteen young ones, seventeen in 1887, and sixteen in 1888, but still there are only the one pair there." Bent [1948] states that two or three broods are raised in a year.

During the years 1935–61, Christmas Bird Count parties listed an average of 24 Carolina Wrens per count in the Great

Smoky Mountains and vicinity. The largest number reported is 63 birds (January 3, 1960).

LONG-BILLED MARSH WREN—
Telmatodytes palustris

This wren is a very uncommon spring and fall migrant and a rare winter resident. In the Cades Cove area I observed it in 1938 (May 20), 1939 (May 17), and 1940 (May 6 and 26) in the wet meadow locally known as the "Oliver Swamp." One bird passed at least part of one winter there, since I recorded it November 20 and 21, 1943, and on January 12, 18, 19, and 25, 1944. Our only other record of this species is one bird reported from Elkmont by Stimson on October 13, 1954.

SHORT-BILLED MARSH WREN—
Cistothorus platensis

The wet "Oliver Swamp" in Cades Cove is the only place in the park where this scarce spring and fall migrant has been observed. On November 25, 1942, I came upon this little wren for the first time and had excellent views of it at close range. In 1943, Walker and I heard it singing and saw it there on April 28; on May 2 of that year Koch and I observed two birds. Again on October 8, 1943, I recorded two birds at that place. One was observed there April 28, 1948 (Stupka).

This secretive little bird is easily overlooked and its preferred habitat is rare in the park.

FAMILY | *MIMIDAE*

MOCKINGBIRD—*Mimus polyglottos*

Along the northern border of the park from Tuckaleechee Cove to Davenport Gap, the Mockingbird is a fairly common permanent resident. North of the park boundary, and especially in the vicinity of towns and cities, this bird becomes so plentiful that its status may be called "abundant" [Howell and Monroe, 1957]; within the park itself, however, the bird is mostly scarce or rare, its penetration of this area being rather shallow. It is definitely not a bird of the mountains although there have been a number of reports of its occurrence in Cades Cove in all excepting the summer season. Latest date for its spring departure from Cades Cove is May 31, 1937 (Walker) ; earliest return to Cades Cove in the fall is October 23, 1934 (Fleetwood) . Elkmont (2200 ft.) , where it has been observed once, each, in February, June, and December, appears to be the uppermost range of the Mockingbird in our area. On the North Carolina side it has been reported from Ravensford (2100 ft.) , Fontana Village (2000 ft.) , Bryson City (1700 ft.) , and Cherokee (1900 ft.) —all on or near the park boundary.

A few Mockingbirds appear in Gatlinburg during October and, after spending the winter there, leave in early spring. Occasionally a lone "Mocker" will winter in the Park Headquarters area. The latest departure date from Park Headquarters is April 24 (1950) .

CATBIRD—*Dumetella carolinensis*

The Catbird is a common summer resident throughout most of the park; at low altitudes it is of rare occurrence in winter. This bird is more plentiful at the lower altitudes, but it does inhabit openings in the spruce-fir forest where it breeds along the main crest of the Great Smokies and on or near the summits of some of the highest peaks. Occasionally it summers and probably nests near Mt. LeConte Lodge, at 6300 ft., and at about the same altitude near the Clingmans Dome Parking Area. Catbirds are common breeding birds on the grass balds in the western half of the park.

Earliest date of arrival is April 13 (1948, Park Headquarters—Stupka) . From 1935 to 1958 there are 7 earliest arrival dates ranging from April 13 to 20, and 11 between April 22 and 24. Most of the Catbirds depart during October, but there are three November records: at Park Headquarters on November 3 (1947) and November 5 (1952) , and in Gatlinburg on November 15 (1953) .

There were no winter records of the Catbird until 1947 when, between February 11 and 16, one came daily to my bird-feeding station, in Gatlinburg. In 1955, Manley had one of these birds under observation in Gatlinburg, throughout November and until December 26. Near the Glades, in the vicinity of Emerts Cove, a Catbird visited Mrs. Janson's bird-feeding station from January 1 to 4, 1960. In Gatlinburg, at Manley's bird-feeder, one of these birds was present from early December 1960, to January 26, 1961. Howell observed one near Laurel Lake, Tuckaleechee Cove, December 31, 1961. There are no winter records from within the park area.

A Catbird was seen carrying nesting material April 20, 1941, in Gatlinburg. On May 9, 1949, the first egg was laid in a nest built close to my home in Gatlinburg. Fleetwood reported the finding of a nest with 2 eggs on May 15, 1935, in Cades Cove.

The earliest date on which I heard the song of this bird was April 17 (1949) in Gatlinburg. On May 8, 1943, in the heath bald below Alum Cave Bluffs (4900 ft.) I was on the verge of calling attention to the "What peeves you?" notes of an Olive-sided Flycatcher when the singer, a Catbird, went on to give equally-good imitations of songs of a Solitary Vireo and a Rufous-sided Towhee, among others. As I had not yet recorded the arrival of the flycatcher up to that time, here was strong evidence that the species was probably on hand since the immediate area was one favored by that late migrant. The Catbird is an excellent mimic and, as Gross has stated [Bent, 1948], "snatches of all the bird songs in the neighborhood appear intermixed with occasional harsher notes."

BROWN THRASHER—*Toxostoma rufum*

The Brown Thrasher is a common summer resident and an uncommon winter resident in our area. The occasional wintering bird makes it difficult to record the times of arrival and departure of those individuals that migrate to and from the park. The earliest spring arrivals were noted in Gatlinburg on February 29 (1956) when Manley reported 2 birds. There are five years when the earliest thrashers put in their appearance between March 1 and 5; five years between March 16 and 18; and nine years between March 21 and 27— all these at elevations below 2000 ft. Most thrashers, like their relatives the Catbirds, leave our area in October, but I have observed the Brown Thrasher in the Park Headquarters vicinity on November 2 (1945), November 4 (1947), and November 5 (1962).

At low altitudes (below 2000 ft.), single birds have been reported wintering during 12 of the 17 years, 1945–61, inclusive. One of these was in Cades Cove (December 31, 1961) while all the others were on, or near, the park boundary.

Ordinarily, thrashers are not as plentiful as Catbirds in the higher mountains and it is very seldom that the former is to be found higher than 5200 ft. (Indian Gap; Heintooga Overlook). Stimson reported one from an elevation of 6000 ft., near the junction of the Appalachian and Boulevard Trails, October 4, 1947, and my highest record was from along the Boulevard Trail, at 5700 ft., on September 25, 1942. The thrasher is fairly common on some of the grass balds in the western half of the park and along the high ridges along the southeastern portions, beyond the limits of spruce and fir, at elevations of 4500–5000 ft. There are no wintering records for either the Brown Thrasher or the Catbird at middle or higher altitudes.

Singing usually begins the latter part of March, although I have heard the song as early as March 4 (1946) in the Park Headquarters area, and March 5 (1961) near Emerts Cove. The "whisper" song of the Brown Thrasher, as described by Mrs. Laskey [Bent, 1948], was heard in Gatlinburg September 18, 1955 (Stupka).

In the Park Headquarters area on August 1, 1951, I discovered a young bird that had just left the nest.

FAMILY | *TURDIDAE*

ROBIN—*Turdus migratorius*

Robins * occur throughout the park at all seasons of the year, but since individuals appear to wander up and down as well as in and out of the area they are not regarded as permanent residents. Ordinarily these thrushes are common and,

* Two races of Robins have been noted in the park. A specimen collected by E. V. Komarek on April 3, 1933, in Greenbrier, and a pair taken by a U. S. National Museum party on June 21, 1937, on Inadu Knob are identified as belonging to the Eastern race (*T. m. migratorius*). One taken in the park 4 miles southeast of Cosby, Tennessee, by a U. S. National Museum party on July 2, 1937, is labeled as a representative of the Southern race (*T. m. achrusterus*). All determinations were made by Wetmore [letter, and 1939].

occasionally, abundant, but for a period of a few weeks after the breeding season, while these birds are undergoing the annual molt, they appear to be uncommon or scarce. It is not surprising to read that Langdon [1887], who spent August 11 to 21, 1886, studying the birds of the Chilhowee and Smoky Mountain regions, observed no Robins here at that time.

Robins breed in considerable numbers in the high-altitude forests of spruce and fir where their songs are often the first to break the pre-dawn quiet. Such birds are usually wild and retiring, quite unlike the fairly approachable lawn-frequenting Robins of the lowlands. There are many records in the high elevations from November through February, single individuals and in flocks of up to 100 birds, especially in years when the mountain-ash trees have borne a heavy fruit crop. (The rarity of hackberry trees in the park may have an important bearing on the appreciably greater flocks of wintering Robins in middle Tennessee than in the park and vicinity.) By far the largest flock recorded in the 25-year period starting in 1936 was one that Manley and I observed flying over Gatlinburg from 5:30 to 6 P.M. February 3, 1949; we estimated that this flock, flying high in a NNW. direction, was comprised of at least 20,000 Robins. Flocks of these birds are most prevalent in January and February. Beginning in April and on into September, one is not likely to find flocks of Robins in the Great Smokies.

Although there are snatches of song in autumn and winter, the familiar singing begins during the latter part of February and continues into July. By the end of July there is a cessation of singing.

In the lowlands, nesting may begin by late March in some years (1945, Park Headquarters) ; the earliest egg date is April 2, 1945, when I found 3 eggs in a nest near the Park Headquarters Building. Along the Appalachian Trail at Sheep Pen Gap (4610 ft.) , Fleetwood reported a half-finished nest April 2 (1935) . Late nests include one with 3 eggs near Heintooga Overlook (5325 ft.) on July 19, and another on Ledge Bald (5175 ft.) on July 24—both records by Fleetwood in 1934. These may represent second or possibly third broods. Ganier [1962] states that most of the nests he examined in the park held but 3 eggs or young. On September 6 (1950) I observed a fledgling with very short tail and down feathers on its head being fed by an adult Robin on the lawn at Park Headquarters.

Robins are hardy birds, but deep snows may present real hazards, as happened throughout the lowlands of the park and vicinity in middle February 1958, and again 2 years later. A 12-inch snow blanketed all out-doors and the weakened hungry birds permitted close approach before flying off from clumps of sumacs where some fruits persisted. The record-breaking cold that followed the heavy snowfall of February 15, 1958, resulted in the death of numerous birds, including many Robins. Over wide areas, highways that had been cleared by snowplows were the only places where a bit of bare ground was in evidence, and those starving birds that alighted there were too weak to escape the traffic.

While the fruits of flowering dogwood, American holly, wild grapes, mountain-ash, and blackgum are favorite food items of the Robin throughout autumn, fruits of sumacs are eaten mostly in February and March.

From 1936 to 1961, Christmas Bird Count parties listed approximately 78 Robins per count, the numbers ranging up to 425 birds (December 26, 1955). No Robins were listed on the count made December 22, 1935, and but 1 on December 30, 1951.

WOOD THRUSH—*Hylocichla mustelina*

This bird is a common summer resident in the lower and middle altitudes of the park. On 13 of the years 1935–55, the first spring arrivals were noted between April 9 and 13; the earliest arrival is April 1 (1955) in Gatlinburg (Manley). October is the time of the fall departure, the latest record being October 20 (1951) at Park Headquarters (Stupka). Records of off-season birds include a freshly-killed specimen found by Manley, November 13 (1957), in Gatlinburg. A Wood Thrush with an injured foot remained close to the Park Headquarters Building on November 20 and 21, 1958; it appeared to be capable of normal flight as was one with a drooping wing that frequented the same area from January 8 to 21, 1960 (Stupka).

This bird occurs in deciduous forests up to the lower limits of the spruce-fir zone. There it may make contact with the Veery which breeds throughout the spruce-fir forests, so that there are a number of places in the park between the 3500 and 5000 ft. altitudes where both these thrushes are to be found. The Veery is more likely to "spill over" into the northern hardwood forests just below the high-altitude conifers than the Wood Thrush is apt to penetrate upward into the forests of spruce and fir. (See Veery).

The highest elevation at which the Wood Thrush has been observed is 5600 ft.—along the Boulevard Trail to Mt. LeConte, on October 4, 1950 (Burns). I have recorded this bird at 5000 ft. or above at Heintooga Overlook, June 19, 1943; at Cosby Knob, July 21, 1942; and at Newfound Gap April 26, 1952, and May 1, 1954. Wetmore [1939] mentions a juvenile collected at White Rock (Mt. Cammerer), 5025 ft., July 1, 1937.

Wood Thrushes are common breeding birds at the lower altitudes. On April 24 (1941) I observed one gathering nesting material in Gatlinburg, and on May 9 (1935) Fleetwood found 2 nests in white pine trees in Cades Cove.

The fine song of this bird is to be heard from the time of its arrival until late July or early August. I have heard it in Gatlinburg on August 2 in 1949 and 1951. Unusual singing dates are September 7 (1936) at Newfound Gap [Foster and McCamey, letter] and October 9 (1934) in the Twentymile Creek area (Fleetwood).

Aldrich and Goodrum [1946] found 12 pairs of Wood Thrushes in the 23-acre virgin hardwood forest area they censused June 23–28, 1946, in Porters Flat (2950–3200 ft.).

HERMIT THRUSH—*Hylocichla guttata*

This bird, a fairly common winter resident, is the only thrush (excluding Robin and Eastern Bluebird) one is likely to encounter in the Great Smoky Mountains between late October and early April. From 1938 to 1950, there were 10 years when the earliest Hermit Thrushes arrived between October 13 and 19. The earliest record is Fleetwood's report of 2 birds along Forney Creek on October 1 (1934); next are my records in the Park Headquarters area on October 6

(1953) and October 8 (1952). A bird observed by Robbins and Coffey on April 27, 1952, in the vicinity of the Clingmans Dome Parking Area (6311 ft.) represents both the latest and highest records of this species in the park.

The great majority of Hermit thrushes winter throughout the lower altitudes. Of a total of 9 records above 3500 ft., 5 are associated with the fall migration (October) and 3 with that of spring (April). The only other high-altitude record was a bird at Alum Cave Bluffs, 4900 ft., December 4, 1939 (Stupka). Severe winters, especially ones when there is considerable snow, usually result in privations and, occasionally, death. There were a number of reports of dead Hermit Thrushes having been found in late February and early March 1947, following a prolonged period of cold snowy weather. Although normally reluctant to visit our bird-feeding area near Emerts Cove, these thrushes did put in their appearance in February 1958 and 1960, when snow and cold prevailed.

To hear the vocal efforts of this fine singer is by no means an unusual experience in the park and vicinity. I have heard the song on 3 occasions in late October, on 24 days in November, 6 in December, 3 in February, 16 in March, and 10 in April. Just before sunrise is a favorite singing time, and evening songs are delivered occasionally. In the Park Headquarters area I have listened to the song under a variety of climatic conditions—warm, cold, clear, overcast, foggy, during a rain, and during a snowfall.

The numbers of Hermit Thrushes listed by Christmas Bird Count parties during the 27-year period 1935–61 ranged from 2 (December 30, 1951) to 29 (December 20, 1942, and December 26, 1955), the average number being 13.

SWAINSON'S THRUSH—*Hylocichla ustulata*

This transient thrush appears to be much more in evidence in its fall migrations than in the spring. As it is exceptionally shy, we are likely to obtain only fleeting glimpses of this olive-brown bird, but its peculiar whistled note, uttered frequently during its autumn sojourn, serves to reveal its presence. Occasionally there comes a morning, usually during the latter half of September, when Swainson's Thrushes appear to be the most common birds in our woodlands. A sudden change from mild to cool temperatures may bring on such an influx.

Between 1937 and 1961 the earliest fall migrants were noted between September 7 and 14 on 8 years, and between September 15 and 17 on 10 years. The earliest record is my observation of a bird in Cherokee Orchard, near Gatlinburg, on September 4 (1939). The latest fall departure record is October 24 (1945) when I examined one of these thrushes that struck a window of the Park Headquarters Building. The earliest of our spring records is April 24 (1952) when Maslowski and others captured a sickly bird at Fighting Creek Gap. One that I heard singing near Emerts Cove on May 15 (1961) represents our latest spring record. In both the spring and fall migrations, Swainson's Thrushes are much more common in the lower altitudes than in the high-mountain forests.

Fruits of flowering dogwood, mountain-ash, black cherry, devils-walkingstick, pokeberry, Virginia creeper, and cucumbertree are eaten here by these thrushes.

GRAY-CHEEKED THRUSH—*Hylocichla minima*

On October 3, 1946, while in the Sugarlands, Downer observed a Gray-cheeked Thrush as it fed upon dogwood fruits. He viewed it for some time in good sunlight. Downer returned on the following day and watched what may have been the same bird in the same general area. On May 8, 1960, Hebard reported one of these birds at 6000 ft. along the Spruce-Fir Nature Trail, on Mt. Collins. At the Cosby Campground (2400 ft.) on October 8, 1961, an East Tennessee Ornithological Society group recorded 5 Gray-cheeked Thrushes on the list of birds observed in that area.

This bird resembles Swainson's Thrush so closely that it may have been overlooked by bird watchers. In the vicinity of ceilometers at the Knoxville Airport, 12 miles northwest of the park line, 4 Gray-cheeked Thrushes perished October 7–8, 1951 [Howell and Tanner, 1951], and 5 on October 6–7, 1954 [Tanner, 1954].*

* In Knox County, Tennessee, Howell and Monroe [1958] regard this bird as an uncommon spring and fall migrant; their dates of migration are April

VEERY—*Hylocichla fuscescens*

This thrush is a common summer resident throughout the higher altitudes, not only in spruce-fir forests in the eastern half of the park but also in the deciduous woodlands west of Clingmans Dome. The earliest of the spring arrival dates is April 25 (1952) when Saunders and Hebard reported this bird in Gatlinburg. On the state-line ridge at Spence Field Bald (5000 ft.) the earliest record is April 29 (1938, Stupka). The latest fall departure date is September 21 (1940), a bird I observed on Mt. Buckley (6582 ft.).

The unique song of this thrush appears to be confined to the period from the latter part of May to near the end of July. I have heard it as late as July 27 (1951) at the Clingmans Dome Parking Area.

As stated in the account of the Wood Thrush, the Veery and the Wood Thrush often occur together between the 3500 to 5000 ft. altitudes—the former elevation marking the approximate lowest breeding range of the Veery while the latter marks the uppermost breeding extension of the Wood Thrush. In the mature deciduous forests to the east and west of Gregory Bald (4948 ft.); along the transmountain road between the tunnel overpass and Newfound Gap; along the trails leading from Cherokee Orchard to Mt. LeConte— here and in many other areas one can hear both Wood Thrushes and Veeries in late spring and early summer.

Aldrich and Goodrum [1946] found one pair of these thrushes in the 23-acre virgin hardwood forest area they censused June 23–28, 1946, in Porters Flat (2950–3200 ft.). There this species is near the lowest fringe of its breeding range.

Ganier [1926] relates that a "nest near the summit of Miry Ridge (at 4700 feet) held three fresh eggs on May 31. It was located in thin cut-out woods on a very steep slope. The location chosen was one of a clump of low spruce, grow-

28–May 20, and September 16–October 4. In Buncombe County, North Carolina, Burleigh [Pearson, Brimley, and Brimley, 1959] says it "normally is rather uncommon in the fall and extremely scarce in the spring. My few records for the spring migration are single birds seen May 18, 19, and 21, 1930, while in the fall my extreme dates of occurrence are September 8 (1931) and October 26 (1933)."

ing up through the branches of a fallen tree, the nest being placed three feet above the ground. Several other nests, containing eggs, were found the first week in June, 1924. All were in low bushes in the woods, close to the ground between elevations 4,000 and 5,000 feet." On June 23, 1948, 2 miles east of Newfound Gap, I came upon a fledgling accompanied by an adult bird; the former had the appearance of having just left the nest.

EASTERN BLUEBIRD—*Sialia sialis*

The bluebird is a fairly common permanent resident. It occurs throughout the park but there are no records of its nesting above 5000 ft. Bluebirds have been observed in flight over some of the highest mountains in the area (Clingmans Dome, Mt. LeConte) ; at Newfound Gap (5040 ft.) it has been recorded on numerous occasions. It is only during the late summer molt that we lack high-altitude records of this species. Bluebirds are appreciably more common at the lower altitudes (especially in Cades Cove) , the vicinity of the park boundary, and in the nearby coves and farmlands near the park.

During the late fall and throughout the winter, bluebirds are more or less gregarious; but the flocks rarely exceed 25–30 birds.

Nesting activities may be under way by late March. On April 3, 1935, Fleetwood found two nests, each containing 4 eggs, while on the following day he discovered another containing 3 eggs—all were in Cades Cove. Again on April 22 and 27, 1935, Fleetwood came upon nests of bluebirds in Cades Cove, the former with 4 eggs and the latter with 3. He recorded the finding of a fledgling out of the nest on May 8, 1935, in Cades Cove. On June 12, 1934, Fleetwood observed bluebirds nesting in a gourd in Emerts Cove.

On April 25, 1953, bluebirds were feeding young in a bird house I had erected near my home near Emerts Cove. I observed a family of these birds in a grove of mature deciduous trees near Gregory Bald (4948 ft.) June 19, 1936.

Among the wild fruits eaten by bluebirds in our area are those of American holly, flowering dogwood, blackgum, pokeberry, and shining sumac.

Christmas Bird Count parties listed from 10 to 83 Eastern Bluebirds on the annual one-day count of winter birds in this area. The average number observed (1935–61) was 34.

FAMILY | *SYLVIIDAE*

BLUE-GRAY GNATCATCHER—*Polioptila caerulea*

In the lower altitudes of the Great Smoky Mountains the Blue-gray Gnatcatcher is a common summer resident. I observed one of these trim little birds at Newfound Gap, 5040 ft., April 27, 1952, and there are 4 records of its occurrence at the 3000–3500 ft. elevation, but for the most part this species is to be found below 2500 ft. From 1935 to 1959, the earliest arrivals were noted between March 25 and 31 on 9 of the years; earliest is March 19 (1945) when I observed one at 3300 ft. along Little River, above Elkmont. An unusually late fall migrant is one I recorded in Gatlinburg on October 21 (1944).

One of several nests discovered in the Park Headquarters area was completed on April 29, 1960. Fleetwood found a number of nests in Cades Cove between April 27 and May 15 (1935). In Gatlinburg on July 4 (1937) I watched an adult gnatcatcher feeding a young bird away from the nest.

The song of this bird is rarely heard, and I have noted it on but two occasions—on April 14, 1946, near Cherokee Orchard and March 26, 1959, at my home in the vicinity of Emerts Cove. It is a soft whisper-like performance somewhat reminiscent of the varied song of the Catbird but faster, softer, and more musical. Lemoyne [1886] calls it a "low jumble of indescribable warbles which defies any representation." To some degree, it resembles the song of the Ruby-crowned Kinglet.

GOLDEN-CROWNED KINGLET—*Regulus satrapa*

This hardy little bird is a common permanent resident throughout the high-altitude forests of spruce and fir. It occurs at all elevations from October until April. Except when occupied with the cares of the breeding season, it is often to be found associated with small loose flocks of chickadees, Red-breasted Nuthatches, and Brown Creepers.

By early April most of the Golden-crowned Kinglets have departed from the lower altitudes; the latest record is a bird observed April 20 (1935) by Fleetwood in Cades Cove (1800 ft.). Tanner recorded this species on September 16 (1949) at 2400 ft. near Cherokee Orchard, and my earliest fall arrival date at Park Headquarters (1460 ft.) is October 2 (1947).

Wetmore [1939] reports a specimen taken in the park June 21 (1937) that was only recently out of the nest and in full juvenal plumage.

During the years 1935–61, parties participating in the Christmas Bird Count reported an average of approximately 70 Golden-crowned Kinglets per count.

RUBY-CROWNED KINGLET—*Regulus calendula*

This bird is a fairly common winter resident. The earliest date of arrival is September 18 (1942) when I found the species common in the fir forest on the summit of Mt. LeConte (6593 ft.). It appears earlier in the high altitudes than in the lowlands, as I have noted it at 5000 ft. or above on Mt. LeConte September 28 (1939); on Mt. Kephart October 1 (1938); and at Newfound Gap October 1 (1940). Stimson and McCamey observed a Ruby-crowned Kinglet on Andrews Bald October 1 (1947). The earliest arrival date at a low altitude is October 4 (1943) at Park Headquarters. The latest departure in the spring is May 5 (1940) when Walker and Baird recorded this bird in Cherokee Orchard (2600 ft.).

These kinglets are much more likely to spend the winter in the lower altitudes where solitary birds are often the rule. In this respect it differs from the related Golden-crowned Kinglet that travels in small flocks. Also, the Ruby-crowned is invariably much more scarce, as a glance at the Christmas Bird Count figures for these two kinglets will reveal. In winter the Ruby-crowned Kinglet is very scarce, or absent, throughout the spruce-fir forests. During the latter half of

April, however, while this species is migrating to its breeding grounds in the far north, it may again be encountered in the higher altitudes of the park.

Like the Winter Wren, the Ruby-crowned Kinglet is a midget with a long and very melodious song. Almost all of the singing is done in the lower elevations during March and April, the latter month being the time of most singing. A warm spell of weather may bring on some early musical efforts during February, as I have noted in Gatlinburg on February 12 and 22 (1950), and on the 24th (1949). In the fall this bird sings very infrequently. At that season I have heard its song on only four occasions—October 19 (1938); October 27 (1946); November 3 (1950); and November 17 (1938)—all in the Park Headquarters or Gatlinburg areas.

An unusual record occurred July 1, 1959, when Assistant Park Superintendent David deL. Condon * reported hearing a Ruby-crowned Kinglet singing repeatedly in the fir forest close to Mt. LeConte Lodge, 6300 ft. Park Naturalist Muller and I arrived at the lodge at 8:30 next morning and spent five hours in that vicinity endeavoring to locate this bird, but we failed to see or hear it.

During the 27 years (1935–61) when a one-day count of winter birds was taken in a portion of the park and vicinity, an average of approximately 5 Ruby-crowned Kinglets per count was listed.

FAMILY | *MOTACILLIDAE*

WATER PIPIT—*Anthus spinoletta*

This bird is an uncommon spring and fall transient and a rare winter visitant in our area. Over the period 1935–62 there are 11 records for the fall migration (October–November), 12 for the spring months (March, April, and May),

---

* Mr. Condon, prior to his transfer to Great Smoky Mountains National Park in June 1959, had served as Park Naturalist in Yellowstone National Park for over 20 years. While there he was quite familiar with the song of the Western Ruby-crowned Kinglet (*R. c. cineraceus*) regarding which Bent [1949] says: "The voice of the western bird seems to be similar to that of the eastern race, with the same variations and with equal charm."

and 3 for the winter season (December, January, and February).

The earliest arrival date in the fall is October 8 (1934) when Fleetwood reported a single bird on Parson Bald (4730 ft.). Four of the five additional October records, each comprising from 1 to 3 birds, are from high-altitude localities —Spence Field Bald (2), Andrews Bald (1), and the Clingmans Dome Parking Area (1). Latest departure in the fall is November 25 (1950) when a few were observed in Gatlinburg. In the spring the earliest arrivals were noted on March 1 (1962) at Park Headquarters (Lix), while the latest departure date is May 6 (1942) when Manley observed the species in Tuckaleechee Cove. Only 1 of the 11 records for the spring months is at a high altitude.

The flock of approximately 200 Water Pipits observed by Manley in Gatlinburg on March 24, 1940, appeared during a snowstorm. This is by far the largest flock on record. On the following day I watched dozens of these birds walking about on the main street of Gatlinburg, surprisingly approachable and little concerned with traffic or pedestrians. In all probability they were weakened by scarcity of food, for the entire park and vicinity lay under a 4- to 5-inch blanket of snow. On one other occasion the appearance of a flock of these birds was associated with a snowstorm—on November 24, 1950, a flock of 30 pipits appeared on the lawn in the Park Headquarters area where the birds remained for several hours. The snowstorm that prevailed at the time was the forerunner of record-breaking low temperatures.

Pipits have been reported from Pigeon Forge, Tennessee, a few miles north of Gatlinburg, on a number of occasions. There, and in the extensive open fields of Wears and Tuckaleechee Coves, they probably occur more commonly than in the park.

FAMILY | *BOMBYCILLIDAE*

CEDAR WAXWING—*Bombycilla cedrorum*

This vagrant species is a common summer resident and is fairly common but erratic the remainder of the year, being scarce or absent at irregular intervals especially from November to April. Cedar Waxwings were reported every month of the year on 3 years (1941, 1947, 1951) during the 20-year period 1934–53; they were reported on every May, June, and July throughout that 20-year period and on all but 2 Augusts, 2 Septembers, and 1 October.

There have been fewer records of these birds in December than in any other month. Both January and February have fully twice as many records as December. After December, March is next with a paucity of records, there being appreciably fewer Cedar Waxwings here that month than during each of the two preceding months, indicating an exodus from the park at that time. Since April records are approximately double the number for March, the former month might be considered the time when this erratic species begins its return to this area. Ordinarily, beginning May 10–15 and continuing throughout the summer, these birds are to be expected here.

Whereas May finds the great majority of these birds in the lower altitudes, beginning in June and continuing through September one is just as likely to come upon waxwings in the high as well as in the low elevations. This distribution changes appreciably during October when these birds show a decided preference for the lowlands; and from November through the following April these gregarious vagrants practically avoid the high altitudes. This pattern of occurrence is to be expected in a species whose diet consists largely of wild fruits.

Fleetwood, in his journal for July 4, 1934, reported the discovery of a nest in a pine tree in which a Cedar Waxwing was incubating; this was at an elevation of 4000 ft. along the trail from near Cosby to Mt. Guyot. Ten days later, along the same trail, and again in a pine tree, he records finding 3 young in the nest of a Cedar Waxwing. It is not known whether this was the same nest. At the Alum Cave Parking Area (3800 ft.) I found the nest of this species on July 10, 1940. My notes reveal that there were young in the nest which was in a yellow birch and about 20 ft. from the ground. The nest was a bulky structure made up largely of *Usnea* lichens. I have notes relating to the nesting of these birds in the Park Headquarters area in four different years: In July 1942, I found a Cedar Waxwing's nest containing 4 young birds 11 ft. from the ground in a tree near the Administration Building. On May 15, 1946, this species was nesting in a sugar maple which grows on the lawn in that area; at that time I was unaware of the fact that the date was an exceptionally early one * and, unfortunately, there was no follow-up in order to obtain additional particulars. On June 7, 1947, I noted a Cedar Waxwing pulling strings from a floor mop that was leaning against a building, presumably to use as nesting material. Again in June 1949, these birds were recorded as nesting in the vicinity of Park Headquarters.

The largest flocks of Cedar Waxwings were observed in winter. In Cades Cove, January 20, 1941, a flock numbering approximately 300 birds was milling about a low springy area; occasionally single birds would alight and drink. On February 6, 1949, some 300–400 birds were feeding upon the fruits of privet and American holly in Gatlinburg. Manley reported a flock of about 150 birds in Gatlinburg during the first week of February 1953.

In addition to American holly, the wild fruits these birds have been observed eating in this park include persimmon, flowering dogwood, pin cherry, serviceberry, mountain-ash, scarlet elder, devils-walkingstick, wild grape, smilax, blueberry, pokeberry, and Christmas American-mistletoe. Fleetwood, in April 1935, watched these birds eating apple blossoms in Cades Cove. On May 26, 1940, in Cades Cove, I noted their feeding upon the recently-emerged adults of the 17-year cicada.

On Christmas Bird Counts for the period 1935–61, Cedar Waxwings were listed on 15 of the 27 years. On January 3, 1960, 224 birds were counted.

---

* For Massachusetts, Forbush [1929] gives egg dates from May 30 to late August; Todd [1940], in his *Birds of Western Pennsylvania*, states, "I have never taken a full set of eggs earlier in the season than June 9, but D. A. Atkinson reports once finding a set on May 18."

FAMILY | *LANIIDAE*

LOGGERHEAD SHRIKE—*Lanius ludovicianus*

This bird has the status of a rare winter visitor to our area. Just outside the park—to the north (Tuckaleechee and Wears Coves), south (Tuckasegee River Valley), and west (Little Tennessee River Valley)—the Loggerhead Shrike is a fairly common winter resident. I noted the earliest fall arrival near Emerts Cove, less than a mile from the park boundary, on July 31 (1953) and in Pigeon Forge on August 1 (1942). My latest spring departure dates are March 31 (1941) in Happy Valley, and April 1 (1944) in Pigeon Forge.

During the 20-year period 1937–56 when Christmas Bird Count parties included the Pigeon Forge area in their territory, a total of 44 shrikes was observed. From 1 to 5 of these birds were counted on 17 of those 20 years.

FAMILY | *STURNIDAE*

STARLING—*Sturnus vulgaris*

The Starling is a common permanent resident along the periphery of the park, especially in towns and on farms. Within the park it occurs in Cades Cove, Elkmont, Cataloochee, the Oconaluftee meadows north of Cherokee, and elsewhere. For the most part its invasion of this area has been rather shallow, for only at rare intervals do these birds make their way into the middle or high elevations. Most of the people who lived on lands now comprising Great Smoky Mountains National Park moved away just prior to the invasion of Starlings, and this abandonment by man must have been a real factor in making the region unattractive to the foreign invader.

What appears to be the first record of this bird from within the park is represented by a specimen collected for the Chicago Academy of Sciences by E. V. Komarek on March

17, 1933, in Greenbrier. In his April 1933, report to Superintendent Eakin of Great Smoky Mountains National Park, Komarek stated that the Starling "has become very abundant at Cades Cove."

Fleetwood's first observation of Starlings in Cades Cove was on October 23, 1934, when he counted 44 birds. He spent many weeks in the Cove and although these birds were noted frequently in his journal, his highest count there was 48 birds on October 30, 1934.

On May 27, 1934, Fleetwood reported 3 Starlings in Gatlinburg; he noted a similar number in Elkmont on March 15, 1935. These appear to be the earliest recorded observations of this species in those places, and Fleetwood's statement of 2 birds nesting in Elkmont on April 25, 1935, is the first reference to the breeding of Starlings in the park.* From Fleetwood's journal for 1934 we learn that he observed 4 birds in Ravensford, August 9; 18 along Deep Creek (just inside the park) September 19; 8 in Bryson City, October 4; and 25 in the Cherokee Indian Reservation, October 20. On December 3, 1934, he reported a flock of several hundred birds in the Deep Creek area. In Cataloochee, Fleetwood's report of 2 Starlings on February 11, 1935, is the first for that part of the park. A specimen collected April 11, 1935, in Bryson City (by Sullivan) is in the park's collection.

J. Huff reported a flock of 10–15 Starlings near Mt. Le-Conte Lodge (6300 ft.) April 1 and 2, 1940. This represents our only high-altitude record. Whether the unusually warm temperatures which prevailed for several days at the close of March and the exceptionally high readings on April 1 and 2 (83° and 86°, respectively, at Park Headquarters) were a factor in the appearance of these birds at such an unlikely place is a matter of speculation.

In addition to the breeding of these birds at Elkmont, as

---

* The first record of the Starling in Tennessee appears to be Tyler's [1922] observation near Bluff City, December 12, 1921, approximately 10 miles south of Bristol and 70 miles northeast of the park. For Buncombe County, North Carolina, C. S. Brimley [1940] states that it was first reported in 1926. Other initial records are Franklin and Highlands, North Carolina, 1937 and 1941, respectively [Stevenson, 1941], and Atlanta, Georgia, 1927 [Burleigh, 1958].

stated above, there are the following reports pertaining to nesting activities:

Cades Cove—May 1, 1935, nest with young in an apple tree (Fleetwood).

Park Headquarters—April 16, 1942, gathering nesting material; May 18, 1943, five half-grown young in nest in building; March 28, 1945, nest about half completed (Stupka).

Gatlinburg—March 29, 1945, gathering nesting material (Stupka).

Christmas Bird Count parties listed an average of 87 Starlings per count in the years 1935–61; practically all were outside but in the vicinity of the park (Pigeon Forge, Tucka-leechee Cove, Gatlinburg).

FAMILY | *VIREONIDAE*

WHITE-EYED VIREO—*Vireo griseus*

This vireo is a common summer resident throughout the lower altitudes. I have come upon it in June (1943) at 3200 ft., along Straight Fork, where it was probably nesting, and that appears to be near the uppermost extent of its breeding range. Ordinarily this bird does not nest above 3000 ft. in the park. Its earliest arrival date is April 1 (1945, Gatlinburg —Stupka), following a period of unusually warm weather.* From 1935 to 1960 there are 8 years when the earliest arrivals appeared April 6–11, and 14 years when the vanguards were noted April 13–18. In most years the White-eyed Vireos departed by the end of September, but in 1938 I observed one in the Sugarlands (1800 ft.) on October 12, which represents our latest record. There are 3 additional October records: I observed one on October 1, 1941, at Park Headquarters and another on October 2, 1943, in Gatlinburg; E. V. Komarek obtained a specimen on October 4, 1933, in Greenbrier.

---

* The mean temperature for March 1945, was higher than that for a normal April.

Bellrose [1938] reported discovering an adult bird feeding young that were almost fully grown August 31, 1937. This would lead one to believe that occasionally a second brood may be reared, even though Burleigh [1958] states that "it is doubtful if in Georgia more than one brood is reared each year." On June 28, 1952, Edwards observed young being fed out of the nest in the Sugarlands.

This bird resumes its singing after a period of molt, so that its distinctive song may be heard throughout September, or until it departs on its fall migration.

With White-eyed Vireos, as with many other summer residents, there is a certain amount of wandering in late summer when the birds are found in places quite distant from their usual haunts. Fleetwood recorded one September 8, 1934, at 5500 ft. on the Noland Divide Trail. Metcalf [1938] reported this vireo from 5000 to 5500 ft. between Newfound Gap and Clingmans Dome on August 26–27, 1937. Along the Appalachian Trail in the eastern half of the park, George and Quay, in 1941, observed this species at 3500–4000 ft. on August 30 and at 5000–5500 ft. on August 31.

YELLOW-THROATED VIREO—*Vireo flavifrons*

This vireo is a fairly common summer resident. Like the White-eyed Vireo, this bird breeds at elevations below 3000 ft. The times of arrival and departure are approximately the same for these two species, but whereas the White-eyed is mostly a bird of shrubs and low brushy tangles, the Yellow-throated frequents the tree-tops. The earliest arrival date in spring is April 7 (1935, Cades Cove—Fleetwood; 1945 and 1947, Gatlinburg—Stupka), and there are 12 years from 1944 to 1960 when the first arrivals were noted between April 8 and 22. The latest departure date in the fall is October 6 (1938) when I observed one in the Park Headquarters area.

In Cades Cove on April 30, 1935, Fleetwood reported two Yellow-throated Vireos at a nest 50 ft. up in an oak tree. On May 3, 1952, one bird was putting the finishing touches to a nest 30 ft. up in a white oak close to my home near Emerts Cove.

After molting, this bird, like the White-eyed and Solitary

Vireos, resumes its singing, and this may continue until the time of its departure.

SOLITARY VIREO—*Vireo solitarius*

On May 29, 1885, William Brewster [1886] obtained at Highlands, North Carolina, a specimen of vireo which differed from the Solitary Vireo of New England "in being larger, with a stouter bill, and duller, darker, and more uniform coloring above." This, which he called the "Mountain Solitary Vireo" (subspecies *alticola*), is a common summer resident at middle and high altitudes in the park. The finest singer of all our eastern vireos, it is also the earliest to arrive in the spring and the latest to depart in the fall.

A bird I saw and heard in Gatlinburg March 14 (1946) is our earliest spring record.* There are 6 years when the earliest arrivals appeared between March 14 and 18, and 11 years between March 20 and 26. On March 29 (1939) this vireo was noted at 4300 ft. on the Alum Cave Trail, and on April 2 (1946) at Indian Gap, 5266 ft. (Stupka). The latest of three November records is November 3 (1950) when I observed this bird and heard it singing in Gatlinburg. At high altitudes the latest record is October 26 (1951) when Howell reported this vireo from Indian Gap (5266 ft.).

This vireo was noted by Wetmore [1939] as high as 6600 ft. on Mt. Guyot on June 25, 1937. The species breeds regularly throughout the highest altitudes and on down to approximately 2000 ft. (Fontana Village, North Carolina— June 5, 1952), but it is not too unusual to find it well below that elevation during the nesting season.** In Gatlinburg (1300 ft.) where I noted the Solitary Vireo throughout the month of June 1950, I have also recorded its occurrence on June 17 and July 1, 1948; June 6–7, 1951; and June 1–2,

* Tanner [1957a] in commenting on the migration of this bird, the so-called "blue-headed vireo," remarks that "A surprising feature of spring migration is the early arrival in the Smokies of some birds that breed there, especially the blue-headed vireo and black-throated blue warbler; they arrive much sooner than do migrants of the same species at Knoxville, Tennessee, 30 miles to the north."

** M. Brooks [1944] writes that in West Virginia, near the northern limit of this race, this vireo is "a common resident in mountainous situations down to about 1,000-foot elevations."

1952. Fleetwood reported it from below 2000 ft., near Cosby, on July 6, 1934.

On April 23, 1935, Fleetwood discovered 2 birds near a nest at 2000 ft. along Abrams Creek. Powers [1936], on May 9, 1936, found one of these vireos incubating 4 eggs in a holly tree in Elkmont; he stated that this bird allowed itself to be stroked while sitting on the eggs. Ganier [1926], on May 31, 1920, found a nest at about 4500 ft. along Miry Ridge that contained 3 eggs which had been incubated about one week; during early June 1924, he discovered 4 additional nests all of which held fresh eggs. At Newfound Gap on June 13, 1947, I watched a Solitary Vireo pulling at strands of *Usnea* lichens with which it flew off. Lovell [1947] describes 2 nests of this bird that were located in the Chimneys Campground (2700 ft.) ; on July 4, 1947, one held 3 or 4 small nestlings. I came upon a Solitary Vireo sitting on a nest in the Chimneys Campground on July 23, 1947, which would indicate that at least two broods may be raised, on occasions, in our area.

The clear whistled song of this bird may be heard from the time of its arrival in early spring until some time in July. Some individuals resume singing during the latter part of August, and there is a fair amount of song throughout September and October.

Aldrich and Goodrum [1946] found three pairs of Solitary Vireos in the 23-acre virgin hardwood forest area they censused June 23–28, 1946, in Porters Flat (2950–3200 ft.) .

RED-EYED VIREO—*Vireo olivaceus*

This vireo is a common summer resident throughout the lower and middle altitudes. Its earliest arrival is April 13 (1948, Gatlinburg—Stupka) . On 12 years during the period 1938–60, the first of the Red-eyed Vireos was recorded between April 14 and 19. The latest departure date in the fall is October 12 (1938, Sugarlands—Stupka) .

During the breeding season this species may occur up the slopes to approximately 5000 ft. although records above 4500 ft. are uncommon. Trautman reported 2 birds at Newfound Gap (5040 ft.) June 17, 1940, and I noted this vireo there June 14, 1944. On May 29, 1953, the Red-eyed Vireo I observed at Heintooga Overlook (5325 ft.) may have been nesting in that area. It is unlikely, however, that Fleetwood's report of this bird on Mt. LeConte (6593 ft.) June 13, 1934, and Trautman's report on Clingmans Dome (6643 ft.) June 22, 1940, represented breeding individuals. Muller's record of one bird at 5500 ft. on the Noland Divide Trail on July 21, 1959, may have been a post-breeding wanderer.

Fleetwood came upon a nest with 3 eggs along the Greenbrier Pinnacle Trail on May 31, 1934. On June 26, 1935, he found a young bird dead in the trail near Walnut Bottoms (3042 ft.). In the Sugarlands (1800 ft.) on July 6, 1950, I observed a young bird only recently out of the nest. On July 15, 1950, Dr. and Mrs. Baldwin watched a Red-eyed Vireo feeding a young cowbird, out of the nest, near Gatlinburg.

Aldrich and Goodrum [1946] found 15 pairs of Red-eyed Vireos in the 23-acre virgin hardwood forest area they censused June 23–28, 1946, in Porters Flat (2950–3200 ft.). Only the Black-throated Blue Warbler was a more common breeding bird in that area.

At the Knoxville airport ceilometer, 12 miles northwest of the Great Smoky Mountains National Park boundary, there were 42 Red-eyed Vireos among 1,044 birds (46 species) that were killed the night of October 7–8, 1951 [Howell and Tanner, 1951]. At the same place, on the nights of October 5–8, 1954, there were 26 Red-eyed Vireos among 267 dead birds (25 species) [Tanner, 1954].

WARBLING VIREO—*Vireo gilvus*

There are but 2 sight records of this bird. During the first week of October 1946, Downer reported one from along the Little Pigeon River, in Gatlinburg. On April 24, 1952, Seeber observed a Warbling Vireo in the Park Headquarters area.

Great Smoky Mountains National Park appears to be near the southern limit of the breeding range of this vireo ("south to . . . northern Alabama, western North Carolina, and the coastal plain of Virginia" [A.O.U. *Check-list of North American Birds,* 1957]). If, as Forbush [1929] indicates, breeding takes place "in farming regions, towns, villages, and suburbs and parks of cities, rarely, if ever, in large wooded tracts," then almost all of the National Park excepting Cades Cove and some of the bordering areas would be unattractive to this bird as a breeding habitat.

Howell and Monroe [1958] regard it as an uncommon summer resident in Knox County, Tennessee.

FAMILY | *PARULIDAE*

BLACK-AND-WHITE WARBLER—*Mniotilta varia*

This warbler is a common summer resident at low and middle altitudes. The earliest arrival date in spring is March 28 (1938, Stupka) ; from 1935 to 1960, the vanguards of this species appeared between March 30 and April 4 on 15 years. The latest fall departure date is October 15 (1934, Fleetwood) .

Black-and-white Warblers breed mostly below 5000 ft., but there are records of their appearance at higher elevations during the nesting season. In 1945 I observed one of these birds on Bunches Bald (5200 ft.) on May 25, and on the Appalachian Trail near Mt. Kephart at an elevation of 5700 ft. on June 15. Wetmore [1939] reports one at 5000 ft. near Inadu Knob on June 26, 1937, and Trautman listed 2 birds on Andrews Bald (5800 ft.) on June 22, 1940. From mid-July until their departure in the fall, these warblers scatter over a wide area and then they may be encountered throughout all altitudes in the park.

On May 28, 1935, near Cades Cove, Fleetwood discovered a female on a nest situated under a pile of leaves; this nest was lined with hair and contained 4 eggs. Another nest record in Cades Cove was on June 16, 1951, when Burns flushed one of these warblers from a nest holding 4 eggs; the disturbed bird acted as if its wing were broken. On June 23, 1954, while I was walking along the Hannah Mt. Trail to Sheep Pen Gap, a Black-and-white Warbler suddenly appeared and dropped to the ground almost at my feet, its wings quivering; the elevation at that place was approximately 4000 ft.

Walker, on May 31, 1937, reported finding young of this species in Cades Cove. Quay, on July 16, 1941, observed a pair feeding young birds along the Laurel Falls Trail. On

June 23, 1951, I came upon a group of 5 of these warblers in Emerts Cove; some of these were young birds. In the Sugarlands on June 28, 1952, Edwards found young being fed out of the nest. On June 14, 1958, Stimson came upon 2 adults and 2 young birds along the trail to Abrams Falls; on the following day he noted 2 adults and 1 young bird near the Alum Cave Parking Area.

Black-and-white Warblers associate with mixed flocks of other warblers after the breeding season. This was noted by Foster and McCamey [letter] on September 3–8, 1936, and by Tanner on July 15, 1952.

PROTHONOTARY WARBLER—
Protonotaria citrea

There are but 3 records of this warbler, all during the spring migration, as follows:

April 25, 1952—One bird along the river between Gatlinburg and Fighting Creek Gap (Mrs. Eifert).

April 25, 1958—One bird in the Park Headquarters area (Tanner and party).

May 9, 1958—One bird near the park line, along the road from Emerts Cove to Cosby (Kincaid).

The Prothonotary Warbler is a fairly common summer resident in Knox County, Tennessee [Howell and Monroe, 1958]. In North Carolina, breeding records appear to be confined to the eastern half of the state [Pearson, Brimley, and Brimley, 1959].

SWAINSON'S WARBLER—*Limnothlypis swainsonii*

Based on 4 sight records, 3 of which are in June, the Swainson's Warbler may be regarded as a very rare summer resident in the park. Tanner [1950a] heard and observed the first of these birds June 8, 1950, at 1900 ft. along the Gregory Ridge Trail in a dense tangled undergrowth of rhododendron. In approximately the same location, Scott heard and observed one of these warblers on April 27, 1952, the loud song reminding him of an aberrant Louisiana Water-thrush. Again in the same general area, on June 26, 1954, Landis reported having seen and heard this bird. The final report is by Stevenson on June 12, 1958, when he identified the species by its song, along Little River, approximately five miles east of its junction with the Middle Prong.

WORM-EATING WARBLER—*Helmitheros vermivorus*

This retiring warbler is a fairly common summer resident in the park. The earliest spring arrival is April 19 (1935) when Fleetwood reported 5 birds in Cades Cove; on 12 of the 25 years, 1935–59, the first of these warblers arrived between April 19 and 30. The Worm-eating Warbler that Fleetwood observed in the vicinity of Deep Creek on September 19 (1934) proved to be our latest record of this species.

Although by no means restricted to that altitude, this warbler prefers forested mountain-sides in the 1800–3000 ft. range. The lower portions of the Laurel Falls, Huskey Gap, and Gregory Ridge Trails are favored breeding areas to which these birds return year after year.

On May 24, 1948, Fawver reported an adult feeding young out of the nest at an elevation of 2800 ft. along the Bull Head Trail to Mt. LeConte. Along the trail to Laurel Falls on June 5, 1947, I also watched an adult feeding young recently out of the nest. Burns, on June 11, 1950, came upon a nest with 4 eggs in the vicinity of Schoolhouse Gap (2000 ft.). Ganier and Clebsch [1938] report immatures being fed by the parent bird along the Anthony Creek Trail on June 16, 1938.

Although there is no direct evidence of nesting at high altitudes, the following records are during the normal breeding period:

June 9, 1940—Bote Mt. Road at an elevation of 4500 ft. (Walker).

June 20, 1940—Rainbow Falls, 4200 ft. (Trautman).

June 22, 1940—Andrews Bald, 5800 ft. (Trautman).

June 25, 1952—Transmountain road, North Carolina side, 4500 ft. (Edwards).

In addition, there are 5 high-altitude records outside the normal breeding period—1 in early May, 3 in August, and 1 in September.

GOLDEN-WINGED WARBLER—*Vermivora chrysoptera*

At low and middle altitudes where old fields and forest clearings are growing up in brush and young trees, this attractive warbler is a fairly common summer resident. In the region of Park Headquarters where it has been observed for more than 20 years, the earliest spring arrival date is April 13 (1948) ; at that place there are 7 years when vanguards of this species arrived between April 15 and 20, and 11 years when the first birds appeared between April 22 and 24. The latest of the fall departure dates is October 5 (1938, Rich Mountain—Stupka) .

Ganier [1956] states that this species nests along the high mountain crests, but within the park it is much more likely to breed at lower altitudes in forest clearings on dry brushy hillsides. In addition to Park Headquarters, its occurrence during the breeding season has been noted in Cades Cove, Emerts Cove, Greenbrier, Oconaluftee Visitor Center area, Deep Creek, and Fontana Dam. Ganier and Clebsch [1938] reported one from near Newfound Gap and a pair at Indian Gap in mid-June 1938, but this warbler does not breed there regularly. It does occur and probably breeds in a number of high-altitude localities in the southeastern part of the park and vicinity, such as Cataloochee Ranch (4888 ft.) , Soco Gap (4300 ft.) , Cove Creek Gap (4062 ft.) , and Pin Oak Gap (4428 ft.) .

Lemoyne [1886] gives May 26–30 as dates of incompleted nests; he found nests with full complements of eggs May 28 and June 3 and 5. On June 26, 1937, I recorded a nest with young along the Laurel Falls Trail. Edwards reported young being fed out of the nest June 28, 1952, in the Sugarlands.

BLUE-WINGED WARBLER—*Vermivora pinus*

This warbler is a very uncommon spring migrant, a rare summer resident, and a rare fall migrant. The earliest of 9 spring arrival records is April 16 (1949) when Howell observed one in the Park Headquarters area. For the fall there are but 2 records—August 30 (1941) in the vicinity of Low Gap, 4242 ft. (George and Quay), and September 16 (1941) near Park Headquarters, 1460 ft. (Quay).

The birds Fleetwood recorded June 5 and 15, 1934, near Injun Creek in the Greenbrier area, may have been nesting there at that time. Stimson's report of this warbler along the trail to Abrams Falls on June 14, 1958, could also have indicated a breeding bird. On June 18, 1949, Hardy [letter] observed an adult feeding 3 fledglings in the Park Headquarters area.

TENNESSEE WARBLER—*Vermivora peregrina*

These birds are fairly common spring and fall migrants. The earliest of the spring arrivals is April 25 (1952, Gatlinburg—Mayfield); latest, May 20 (1953, Park Headquarters—Stupka). Fall arrivals appeared as early as September 1 (1941, Appalachian Trail near Pecks Corner, 5500–6000 ft.—George and Quay) and some tarried as late as October 28 (1937, Gatlinburg—Stupka).

The large numbers of Tennessee Warblers killed in the immediate vicinity of the lights at the Knoxville airport's ceilometer, located approximately 12 miles northwest of the park line, would tend to indicate that there are times during the fall migration when this bird may become quite numerous. On the night of October 7–8, 1951, when altogether 1,044 birds (46 species) were killed at that place, 80 proved to be Tennessee Warblers [Howell and Tanner, 1951]. Three years later, when a total of 267 birds died on the nights of October 5–8, 1954, 25 were identified as Tennessee Warblers [Tanner, 1954].

ORANGE-CROWNED WARBLER— *Vermivora celata*

This appears to be a scarce bird in our portion of the Southern Appalachian Mountains. In the park and vicinity there are but 3 records of this rare migrant—May 5, 1940, Cherokee Orchard (Walker); November 28–December 3,

1956, Gatlinburg (Manley and Stupka); and October 20, 1957, Cades Cove (Mrs. West). The bird that Manley and I had under observation from November 28 through December 3, 1956, frequented a brushy streamside at the north end of Gatlinburg, within a stone's throw of the main highway.

Near the ceilometer at the Knoxville airport, 12 miles northwest of the park line, 4 Orange-crowned Warblers were among the 1,044 birds that died on the night of October 7–8, 1951 [Howell and Tanner, 1951]. There are but 3 records of this bird in Knox County, Tennessee, where the species is considered a rare fall migrant [Howell and Monroe, 1958]. In the region of Asheville, North Carolina, Burleigh [Pearson, Brimley, and Brimley, 1959] regarded it as being decidedly scarce in the spring and fairly common in the fall.

NASHVILLE WARBLER—*Vermivora ruficapilla*

Our records for this scarce transient total 4 in the spring and 3 in the fall, as follows: April 24 and 26, 1952, Park Headquarters (Seeber); April 29, 1935, Cades Cove (Fleetwood); May 1, 1956, Cades Cove (Watkins); September 14, 1938, Elkmont (Stupka); October 4, 1949, Newfound Gap (Stupka); and October 16, 1940, Park Headquarters (Stupka). In Knox County, Tennessee, Howell and Monroe [1958] regard it as an uncommon spring and fall migrant. Burleigh [Pearson, Brimley, and Brimley, 1959] said it was not uncommon about Asheville, North Carolina, in the fall.

PARULA WARBLER—*Parula americana*

This small warbler is a fairly common summer resident occurring from the lowest altitudes to approximately 5200 ft. The earliest arrival date is April 4 (1946, Gatlinburg— Stupka) and from 1935 to 1960 there are 8 years when the first birds were noted between April 18 and 25. The latest departure date is October 1 (1947, Park Headquarters—Stimson and McCamey).

During the breeding season the Parula Warbler has been observed in the vicinity of the park boundary from Gatlinburg east to Davenport Gap, south along the Cataloochee Divide, and on to Soco Gap. I have heard the bird singing on

Bunches Bald (5200 ft.) where it appears to reach its highest breeding altitude. Trautman, in 1940, reported it from Trillium Gap (4717 ft.), Rainbow Falls (4200 ft.), and Newfound Gap (5040 ft.) on June 19, 20, and 22, respectively. Fleetwood, in 1935, observed 6 birds at Black Camp Gap (4522 ft.) on June 12, and 13 birds at widely scattered localities in the Cataloochee area on June 20.

On May 4, 1950, Burns and I watched a Parula Warbler gathering lichens in the Park Headquarters area; a male was singing close by. During May 1961, one of these birds constructed a nest in a clump of "Spanish moss" which Snowden had brought up from the deep South and hung in a small tree near his home in the Glades, approximately a mile north of the park line (near Emerts Cove). On June 4, Snowden found 2 dead fledglings, possibly a week old, on the ground beneath this nest, after which the rather flimsy structure was deserted. The inside of this nest was lined with lichens and contained bits of hair (cottontail ?).

YELLOW WARBLER—*Dendroica petechia*

This warbler is a common summer resident throughout the lower altitudes. Trautman reported 5 birds in Cherokee Orchard (2600 ft.) June 20, 1940, and I have observed it June 6, 1947, along Straight Fork at 3135 ft. where the species appeared to be nesting. Above these altitudes it is rare or absent * with the exception of Cataloochee Ranch, 4888 ft., where I have noted it May 28, 1952, and June 4–5, 1961, and where it probably breeds regularly. The earliest arrival date is April 3 (1952 and 1953, Manley); from 1935 to 1960, the first of these warblers was reported between April 9 and 15 on 15 years. There are no records after August 8 (1934) at which time it was observed by Fleetwood.

At Park Headquarters on May 5, 1945, I watched one of these birds gathering nesting material (feathers). Fleetwood reported adults feeding young birds on May 30, 1934, in Greenbrier. On June 1, 1936, near Fighting Creek Gap (2300 ft.) I observed parent birds feeding almost fully-fledged

---

* Ganier and Clebsch [1938] report a Yellow Warbler at 4800 ft. along the transmountain road (Tennessee side) June 15, 1938. Since the habitat there is quite unsuited to this species, the bird was probably a stray.

young in a nest in an apple tree. Edwards notified me that on June 28, 1952, he watched young being fed out of the nest in the Sugarlands (1800 ft.).

Yellow Warblers favor open areas. Their absence from the grass balds on or near the state-line ridge may be due to the isolation and relatively small size of these meadowlands, since the birds breed at Cataloochee Ranch, 4888 ft., where the elevation is comparable. To quote Odum's [1945] comments on the absence of these warblers from high-altitude clearings and orchards in the mountains of Virginia: "If the clearings at high altitudes became more extensive and sufficiently connected with lower areas I would be willing to predict that the Yellow Warbler would eventually invade them. The extent and position of apparently suitable habitat must be taken into consideration."

MAGNOLIA WARBLER—*Dendroica magnolia*

Although a fairly common bird during the fall migration, this transient warbler is scarce in the spring. The earliest of the spring arrivals was recorded April 25–27 (1952) when Hebard [letter] noted one singing in Gatlinburg. Robbins [letter] observed one April 28, 1952, in the same locality. In 1935, Fleetwood listed this species on May 4, 8, and 18 in Cades Cove. Three additional records, all in early May, complete the spring list. There are 22 September records of this attractive warbler and a similar number in October; the earliest observation is September 3 (1936, Cades Cove—Foster and McCamey) and the latest is October 28 (1937, Gatlinburg—Stupka). During its autumn sojourn in the park, this bird has been found at all altitudes.

On the night of October 7–8, 1951, when 1,044 birds representing 46 species were killed at the ceilometer beacons near the Knoxville airport, 61 Magnolia Warblers were included [Howell and Tanner, 1951]. Three years later, on the nights of October 5–8, there were 15 Magnolia Warblers among the 267 birds that died at that place [Tanner, 1954]. In both instances, these warblers were fifth highest on the list of species killed. The airport is located 12 miles northwest of the park boundary.

Cairns [1902], in a list of birds of Buncombe County,

North Carolina, states, "I think this bird must breed, as young are common in July." In Pearson, Brimley, and Brimley's *Birds of North Carolina* [1959] we read that "Minot Davis, in a migration schedule from Asheville, for 1899, states that a nest and eggs had been taken by Cairns . . ." Nevertheless, there appear to be no generally-accepted breeding records south of Giles County, Virginia [A.O.U. *Check-list of North American Birds,* 1957]—approximately 150 miles northeast of Great Smoky Mountains National Park.

CAPE MAY WARBLER—*Dendroica tigrina*

This handsome warbler is a fairly common spring and fall transient. The earliest arrival date in spring is April 24 (1952, Robbins) ; the latest departure date, May 12 (1953, Stupka) . In the fall the earliest arrival date is September 18 (1951, Stupka) ; the latest departure date, November 3 (1948, Stupka) . There is one other November record—a male on November 1, 1949, gleaning bits from the rough bark of an elm tree only a few feet from my office window, at Park Headquarters.

BLACK-THROATED BLUE WARBLER—
Dendroica caerulescens

This bird * is a common summer resident above 2800 ft. in the park. The earliest arrival date is April 13 (1952, Smokemont—Phillips) ; from 1936 to 1957 the first arrivals were noted between April 16 and 23 on 19 years. The latest date of departure is October 24 (1934, Cades Cove—Fleet-

* The local race of this warbler, *Dendroica caerulescens cairnsi,* was named by Dr. Elliott Coues [1897] in honor of the late John S. Cairns of Weaverville, North Carolina, who, in 1896, had presented a paper to the World's Congress in Ornithology entitled, "The Summer Home of *Dendroeca caerulescens.*" Coues had named the new warbler before he had seen any specimens because he "was satisfied that the bird could not have thus been localized without developing distinctive characteristics." Its range is from northeastern West Virginia and western Maryland south to northeastern Georgia and northwestern South Carolina [A.O.U. Check-list, 1957]. The northern race, *D. c. caerulescens,* which breeds from Pennsylvania northward, was recorded here by Hicks on April 29, 1939 (specimen collected and now in the Ohio State Museum) , and by Stimson [letter] who observed one in good light on Mt. LeConte, October 4, 1947.

wood; and 1944, Alum Cave Parking Area—Stupka) . Fleet-wood reported a female of this species on November 17 (1934) along Little River, above Elkmont.

On May 29, 1886, Lemoyne [1886] discovered 3 nests in a laurel "swamp"—one held 4 fresh eggs, one contained 2 eggs, and the third was empty. Ganier [1956] reports finding a nest at 4000 ft. in the Great Smoky Mountains that contained 3 nearly fresh eggs on May 30, 1920. On June 14, 1924, and on June 2, 1925, he came upon 2 more nests; the first, at 5000 ft. on the north slope of Silers Bald, held 3 eggs incu-bated four days, while the second had 4 eggs incubated five days. Again on June 15, 1938, near the foot of the Chimney Tops, he found a nest with 4 small young. "All of about a dozen nests found were near a brook or spring" [Ganier, 1962]. Fleetwood, on June 20, 1934, found a young bird out of the nest near Greenbrier Pinnacle. Wetmore [1939] re-ports the finding of a young bird recently out of the nest on June 19, 1937, at Low Gap.

Although 2800 ft. is the approximate low altitude for the nesting of this warbler, it breeds down to 2400 ft. on the Gregory Ridge Trail, 2500 ft. along the Laurel Falls Trail and near Elkmont, and 2600 ft. at Chimneys Campground and the Ramsey Cascades Trail. In mid-September, following the post-nuptual molt, these birds may begin to appear in the lower altitudes.

Bent [1953], quoting Saunders, states that the song of the northern race of this warbler "is rarely revived in August, after the molt." The breeding birds of the Great Smoky Mountains, however, have been known to deliver their buzzing song often enough in August and September so that the effort is by no means a rare performance here.

The Black-throated Blue is one of the most abundant breeding warblers in the higher elevations throughout the Southern Appalachian region. Aldrich and Goodrum [1946] found 19 pairs in the 23-acre virgin hardwood forest area they censused June 23–28, 1946, in Porters Flat (2950–3200 ft.) . This would give a population of 83 pairs per 100 acres in that type of habitat. Where the original high-mountain forest is interrupted by heath balds or grass balds, or where it has been affected by fires, lumbering, or both, the Chestnut-sided replaces the Black-throated Blue as the most prevalent breeding warbler.

MYRTLE WARBLER—*Dendroica coronata*

This is the only warbler that winters in our area in any appreciable numbers. Locally, it may be a fairly common winter resident, but over the park as a whole it is an uncommon bird. Ordinarily this species is most plentiful in limestone areas, especially Tuckaleechee Cove, where the fruits of the red cedar appear to comprise one of its favorite food items.

The earliest fall arrivals were noted September 29 in the vicinity of Park Headquarters (1948 and 1952). Fleetwood's report of 3 birds in Cades Cove on May 9 (1935) represents the latest of our spring departure dates. Myrtle Warblers have not been observed in the higher altitudes during the winter season, but this species has been noted on Mt. LeConte and along the crest of the main divide in October, at Collins Gap on November 9, 1939, and at Newfound Gap and Flat Creek in April.

Fleetwood reported between 30 and 40 birds in Cades Cove on October 22 and 23, 1934, and I observed a flock of approximately the same size on March 28, 1937, in Gatlinburg. The song of this warbler has been heard between March 27 (1945) and April 28 (1943 and 1952).

Christmas Bird Count parties listed the Myrtle Warbler on 20 of 27 counts (1935–61), the average per count being 9 birds.

BLACK-THROATED GREEN WARBLER— *Dendroica virens*

This is one of the few summer resident warblers that occur at all altitudes in the park. At the lower elevations it is locally common in ravines where hemlocks prevail although it may occur in other habitats; in the spruce-fir forests it is a fairly common breeding bird. The earliest arrival date in spring is March 24 (1935, Fleetwood; 1955, Lix), and on 10 of the years from 1939 to 1956 the first birds were recorded between March 27 and 31. The latest departure date in the fall is October 23 (1939, Stupka).

A specimen obtained June 28, 1959, near the Abrams Creek Ranger Station (1200 ft.) is an immature with many pin feathers. On April 27, 1962, approximately one-half mile above Alum Cave Bluffs, Howell [letter] observed a Black-throated Green Warbler bringing material for a nest located on a horizontal limb 35 ft. up in a red spruce tree; the nest was 3 ft. from the trunk of the tree. On the following day, along the Buckeye Nature Trail, he watched another of these warblers transporting material to the site of a nest located in a crotch about 35 ft. up in a buckeye sapling.

While hiking from Newfound Gap to Bryson City via Deep Creek, on August 31, 1934, Fleetwood counted more than 50 Black-throated Green Warblers. In Cades Cove and vicinity, in 1935, he listed 57 birds on April 19 and 33 birds on May 1. Walker [1937] observed 30 of these warblers in Cades Cove on May 31, 1937.

There were 25 Black-throated Green Warblers among 1,044 birds that died in the immediate vicinity of the ceilometer at the Knoxville airport on the night of October 7–8, 1951 [Howell and Tanner, 1951]. Again on the nights of October 5–8, 1954, six of these warblers were among 267 birds that died at that same place [Tanner, 1954], approximately 12 miles northwest of the park boundary.

CERULEAN WARBLER—*Dendroica cerulea*

This attractive warbler is a very uncommon spring migrant and summer resident. The earliest record is represented by a specimen collected April 10 (1933, Greenbrier—E. V. Komarek). I observed one in the Park Headquarters area on April 11 (1939) and Mrs. Eifert reported one on April 23 (1952, Gatlinburg). Walker noted one in Cades Cove on May 22 (1938).

Howell [letter] heard the Cerulean Warbler singing near the Abrams Creek Ranger Station on June 5, 1955, and Stimson reported one at Mollies Gap, 5358 ft. on June 13, 1958. On June 13, 1952, upon being notified by Schweinfurth that he had just heard this warbler singing at 1900 ft. in the Sugarlands, Lix and I hurried to the place (a grove of mature walnut trees) where we heard and soon discovered this bird. Fifteen days later (June 28) Edwards reported a Cerulean Warbler in the same grove of trees.

BLACKBURNIAN WARBLER—*Dendroica fusca*

This handsome warbler is a common summer resident, mostly at elevations above 3000 ft. The earliest arrival date is April 11 (1932 and 1933, E. V. Komarek); on 9 years from 1936 to 1952 the first arrivals were noted between April 13 and 19. The latest departure date is October 14 (1933, E. V. Komarek).

The majority of these birds frequent the evergreen spruce-fir forests of the park where they may breed on the highest summits. Aldrich and Goodrum [1946] did not record the Blackburnian Warbler at 2950–3200 ft. in the 23-acre virgin hardwood forest area they censused June 23–28, 1946, in Porters Flat, and Tanner [1955] listed it as occurring only above the 3750 ft. elevation in his report on the altitudinal distribution of birds in the valley of LeConte Creek.

Although generally regarded as a bird of the Canadian Zone [Chapman, 1926], it has been found, occasionally, well below the lower limits of the spruce-fir forests. Stevenson and Stupka [1948] report this warbler from Fontana Village, 2400 ft. June 11, 1948, and Brewster [1886], M. Brooks [1936], and Burleigh [1958] report its occurrence outside the Canadian Zone in North Carolina, West Virginia, and Georgia, respectively.

Lemoyne [1886], in his "Notes on Some Birds of the Great Smoky Mountains," describes the finding of a nest of the Blackburnian Warbler on May 31, 1886, which contained one egg. Apparently the egg-laying period had just begun. Fleetwood, in 1934, recorded the discovery of 3 adults and 3 young on June 20, an adult and 2 young on June 28, and 3 young on July 14. Edwards reported that on June 27, 1952, on Mt. Kephart, he observed an adult bringing food to the nest.

Among 1,044 birds that died on the night of October 7–8, 1951, in the vicinity of ceilometer beacons at the Knoxville airport were 39 Blackburnian Warblers [Howell and Tanner, 1951]. At the same place on the nights of October 5–8,

1954, there were 7 Blackburnian Warblers among 267 dead birds [Tanner, 1954]. The airport is approximately 12 miles northwest of the park line.

YELLOW-THROATED WARBLER—
Dendroica dominica

This warbler * is a common summer resident in the lower altitudes. The earliest spring arrival date is March 22 (1948) when I observed 3 birds in the Park Headquarters area; from 1935 to 1961 there are 10 years when the first arrivals were noted between March 25 and 30. The latest departure date is October 1 (1941 and 1961, Stupka).

Pine trees are the favored haunts of this bird, especially at elevations below 2500 ft. Seibert [letter] reported one at 3500 ft. on Cove Mountain July 8, 1936, which is well above the usual range of this warbler.

On June 18, 1938, Ganier and Clebsch [1938] reported an adult with 2 young along the trail to Laurel Falls. On June 15, 1942, MacArthur observed an adult feeding a young bird out of the nest at 1500 ft. along the Cove Mountain Trail.

In the spring of 1961 and again from September 25 to October 1 of that year, a Yellow-throated Warbler paid frequent visits to a birdfeeder near my home, close to Emerts Cove, where miscellaneous seeds imbedded in suet comprised the bill of fare.

CHESTNUT-SIDED WARBLER—*Dendroica pensylvanica*

This warbler is a common summer resident from 3000 ft. to the summits of the highest mountains. The earliest spring arrival date is April 17 (1940, Stupka) ; from 1935 to 1955 there

* According to the A.O.U. Check-list [1957], the park area is within the breeding range of the subspecies *albilora*, sometimes known as the Sycamore Warbler. That is the name Lewy [1945] applied to the Yellow-throated Warbler in his account of the birds he noted in this area during the first week of May 1945; Ganier and Clebsch [1938] included both subspecies in their account. These determinations were based upon the coloration of the lores, a character that Peterson [1947] does not regard as a constant and infallible criterion.

are 11 years when the first of these warblers was noted between April 23 and 29. The latest fall departure date is October 14 (1949, Stupka).

At the higher elevations, wherever openings have been created in the forest by fire, lumbering, chestnut blight, windthrow, landslide, or by other means, the Chestnut-sided Warbler is one of the most plentiful breeding species. This situation seems to have come about some time after the turn of the century in view of such remarks as the following: Brewster [1886], who in 1885 pioneered a study of Southern Appalachian birds, regarded this warbler as being "nowhere really numerous. Indeed, I rarely saw more than one or two in any single day." (Fifty years later, on June 12, 1935, Fleetwood listed 20 Chestnut-sided Warblers during the course of a day spent in the field in the southeastern corner of the park). Cairns [1889] reported this to be an uncommon summer visitor in the region of the Craggy Mountains. Arthur H. Howell [1909] did not encounter this bird in 1909 in the highlands of northern Georgia where, according to Burleigh [1958], it was not definitely recorded as a breeding species until 1925. Burleigh states further that "it is now known to nest commonly" on a number of mountains there. Odum's [1945] comments are pertinent:

"The Chestnut-sided Warbler 'push' is especially interesting because it demonstrates how a wholesale change in habitat may change the range of a species, even though the climate remains the same. Thus, before the blight and lumbering operations by white man, there was probably little suitable habitat for the Chestnut-sided in the Georgia mountains other than the isolated 'balds.' With the destruction of the overstory trees, however, the bushy second growth became the dominant habitat, forming a continuous broad highway into formerly unoccupied regions. Birds, of course, are not always able to take advantage of such windfalls, but species which are able to build up large populations and are tolerant of the climatic conditions often do take advantage of such large scale changes as apparently the Chestnut-sided and the Song Sparrow have done . . ."

Fleetwood observed a pair of these warblers constructing a nest May 23, 1935, along the state-line ridge above Cades Cove. On June 12, 1936, while on Andrews Bald (5800 ft.), I watched one carrying nesting material. Ganier and Clebsch [1938] reported the discovery of a nest that had just been completed on Clingmans Dome on June 14, 1938. My notes pertaining to young birds include the following: (a) An adult carrying food to the young in a nest near Sunup Knob, on the state-line ridge, near 4800 ft. on June 15, 1937; (b) a nest with 3 small fledglings in a low shrub near Alum Cave Bluffs (4900 ft.) on June 15, 1943; (c) three birds, approximately a day old, in a nest near Alum Cave Bluffs on June 12, 1947. Occasionally, as along the Gregory Ridge and Hannah Mountain Trails to Gregory Bald, the Chestnut-sided Warbler may breed somewhat below the 3000 ft. altitude in an acceptable habitat.*

On June 4–6, 1951, I was surprised to hear the song of one of these warblers in the Park Headquarters area (1460 ft.). After the breeding season this species rarely sings, but on September 12, 1946, I heard the song at Collins Gap (5720 ft.).

On the night of October 7–8, 1951, attracted by the ceilometer beacons near the Knoxville airport, a total of 1,044 birds representing 46 species were killed. Among that number were 90 Chestnut-sided Warblers [Howell and Tanner, 1951]. Three years later, on the nights of October 5–8, a similar tragedy overtook 267 birds at that locality; included in that number were 18 Chestnut-sided Warblers [Tanner, 1954]. This airport is approximately 12 miles northwest of the park boundary.

BAY-BREASTED WARBLER—*Dendroica castanea*

This transient warbler is uncommon in the spring and fairly common in the fall migrations. A bird reported by Mayfield in Gatlinburg on April 25 (1952) represents our earliest spring occurrence, while one I observed in the Park Head-

---

* During the breeding season, this warbler has been reported from as low as 2100 ft. at Sylva, North Carolina [Stevenson, 1957], and 2000 ft. at Franklin, North Carolina [Stevenson and Stupka, 1948]—these localities being approximately 10 and 20 miles, respectively, south of the park boundary.

quarters area on May 22 (1947) marks the latest departure for that season. Its earliest reappearance in the fall is September 4 (1936, Foster and McCamey [letter]) while the latest record is on October 29 (1947, McCamey).

Fleetwood observed 21 of these birds in Cades Cove and vicinity from May 3 to 18, 1935. Burns reported a Bay-breasted Warbler singing in Cades Cove on May 3, 1951. There are two additional records from Cades Cove—single birds were noted there May 17, 1941 (Goddard) and April 27, 1952 (Howell). Our only other spring record is by Hebard who listed the species from the park area May 6–8, 1960.

There are fully twice as many records for the fall as for the spring migrations, and the former occur at all altitudes throughout the park. E. V. Komarek collected 9 specimens for the Chicago Academy of Sciences between October 4 and 20, 1933 (Gatlinburg, Greenbrier, Mt. Kephart) and Fleetwood observed a total of 20 birds in the southwestern part of the park between October 3 and 16, 1934. There are 15 additional reports of Bay-breasted Warblers ranging from September 4 to October 29, in numbers of from 1 to 10 birds.

Among 1,044 birds (46 species) killed in the vicinity of ceilometer lights at the Knoxville airport during the night of October 7–8, 1951, there were 63 Bay-breasted Warblers [Howell and Tanner, 1951]. Again, at the same place, on the nights of October 5–8, 1954, among a total of 267 birds (25 species) killed, there were 13 of these warblers [Tanner, 1954]. This airport is approximately 12 miles northwest of the park boundary.

BLACKPOLL WARBLER—*Dendroica striata*

In contrast to the Bay-breasted Warbler, which it resembles so closely in the fall plumage, the Blackpoll is fairly common as a spring migrant; its scarcity in the fall, in all probability, is due partly to the difficulties involved in its identification at that time of year and partly to the fact that the bird sings rarely, if at all, during its southward passage. It is one of the last of the transients to pass through on its northward migration. Based on more than 30 spring records for this warbler (1935–60), its earliest arrival is April 27 (1952) when D. S. Miller and Gunn recorded the bird in Gatlinburg. The latest spring departure record is May 21 (1952) when I observed this species in the same locality.

There are but 3 autumn records. Stimson observed this warbler October 3, 1947, along the Ramsey Cascades Trail, and again on the following day on Mt. Kephart. On October 14, 1933, E. V. Komarek collected a specimen in Greenbrier.

PINE WARBLER—*Dendroica pinus*

At low altitudes and where pines predominate, this warbler is a fairly common spring and fall transient and an uncommon summer resident. It has been observed rarely in winter. It is the earliest of the warblers to arrive, there being a number of February records the first of which is February 22 (1957, Stupka). The latest departure date in the fall is November 1 (1950, Stupka). Birds were heard singing on both these extreme dates. Pine Warblers do little or no singing for some weeks after the breeding season is over, but from early September until they depart, some renewal of singing may be expected.

On July 28, 1947, McCamey reported an adult and 4 young birds out of the nest, in Gatlinburg.

This warbler appears to be restricted to the lower elevations. During the spring it is to be expected in Cades Cove and along the western boundary of the park where extensive stands of pines prevail; at the latter place, in all probability, it may not be as scarce in winter as the one record (December 21, 1958—Mrs. Monroe) would indicate. Fleetwood's report of one bird near the fire tower on Look Rock (2600 ft.) on June 3, 1935, is the highest altitude at which it has been recorded.

PRAIRIE WARBLER—*Dendroica discolor*

This warbler is a fairly common summer resident in the lower altitudes where it occurs on fairly open hillsides. The earliest spring arrival date is April 3 (1935) when Fleetwood reported it from Cades Cove; from 1936 to 1958 there are 11 years when the first birds appeared between April 15 and 19. The latest departure date is October 4 (1949) when I was surprised to observe one at Newfound Gap (5040 ft.), the highest altitude at which the species has been recorded here. During the breeding season it has occurred up to 2700 ft. where I observed one at Sam Gap, on Hannah Mountain, on June 12, 1937.

On June 29, 1934, Fleetwood noted 7 adults and 1 young bird along a trail from Cosby to Low Gap.

After the breeding season the distinctive song of this warbler is rarely heard. The latest date I heard it was August 4, 1945, in Wears Cove.

PALM WARBLER—*Dendroica palmarum*

This warbler * is a fairly common spring and fall migrant and a rare winter visitor in the park. In view of its preference for open fields and cultivated land this bird is probably more common just outside the park's boundaries. The earliest arrival date in spring is April 1 (1941, Stupka); from 1935 to 1959, the first birds were recorded between April 18 and 28 on 13 years. The latest departure date in spring is May 31 (1937) when Walker [1937] observed what must have been an unusually late migrant in Cades Cove. On September 1 (1945) I recorded 3 birds in the Park Headquarters area which represent our earliest fall arrivals. The latest of three November records is November 20 (1952, Stupka); I observed a single bird at Park Headquarters on December 30 and 31, 1946, and again on January 3, 1947; in December 1947, McCamey and I watched a lone bird in the immediate vicinity of Park Headquarters Building on the 16th and 19th.

On October 16, 1940, I observed a flock consisting of several hundred birds in the Sugarlands area, near Park Headquarters. Near the same location, flocks of over 100 Palm Warblers were noted October 17, 1941; September 21, 1942; September 24, 1943; and October 9, 1945.

* Both the subspecies *D. p. palmarum*, sometimes referred to as the Western Palm Warbler, and *D. p. hypochrysea*, the so-called Yellow Palm Warbler, have been observed in the park on a number of occasions. As Peterson [1947] has stated, both races of this bird can be identified in the field, but since there is always the possibility of error with sight records, I have decided against any distinction between these two subspecies in the above text. Based on my own records, it can be stated that the subspecies *palmarum* is appreciably more numerous in the fall than *hypochrysea*, a situation which, according to Burleigh [1958], is also true in Georgia. According to Pearson, Brimley, and Brimley [1959] quite the reverse is true in North Carolina.

There are 11 records of the appearance of this species at
high altitudes (4300–6300 ft.) ; of this number, 9 are for the
fall and 2 for the spring migrations. There are no records of
large flocks at the higher elevations, most of these reports involving single birds.

OVENBIRD—*Seiurus aurocapillus*

This warbler is a common summer resident at low and
middle altitudes. Three-quarters of a century ago Brewster
[1886] regarded the Ovenbird as one of the commonest and
most characteristic summer birds, and its status has remained
unchanged over the years. The earliest spring arrival date is
April 8 (1959, Stupka) ; during the period 1935–61 the first of
these birds was noted between April 16 and 19 on 11 years.
The latest October record is on the 21st (1949, Stupka), but
there are 2 records in November. Along Little River, on November 13, 1934, Fleetwood listed a total of 12 Ovenbirds in
the course of the day; on November 30, 1959, with snow in
patches on the ground and the temperature reading 10°
above zero, I observed one of these birds walking on the lawn
close to the main building in the Park Headquarters area.*

Ordinarily this warbler reaches its upper limits at around
4200–4500 ft. [Brewster, 1886; Burleigh, 1941; Tanner,
1955], but it is not unusual to find it in forests up to 5000 ft.
(Newfound Gap, vicinity of Gregory Bald, Heintooga Overlook), and, on occasions, it occurs at higher altitudes. Ganier
and Clebsch [1938] report 2 birds at Silers Bald, 5620 ft., on
June 18, 1938, and Trautman, in 1940, observed one near the
lodge on Mt. LeConte, near 6300 ft., on June 20.

Ganier [1926] reported finding a nest with young birds
about 6 days old on Miry Ridge on June 1, 1920. In the vicinity of Cades Cove, Fleetwood came upon a nest with young
birds on May 28, 1935; Ganier and Clebsch [1938] reported
a nest containing 4 young on June 16, 1938; and I discovered
a nest with 4 eggs on May 26, 1940. A nest with 3 eggs was
found along Laurel Creek by Koch on May 24, 1944. Fawver,
on May 20, 1948, reported a nest with at least 3 young birds
along Roaring Fork.

* Bent [1953]: "There are records of the ovenbird wintering or attempting to winter as far north as New England."

Fleetwood counted 12 to 29 Ovenbirds per day on 8 of the days between April 19 and May 28, 1935—all were observed in or near Cades Cove. Aldrich and Goodrum [1946] found 4 pairs in the 23-acre virgin hardwood forest area they censused June 23–28, 1946, in Porters Flat (2950–3200 ft.).

In the Great Smoky Mountains the song of this woodland bird is unlike that I have heard in Ohio. Ordinarily a single note is repeated instead of the two-note phrase usually written as "teacher-teacher-teacher . . ." Also, as noted by Odum [1944] in Georgia, "the phrases tend to be more uniform in volume (like the Carolina Wren) rather than increasing in volume as in typical 'teacher' version of New York birds . . ."

On the night of October 7–8, 1951, attracted by the strong vertical beam of the ceilometer at the Knoxville airport, 1,044 birds of 46 species were killed when they struck the concrete pavement of the lighted area in that vicinity [Howell and Tanner, 1951]. By far the most numerous of this ill-fated lot were Ovenbirds, there being 387 of that species of warbler alone. Again at the same location, on the nights of October 5–8, 1954, Ovenbirds comprised approximately one-third of all the 267 birds that were killed, there being 81 of these warblers [Tanner, 1954]. The Knoxville airport lies about 12 miles northwest of the boundary of Great Smoky Mountains National Park.

NORTHERN WATERTHRUSH—*Seiurus noveboracensis*

This warbler is a very uncommon spring and fall migrant. There are but three records for the spring: April 26, 1952, Park Headquarters area, 1 bird observed and heard singing (Hebard and Street); April 27, 1935, Cades Cove, 2 birds (Fleetwood); and May 8, 1935, Cades Cove, 1 bird (Fleetwood). All of the fall records are of birds I observed from my office window in the Park Headquarters area. The earliest is on September 14 (1953) and it is possible that this was the same individual I noted in that location on the two following days. On October 1–3, 1947, a lone bird frequented the spacious lawn there. The latest fall record is October 7 (1959).

LOUISIANA WATERTHRUSH—*Seiurus motacilla*

This warbler is a common summer resident at altitudes below 3500 ft. The earliest arrival date in spring is March 17 (1957, Lix); during the period 1935–56 there are 15 years when the first Louisiana Waterthrushes were noted between March 18 and 23. In the fall the latest departure date on record is October 1 (1941, Stupka), and there is an unusual record of one of these birds' having frequented the center of Gatlinburg from December 8, 1954, to January 25, 1955. This wintering individual was under almost daily observation by Manley, who discovered it, and the bird was also viewed by Tanner and me.

This waterthrush has been observed above 3500 ft. on a number of occasions. Its occurrence at the Alum Cave Parking Area, at 3800 ft., has been noted a few times, and Tanner [1955] has recorded it at the same elevation in the LeConte Creek valley. On September 3, 1947, McCamey saw one at Newfound Gap, 5040 ft. while on July 13, 1949, Baldwin reported this warbler near the 5700 ft. altitude along the Appalachian Trail, approximately one mile west of Charlies Bunion.*

In 1934, Fleetwood observed an adult and a young bird on June 6 near Greenbrier; on June 20 he reported a young Louisiana Waterthrush along the trail to Greenbrier Pinnacle. On May 31, 1946, the first of four birds hatched in a nest I discovered near Gatlinburg. Along Deep Creek on July 28, 1950, I was surprised to find 2 young birds only recently out of the nest and capable of a weak flight.

This warbler sings but rarely after its nesting cares are over. I heard the song July 19, 1948, and August 18, 1939, near Gatlinburg.

KENTUCKY WARBLER—*Oporornis formosus*

Below the 3500 ft. altitude, in ravines and along stream courses where there is dense undergrowth, this warbler is a fairly common summer resident. The earliest arrival date is

---

* In western North Carolina, outside the park, Brewster [1886] reported this species to 4500 ft. near Highlands, and Wetmore [1941] mentions one at 5000 ft. 12 miles west of Franklin.

April 20 (1939, Stupka), and during 1937–60 there are 18 years when the first birds appeared between April 22 and 29. The latest departure date is September 24 (1950, Burns).

Wetmore [1939] mentions the occurrence of this species at Low Gap (4242 ft.) on June 19, 1937, which represents the highest of the park records. I have observed it up to 3500 ft. along the Gregory Ridge Trail on June 19, 1953.*

Ganier [1926] discovered a nest containing very small young on May 27. In 1934, near Greenbrier, Fleetwood came upon a nest with 5 young birds on May 31 and another nest occupied by a close-sitting adult on June 2. Along Porters Creek on June 13, 1934, Fleetwood reported one young bird with an adult. In Cades Cove, Keating found two nesting pairs of Kentucky Warblers on June 11, 1937. Muller, on May 28, 1959, discovered a nest with 5 eggs near the Abrams Creek Ranger Station.

In Cades Cove, Fleetwood listed 15 of these warblers on May 1, 1935, while Walker [1937] counted 33 birds on May 31, 1937. Aldrich and Goodrum [1946] found one pair of Kentucky Warblers in the 23-acre virgin hardwood forest area they censused June 23–28, 1946, in Porters Flat (2950–3200 ft.).

YELLOWTHROAT—*Geothlypis trichas*

This warbler ** is a common summer resident at all altitudes, occurring where streams are margined with deciduous shrubs, especially in fairly open situations. The earliest record of its arrival in the spring is April 14 (1938, Stupka); from 1935 to 1959 there are 15 years when the first of these warblers was noted between April 17 and 23. The latest depar-

---

* Brewster [1886] gives 3500 ft. as its upper limit in western North Carolina; Stevenson [1957] mentions three localities in western North Carolina, outside the park, where the highest range of this bird during the breeding season was 3550–3800 ft.; Pearson, Brimley, and Brimley [1959] state that this species occurs up to 4000 ft. in North Carolina but give no particulars.
** Specimens of this warbler obtained in Cades Cove by E. V. Komarek (May 3, 1933) and at 6100 ft. on Inadu Knob by a party from the U. S. National Museum (June 26, 1937) were identified as belonging to the so-called northern race *G. t. brachidactyla* by Wetmore [1939]. That is also the determination placed on specimens obtained outside the park in western North Carolina, in 1939 [Wetmore, 1941].

ture date in the fall is October 28 (1947) when I found 2 of these birds in the Sugarlands.

Brewster [1886], in western North Carolina, did not observe this warbler above 2100 ft., and Ganier [1926] likewise listed it only from the lower altitudes. It is possible that here as in the Central Allegheny Mountain Region the Yellowthroat has invaded the highest mountains following the removal of the spruce [M. Brooks, 1940]. In the Great Smoky Mountains where precipitation at the higher altitudes exceeds that in the lowlands by 50 percent [Shanks, 1954], this bird may find an acceptable environment in extensive clearings. Thus we find it high up on the slopes of Clingmans Dome at altitudes exceeding 6000 ft. (10 or more records during May, June, and July, from 1938 to 1949—Stupka) and on Andrews Bald, nearby, at 5800 ft. (June 12, 1936, and June 13, 1941—Stupka; Ganier and Clebsch [1938]). It has also been reported from approximately 6000 ft. by Wetmore [1939], Stupka (June 29, 1936), and McCamey (August 30, 1947), and from near Charlies Bunion, 5375 ft., by Edwards (June 27, 1952), and Stupka (June 1939 and 1943; July 1936 and 1943). On June 11, 1935, Fleetwood observed 3 Yellowthroats on Hemphill Bald, 5573 ft., on the southeastern boundary of the park.

Although it is unusual for this warbler to sing late in the season [Bent, 1953], on September 26, 1953, near Emerts Cove, I listened to a weak vocal performance by one of these birds.

On the night of October 7–8, 1951, 32 Yellowthroats were among 1,044 birds killed in the vicinity of ceilometer beacons at the Knoxville airport, 12 miles northwest of the park boundary [Howell and Tanner, 1951].

YELLOW-BREASTED CHAT—*Icteria virens*

This large warbler is a common summer resident at low and middle altitudes on mountainsides where low thickets and brush prevail. The earliest spring arrival date is April 14 (1948, Stupka); from 1935 to 1960 there are 18 years when the chat's first appearance was noted between April 19 and 27.

Its latest date of departure in the fall is October 7 (1949, Burns).

Whereas in some watersheds this bird may not occur above 3500 ft., elsewhere its upward range may go to 5000 ft. as I have observed along the Appalachian Trail west of Cosby Knob (June 29, 1936). Above that elevation chats are scarce; Stevenson [Stevenson and Stupka, 1948] reported the species from 5400 ft. on the slope of Mt. LeConte on June 9, 1948, and Fleetwood mentions its occurrence in brier thickets near the summit of Hemphill Bald, 5573 ft. on June 11, 1935.

Cades Cove (1800–1900 ft.) is one of the areas within the park where these warblers are quite plentiful. Fleetwood listed 18 of these birds there on May 30, 1935, while Trautman, on June 18, 1940, counted 20.

Seibert flushed a chat from a nest containing 3 eggs, near Elkmont, on July 10, 1936.

HOODED WARBLER—*Wilsonia citrina*

This bird is a common summer resident in forests at low and middle altitudes. The earliest arrival date is April 5 (1935) when Fleetwood observed this warbler in Cades Cove; from 1937 to 1960 there are 19 years when this bird was first noted between April 11 and 18. The latest departure date in the fall is October 25 (1934, Fleetwood), but on November 29, 1955, Burns had a male Hooded Warbler under observation for 15 minutes in the vicinity of the main parking area in Cades Cove.

During the breeding season this bird seldom ascends above the 4000 ft. altitude. Wetmore [1939] reports on its occurrence at Low Gap, 4242 ft., June 19, 1937; Trautman, in 1940, mentions it at 4600 ft. along the transmountain road (Tennessee side) on June 22, and at Trillium Gap, 4717 ft., on June 19; Fleetwood, on June 7, 1934, came upon a pair of these birds on Brushy Mountain, 4911 ft., where he heard the cries of their young.*

In late summer some Hooded Warblers may wander into areas well above their breeding grounds. On August 23, 1950,

* In Monroe County, Tennessee, on the western boundary of the park, Lemoyne [1886] describes a nest with 4 eggs that was found June 3, 1883. On June 9, another nest held 4 eggs "nearly fresh."

Burns encountered one of these birds along the Boulevard Trail, 5500–6000 ft., while Metcalf [1938], on August 26, 1937, reported one in the young forest just below the Clingmans Dome Parking Area, 6311 ft. In early September 1936, Foster and McCamey [letter] reported this species "in most warbler flocks at all elevations."

In Cades Cove, where these birds are plentiful, Fleetwood reported finding up to 71 individuals in one day (April 27, 1935), which probably marked the peak of the spring migration. On May 31, 1937, by which time the birds were engaged in their nesting activities, Walker [1937] counted 16 Hooded Warblers in that area.

There appears to be no member of the warbler family that sings so persistently throughout the summer.* In fact there are but few birds that sing as frequently during the latter part of that season.

On the night of October 7–8, 1951, 35 Hooded Warblers were among 1,044 birds killed in the vicinity of ceilometer beacons at the Knoxville airport, 12 miles northwest of the park boundary [Howell and Tanner, 1951].

WILSON'S WARBLER—*Wilsonia pusilla*

There is only one record of this transient warbler in the spring migration and but four in the fall. On May 11, 1944, I observed a single bird in the Park Headquarters area. Of the fall occurrences, the earliest is August 31 (1941) when George and Quay listed one on the Appalachian Trail, near Cosby Knob, at 4500–5000 ft. At Park Headquarters I observed one on September 11, 1944. Fleetwood's only record of this species is September 18, 1934, when he noted two birds along Deep Creek. The latest, again in the Park Headquarters area, is one I saw on October 2, 1939.

CANADA WARBLER—*Wilsonia canadensis*

In cool dark tangles of rhododendrons and other shrubs, especially near small watercourses, the Canada Warbler is a common summer resident from 3400 ft. to the tops of the highest mountains. The earliest arrival date in the spring is

* Burleigh [1958], in his book on *Georgia Birds*, makes the same comment.

April 24 (1955, Watkins) ; from 1935 to 1954, the first were noted between April 26 and May 3 on 15 years. The latest departure date in the fall is September 17 (1934, Fleetwood; 1950, Burns) .* Before the middle of May and again after the middle of August this bird may appear at any altitude.

Ganier and Clebsch [1938] report the finding of a nest on June 15, 1938, near the trail from the Clingmans Dome Parking Area to Andrews Bald; it contained 3 nearly fresh eggs. On June 23, 1947, at Arch Rock (4200 ft.) , I came upon an adult Canada Warbler feeding a young bird out of the nest. On June 13, 1958, at 5200 ft., within a few feet of the spur road to Heintooga Overlook, I examined a nest containing 3 birds approximately a week old. Along the Hannah Mountain Trail to Gregory Bald, at 3800 ft., I discovered an adult feeding a young bird out of the nest on June 17, 1961.

There is some singing in August, but for the most part these warblers are quiet after the breeding season.

Trautman listed 16 of these birds in going from Trillium Gap to Mt. LeConte, June 19, 1940, and 14 (next day) from Mt. LeConte to Rainbow Falls.

AMERICAN REDSTART—*Setophaga ruticilla*

This attractive warbler is a fairly common summer resident, mostly at the lower altitudes. The earliest spring arrival date is April 8 (1959, Stupka) ; from 1936 to 1960 the first appearance of this bird was noted between April 11 and 15 on 13 years. The latest fall departure date is October 18 (1934, Fleetwood) , but on November 12, 1953, Manley observed a male redstart with a flock of Myrtle Warblers in Gatlinburg.

During the breeding season most of the American Redstarts remain below the 2500 ft. altitude. There are a few high-altitude records at that time of year, however, such as Fleetwood's report of 3 birds along the Boulevard Trail, at approximately 5500 ft., on June 13, 1934, and my observation of single birds near Flat Creek on June 11, 1937, and on Gregorys Bald on June 12, 1937—both these latter places being at about the 4900 ft. elevation. After the breeding season red-

* For Knox County, Tennessee, the latest fall date is October 5 [Howell and Monroe, 1957]; for Buncombe County, North Carolina, it is October 10 [Pearson, Brimley, and Brimley, 1959].

starts range widely over the park prior to their fall migration, occasionally reaching the highest elevations.

The largest number of these warblers recorded in one day was 18; these were observed by Fleetwood on April 25, 1934, near Elkmont.

FAMILY | *PLOCEIDAE*

HOUSE SPARROW—*Passer domesticus*

Langdon [1887] in 1886 observed a few of these introduced birds at Knoxville and Maryville, Tennessee, but makes no mention of them in the mountains nor in Miller's and Tuckaleechee Coves where he spent several days in August studying birds.

During the first quarter of the present century, with extensive logging operations underway and hundreds of families living in what is now the park area, such livestock and poultry as were raised probably attracted a considerable population of House Sparrows. Their numbers dwindled after the National Park was realized, not only because livestock and poultry disappeared along with the exodus of the families who had lived here but because motorpower was fast replacing horsepower.

In Cades Cove, where horses and other livestock continue to graze, the House Sparrow is a common permanent resident, and this status prevails on farm lands and in communities adjacent to practically the entire boundary of the park. Elsewhere this bird is mostly scarce or absent.

In 1934, the largest number of House Sparrows counted by Fleetwood in Cades Cove was 26 (October 30) ; along Deep Creek, 42 (November 9). Christmas Bird Count parties listed an average of approximately 75 of these birds on 27 counts (1935–61) ; largest single count was 260 on January 1, 1950.

FAMILY | *ICTERIDAE*

BOBOLINK—*Dolichonyx oryzivorus*

This bird is an uncommon spring migrant in our area. The flocks of Bobolinks appear to bypass the mountains in their migratory flights, particularly in the fall. On April 18 (1935) Fleetwood reported a lone male in Cades Cove which is our earliest record. Watkins observed the species in the park on April 24, 1955, and again on April 28, 1954. I saw and heard 3 male birds in Tuckaleechee Cove on April 30, 1953.

Fleetwood noted 6 Bobolinks in Cades Cove on May 2 and 4, 1935, and I have a record of 10–12 birds in that place on May 6, 1940. Our only high-altitude report is of a lone male perched in the top of a spruce tree at Newfound Gap, 5040 ft., on May 12, 1953 (Mrs. Weig and Mrs. Appleby).

I observed a lone male on May 9, 1950, near Fontana Dam. On May 19, 1953, a male and a female were on the lawn in the Park Headquarters area. What must have been a belated male was viewed June 21 and 22, 1950, by Burns, Pfitzer, and me in a hayfield along Deep Creek, approximately one-fourth mile south of the park boundary.*

The largest flock on our records, comprised of 12 to 15 birds, was in a field along the Tuckasegee River, between Ela and Bryson City, on May 5, 1944 (Stupka).

EASTERN MEADOWLARK—*Sturnella magna*

Wherever there are openings in the forest, this bird is a common spring and fall transient. It has the status of fairly common permanent resident in Cades Cove as well as in the adjacent or nearby coves and broad stream valleys and on lands along much of the park's boundary. Prior to 1930 before the National Park became a reality, meadowlarks were probably permanent residents on the cultivated lands at the lower altitudes, but with the rapid return of the forest following the abandonment of the land by man these birds disappeared.

---

* There are records of belated stragglers on June 17 and 28, 1903, at Durham, North Carolina [Pearson, Brimley, and Brimley, 1959], and on June 23 (year ?) in South Carolina [Sprunt and Chamberlain, 1949].

Disregarding what appear to be records of a few vagrant birds in January and early February, the first of the spring migrants was observed February 14 (1949) when Davis noted single birds at Newfound and Indian Gaps; from 1935 to 1961, there are 12 years when the first arrivals were noted between February 18 and 29. In the fall, in areas other than the lower altitude coves (where meadowlarks are permanent residents), the latest departure date is November 17 (1951) when Ealy encountered a few birds near Indian Gap.

At Park Headquarters where the clearing adjacent to the Administration Building has been a landing field and a temporary feeding area for meadowlarks for a number of years, the birds were readily observed and their presence recorded during the period 1937–60. The following summary reveals the total number of days meadowlarks were noted there (1460 ft.) as well as at various places above 4000 ft.:

NUMBER OF MEADOWLARKS AT PARK HEAD-
QUARTERS AND IN THE HIGHER ALTITUDES
(1937–60)

Month	Headquarters (1460')	4000' or over
January	0	0
February	19	6
March	53	12
April	43	9
May	0	2
June	0	0
July	0	0
August	0	0
September	0	0
October	18	11
November	13	4
December	0	0
Total	146	44

At Park Headquarters, the earliest spring arrival date is February 15 (1949) and the latest spring departure date, April 30 (1951); the earliest fall arrival date is October 3 (1945) and the latest fall departure date, November 27 (1951).

During their migrations these birds have appeared at Newfound (5040 ft.) and Indian Gaps (5266 ft.) on a number of occasions. There also are records for various other places along the main divide of the Smokies, such as Charlies Bunion, Collins Gap, Spence Field, and Russell Field. On April 21, 1940, J. Huff reported 2 meadowlarks near the lodge on Mt. LeConte (6300 ft.).

On April 27, 1952, Howell discovered a nest and 5 eggs in Cades Cove.

The largest recorded flock, comprising approximately 300 birds, was noted by Manley on October 18, 1957, in Gatlinburg. At Park Headquarters I observed a flock of about 100 birds on March 23, 1938. On October 21, 1960, I found 5 dead meadowlarks within a stretch of one-half mile of road less than a mile east of Gatlinburg; passing vehicles had run into a flock of these birds that had moved into the area during a sudden change to much colder weather.

Parties engaged in the Christmas Bird Count during the years 1935–61 listed approximately 50 meadowlarks per count. (For the 5-year period 1957–61, when the area of the count included Cades Cove and Tuckaleechee Cove, the average number of these birds per count was 139.)

REDWINGED BLACKBIRD—*Agelaius phoeniceus*

This bird, like the meadowlark, is a common spring and fall transient; due to the scarcity of its preferred habitat it is a very uncommon breeder and winter visitor. Just north of the park where the streams become larger and slower-moving, the Redwinged Blackbird is a common summer resident.

At Park Headquarters the earliest of 11 February records (1943–61) is February 16 (1945); this represents the earliest spring arrival date at that place. There are earlier records in Cades Cove and the coves just north of the park, but there the situation is affected by the occasional winter visitation or wintering of this species. What is probably the earliest arrival date for the park is February 9, (1950) when Burns noted one of these birds at Collins Gap (5720 ft.) on the state-line ridge. Ealy counted approximately 70 birds at Collins Gap on February 15, 1949, and Burns observed about 50 there on March 14, 1950. That is the highest elevation at which the species has been noted.

Flocks numbering 50–100 birds have been observed late in November in Gatlinburg (1948) and in Cades Cove (1938, 1950). Occasionally Redwinged Blackbirds appear in Cades Cove during the winter months but these are probably vagrants from flocks that winter outside the park.

In Cades Cove, one or more pairs have nested in the wet Oliver meadow for a number of years. On May 20, 1938, when I discovered a nest with 2 eggs at that place, I also observed a few young birds that had recently left the nest. This species was nesting there again in 1943, 1944, and 1946. On May 22, 1944, there were 2 nests, one with 3 eggs and the other with 4 eggs.

The largest flock, containing 300–400 birds, was found along Big Creek, near Mt. Sterling, North Carolina, on February 24, 1955 (Stupka). On the opposite extremity of the park, at Chilhowee, Tennessee, Burns reported a flock of approximately 200 birds on February 27, 1951. During 1935–61, Christmas Bird Count parties listed an average of 3 Redwinged Blackbirds per count, mostly from outside the park near Pigeon Forge and Tuckaleechee Cove.

ORCHARD ORIOLE—*Icterus spurius*

Although this species is a fairly common summer resident in the vicinity of the park, its status within the area is that of an uncommon transient. Like the Chuck-will's-widow, Mockingbird, and Loggerhead Shrike, the Orchard Oriole becomes a much more frequently-encountered bird almost as soon as one leaves the mountains going in a northward or westward direction, the change of status corresponding to the rather sudden change in the topography.

This oriole was noted on 14 of the 27 years, 1935–61. The earliest arrival date in the spring is April 16 (1936, Stupka), and there are 5 records of this species arriving between April 24 and 28. The latest departure date in the fall is September 3 (1936) when Foster and McCamey [letter] observed this bird at 3000 ft. on the Gregory Ridge Trail.

Fleetwood, in 1935 (Cades Cove), and Manley, in 1953 (Gatlinburg), observed this species on a number of days during the latter half of May and on into June 1, but no nesting activities were reported in either instance.

Dense forests, so characteristic of much of this area, do not appeal to the Orchard Oriole. Ordinarily it inhabits the trees near human dwellings and occurs in the vicinity of cultivated lands along the boundaries of Great Smoky Mountains National Park.

BALTIMORE ORIOLE—*Icterus galbula*

This handsome bird is a rather uncommon transient in our area.* The earliest spring arrival date is April 24 (1952, Seeber), and there are 12 additional records ranging from April 25 to May 11. On May 31, 1939, Manley observed one along the transmountain road (Tennessee side), while in June 1962 a lone male was reported in Gatlinburg on the 1st (Stupka), 3rd (Howell), and 21st (Manley). Our only August record (August 24, 1961—Stupka) marks the beginning of the fall migration. Foster and McCamey [letter] reported this bird on September 3, 1936; Manley noted it on September 7, 1940; and I observed it on September 11, 1940—this last-mentioned date denoting the time of its latest fall departure.

The above records of May 31, 1939, and September 3, 1936, are at elevations of approximately 3500 ft.; all the others are below 1800 ft. At least three-fourths of all the observations were made in Gatlinburg, near Park Headquarters, or in Cades Cove.

RUSTY BLACKBIRD—*Euphagus carolinus*

The Rusty Blackbird is mostly an uncommon spring and fall transient; it winters here only on rare occasions. From 1934 to 1960, spring migrants were reported on 11 years and fall migrants on 12 years.

For the spring migration our earliest record is March 1 (1940) when Manley observed 10–12 birds in Tuckaleechee Cove. There are 5 first-arrival records during the March 14–17 period. The latest departure date in spring is April 22 (1935) when Fleetwood noted 5 birds in Cades Cove.

* Baltimore Orioles have been reported breeding north (Greeneville, Tennessee [Darnell, 1956]), east (Asheville, North Carolina [Cairns, 1889]), and west (Athens, Tennessee [Ganier, 1935]) of the park. According to Stevenson [1941], this bird also nested south of the park at Highlands, North Carolina, up to 1911.

The flock of 25–30 Rusty Blackbirds that appeared near my home in the vicinity of Emerts Cove on October 26 (1957) proved to be the earliest of our fall records for this species. On 3 additional years the autumn vanguards arrived in late October, but in most instances this takes place in November. The small flock I noted in Tuckaleechee Cove on November 29 (1938) and a flock of approximately 25 birds that Burns reported in Cades Cove on November 29 (1950) represent the latest fall departures.

There are 3 winter records: A flock of 8 birds in Cades Cove on February 5, 1938 (Stupka) ; a lone bird that appeared in the immediate vicinity of the Park Headquarters Building on November 30, 1959, and remained until January 8, 1960 (Stupka) ; and 2 birds observed in Cades Cove on December 24, 1960 (Russell).

Single birds have been observed more often in spring than in the fall. Flocks are larger in the fall migration; by far the largest, comprised of approximately 200 birds, was in the Park Headquarters area November 10, 1939 (Stupka). Only once was this species found associating with other birds—on March 14, 1950, when a lone Rusty Blackbird was observed in a large flock of Redwinged Blackbirds on the lawn at Park Headquarters.

I recorded 1 high-altitude record in the spring (Newfound Gap, 5040 ft., March 23–24, 1949) and 2 in the fall (between Black Camp Gap and Heintooga Overlook, at 4900 ft., October 28, 1948; and along the Tennessee side of the transmountain road at 4800 ft., November 16, 1951) —each involving single birds. All other records are from places below 2200 ft.

On one occasion (March 31, 1936), I heard a Rusty Blackbird singing in Elkmont.

COMMON GRACKLE—*Quiscalus quiscula*

Grackles are fairly common summer residents at the lower altitudes, especially in communities and on farms near the park boundary. During the winter these birds are rare in the park. The earliest date on which they were noted in spring is February 15 (1956) when Manley reported 4 birds in Gatlinburg; during 1937–61 there are 9 years when the first grackles put in their appearance between February 26 and March 4.

In the fall, Manley observed a flock of approximately 50 birds at Fighting Creek Gap (2300 ft.) on November 8, 1940; at Park Headquarters I noted 1 grackle on December 14 and 15, 1944, and Walker counted 5 birds at that place on December 17, 1944. There are a few records for the late fall and early winter in some of the towns adjacent to the park.

On May 5, 1945, I heard young grackles crying for food near Pigeon Forge. For many years, these birds have nested in a close stand of mature white pines near the Mountain View Hotel, in Gatlinburg. Fleetwood, on April 11, 1935, counted 14 grackles in Cades Cove; Trautman, on June 18, 1940, listed 40 birds in the pine stands there.

A flock of approximately 300 grackles that I observed in the Park Headquarters area on October 29, 1940, is the largest aggregation to be recorded here.

On April 26, 1952, I watched 2 grackles fly over Newfound Gap (5040 ft.) . This represents our only high-altitude record of this species.

BROWN-HEADED COWBIRD—*Molothrus ater*

This bird is a fairly common transient, an uncommon summer resident, and a scarce winter visitor. Generally speaking, the cowbird, like other blackbirds, is more plentiful on farmland just outside the park. In the Park Headquarters area the earliest spring migrants arrived February 20 (1948) when I observed 2 cowbirds with a large flock of Redwinged Blackbirds. Other February records at that place, all relating to single birds, are February 22 (1949) , February 25 (1954) , February 26 (1944) , and February 29 (1952) .

During March, April, and May (1935–61) there are 22, 38, and 9 records of cowbirds, respectively, mostly single birds or in twos and threes. All these, plus the few records for June, are at elevations below 2000 ft. Only 2 records are above that altitude, and both are for Newfound Gap (5040 ft.) in summer—one bird on August 3, 1944, and another on July 29, 1952 (Stupka). The latter bird, a young-of-the-year, remained at that locality for approximately 2 weeks during which time it became so approachable that it would accept live grasshoppers from one's hand and would perch on the finger or shoulder of the ranger who was stationed there. (Photographs of such intimacies were obtained.)

During all of June 1961, a pair of adult cowbirds frequented the lawn in the Park Headquarters area. On July 15, 1950, Dr. and Mrs. Baldwin observed a Red-eyed Vireo feeding a young cowbird out of the nest, 2 miles north of Gatlinburg. On July 14, 1953, I recorded an immature cowbird at Park Headquarters, and on July 17, 1961, a young-of-the-year appeared at my bird-feeding station, near Emerts Cove.

The birds have not been observed as often in the fall as in the spring migration, there being but 8 low-altitude records ranging from October 26 (1950, Burns) to December 6 (1954, Stupka). On January 5, 1946, I noted a flock of 20 cowbirds in Cades Cove.

FAMILY | *THRAUPIDAE*

SCARLET TANAGER—*Piranga olivacea*

This strikingly-attired bird is a common summer resident mostly between 1500 and 5000 ft. The earliest spring arrival date is April 17 (1935, Fleetwood) ; from 1937 to 1961 there are 14 years when the first Scarlet Tanagers were noted between April 18 and 25. The latest fall departure date is October 19 (1951, Stupka). During the breeding season, there are but few records of this species at altitudes below 1500 or above 5000 ft. Murray [1940] has indicated for the West Virginia mountains that the line of division between the Summer and Scarlet Tanagers is near the 1500 ft. altitude—for the Great Smoky Mountains I would place this at 1500–2000 ft. My home near Emerts Cove is at an elevation of approximately 1650 ft. on a south-facing hillside where oaks and pines predominate. There the Summer Tanager is common and breeds regularly, but the Scarlet is of irregular occurrence breeding less than half of the summers (1952–61). Above that elevation the Scarlet Tanager soon prevails; below, it disappears over wide areas.

Trautman reported 2 Scarlet Tanagers from Andrews Bald, 5800 ft., on June 22, 1940. That represents our upper limit for this bird and one of the few records above 5000 ft. It is a common species up to approximately 4500 ft. as almost anyone can testify who hikes to Gregory Bald, in June, over either the Gregory Ridge or the Hannah Mountain Trails.

Along the trail to Laurel Falls on June 28, 1950, I came upon a young bird out of the nest attended by the parents. Along the same trail on July 17, 1946, I noted an adult female feeding a young bird just out of the nest. Aldrich and Goodrum [1946] found 5 pairs of Scarlet Tanagers in the 23-acre virgin hardwood forest area they censused June 23–28, 1946, in Porters Flat (2950–3200 ft.).

On the night of October 7–8, 1951, 33 Scarlet Tanagers were among 1,044 birds killed in the vicinity of ceilometer lights at the Knoxville airport, 12 miles northwest of the park boundary [Howell and Tanner, 1951].

SUMMER TANAGER—*Piranga rubra*

This bird is a common summer resident at the lower altitudes, mostly below 2000 ft. The earliest spring arrival date is April 12 (1952, Stupka); from 1935 to 1960 there are 14 years when the first Summer Tanagers were noted between April 17 and 21. The latest fall departure date is October 19 (1943, Stupka).

Trautman reported 2 of these birds at Cherokee Orchard, 2600 ft., on June 19, 1940, which appears to be the uppermost range during the breeding season. As stated in the comments (above) relating to the Scarlet Tanager, these two species meet near the 1500–2000 ft. altitude, the Summer prevailing below that range. Even after the breeding season this bird remains in the lower altitudes, the highest late summer record (August 21, 1932) being at 2800 ft. in the Greenbrier area (E. V. Komarek).

On May 17, 1941, Goddard reported the nest of a Summer Tanager in a pine tree in Cades Cove. Five days later Manley discovered a nest in a pine tree in Gatlinburg. Since both Forbush [1929] and Burleigh [1958] state that this species is single-brooded,* the report that a fledgling left the nest on August 11, 1959, close to the Morrell residence 2 miles north of Gatlinburg, is of considerable interest. This nest had been under observation by the Morrells for some days.

Some Summer Tanagers sing throughout July, and the song period may be resumed again in September.

FAMILY | *FRINGILLIDAE*

CARDINAL—*Richmondena cardinalis*

Cardinals are common permanent residents at elevations below 3500 ft. Fleetwood's report of hearing one near Black Camp Gap, 4492 ft., on June 16, 1935, is by far the highest record during the breeding season. My observation of one at Newfound Gap (5040 ft.) on October 12, 1943, came as a surprise since this species rarely invades the higher elevations.

On May 30, 1934, Fleetwood came upon adults feeding young birds in the Greenbrier area. Along Roaring Fork, near Gatlinburg, I found a female Cardinal incubating 3 eggs on May 10, 1944. Bellrose [1938] reports several young being fed by adults on September 1, 1937, in the Park Headquarters area.**

From August through December this bird sings very infrequently, but the song period may be resumed by late January or early February, even under conditions of very cold temperatures.

Christmas Bird Count parties observed an average of 71 Cardinals per count during the 27-year period beginning in 1935. The largest number, 148, was listed on January 3, 1960. In 1885, prior to the nationwide protection accorded all songbirds, the Cardinal, occasionally confined as a cage bird, was relatively uncommon. The eminent ornithologist William

---

* At Memphis, Tennessee, however, Mrs. Klyce [1936] reports: "A pair of Summer Tanagers have spent the past three years with us, building their nests near the house and raising two broods each year."

** Cairns [1889] found a nest near Asheville, North Carolina, on September 25.

Brewster [1886], in his excellent report on the birds of western North Carolina, "rarely saw more than two pairs in a single day."

ROSE-BREASTED GROSBEAK—*Pheucticus ludovicianus*

At altitudes of 3200 to 5000 ft., the Rose-breasted Grosbeak is a common summer resident in the park. It also occurs well above 5000 ft. but is less common in the spruce-fir forests that prevail above that altitude east of Clingmans Dome.* Mature stands of the northern hardwood forest are a favored habitat. Aldrich and Goodrum [1946] found one pair of Rose-breasted Grosbeaks in the 23-acre virgin hardwood forest area they censused June 23–28, 1946, in Porters Flat (2950–3200 ft.) where this species is at the lowest limits of its breeding range.

The earliest spring arrival date is April 18 (1940, Needham), and from 1935 to 1960 there are 15 years when the first birds were noted between April 22 and 27. The latest record in the fall is October 24 (1948, Stimson; 1950, Stupka). On December 1–3, 1959, a lone male of this species remained close to the Park Headquarters Building where it fed upon fruits of the flowering dogwood trees; the bird, although somewhat less wary than expected, was capable of normal flight.**

There are a few low-altitude records of the Rose-breasted Grosbeak during the breeding season, as follows: Mrs. Stupka picked up a male bird that was killed when it flew into a window at our home near Emerts Cove, 1650 ft., on June 10, 1959; Trautman reported two in Cades Cove, 1800 ft., on June 18, 1940; Manley observed two females in the Sugarlands, 1800 ft., on June 30, 1942; I heard one sing repeatedly in the Park Headquarters area, 1460 ft., on July 2, 1949.

Ganier [1962] describes a nest he found on June 1, 1920, on Chestnut Ridge at 4300 ft. that contained 3 eggs "with

* Tanner [1955], in his study of the birds of the valley of LeConte Creek, includes a chart that gives 3200–6500 ft. as the breeding range of this bird.
** Mrs. Monroe [1952] reports the occurrence of a Rose-breasted Grosbeak at a feeding station in Knoxville, Tennessee, from December 7, 1951, to January 26, 1952; and H. P. Langridge [1957] mentions one on December 1, 1956, at Elizabethton, Tennessee.

incubation advanced." A nest with 3 eggs was discovered May 14, 1944, along the trail below Rainbow Falls by H. Meyer. On the morning of May 22, 1946, near the Alum Cave Parking Area (3800 ft.), I came upon a male sitting in a nest 10 ft. from the ground in a rhododendron; that afternoon, when I again passed by this nest, a female Rose-breasted Grosbeak occupied it.

In addition to the fruits of flowering dogwood, this bird has been observed feeding upon the fruits of scarlet elder, pin cherry, and yellow-poplar.

The Rose-breasted Grosbeaks that appear in the lower altitudes in early summer are probably birds from the nearby mountains. During the latter half of September this local population is augmented by large numbers of migrants from the north, for this species then becomes quite plentiful.

BLUE GROSBEAK—*Guiraca caerulea*

This bird has been extending its breeding range northward in recent years. The first park record was on May 8, 1943, when I observed a male at Park Headquarters [Stupka, 1946b]. Almost 9 years later, on April 23, 1952, Mrs. Eifert reported a lone male from near Fighting Creek Gap. In Gatlinburg, on April 28, 1952, Manley was on the verge of picking up a stunned male bird when it suddenly flew off.

The additional records, like those already mentioned, are of spring migrants. The single bird observed on May 1, 1954, at Newfound Gap (5040 ft.) by Howell and party may have set a high-altitude record for this species. On May 3, 1956, Watkins reported at least 3 Blue Grosbeaks within a mile of the Cable Mill in Cades Cove. The Kincaids [letter] in 1958 observed one bird on May 9 along the park boundary between Gatlinburg and Cosby, and one on May 10 in Cades Cove. Russell noted this species on May 21, 1960, in the Park Headquarters area. In Gatlinburg, at his feeding station, Manley had an immature male from April 23 to 26, 1961, and 2 females on April 26 and 27, 1962.

To date, there have been no breeding records here and no observations of this species during the fall migration, but in view of its present status in Knox County and elsewhere in East Tennessee [Howell and Monroe, 1958; Nevius, 1955], the prospects of the Blue Grosbeak becoming one of the breeding birds of the park appear encouraging.

INDIGO BUNTING—*Passerina cyanea*

This bird is a common summer resident at low and middle altitudes. The earliest arrival date in spring is April 18 (1956, Manley), and from 1935 to 1959 there are 12 years when the first birds were noted between April 23 and 25. The latest fall record is November 1 (1949, Park Headquarters area—Stupka). There are two winter records—Manley and I observed one bird January 7, 1957, at the north end of Gatlinburg; Manley had one bird at his feeder, in Gatlinburg, from December 14, 1960, to January 15, 1961, during which time the minimum temperature registered 2 degrees above zero (December 22).*

There are numerous high-altitude records of this species in the park, but as has been noted by Burleigh [1941] in his report on Mt. Mitchell birds, only adult males are seen, no females or young of the year having been noted above an altitude of 5000 ft. In more than 100 trips made to the lodge near the summit of Mt. LeConte (6300 ft.), I have recorded the Indigo Bunting there but twice and, in view of the dates (June 28, 1936, and July 15, 1936) this, in all probability, represented one singing male. On July 1, 1936, a singing male was seen and heard near the fire tower on Mt. Sterling (5835 ft.), and in June 1940, at Andrews Bald (5800 ft.) and Charlies Bunion (5375 ft.). Fleetwood reported one from Hemphill Bald (5573 ft.) on June 11, 1935, and there are a number of records from Newfound Gap (5040 ft.), Indian Gap (5266 ft.), and other localities at comparable elevations.

In the Elkmont area on July 10, 1936, Seibert discovered a nest in a maple tree that contained 3 young estimated to be about 5 days old. Bellrose [1938], on September 3, 1937, came upon adults feeding a young bird nearly fully grown in the Park Headquarters area. Again in the Park Headquarters vicinity on May 28, 1939, I found a nest with 3 eggs.

The largest number of Indigo Buntings observed in one

* Mrs. Laskey [1941] reports one bird at Nashville, Tennessee, December 6–16, 1940, while Pearson, Brimley, and Brimley [1959] mention a January 28 (year ?) record at Wilmington, North Carolina.

day is 40—a record made by Trautman, June 18, 1940, in Cades Cove.

Although this bird is a persistent early- and mid-summer singer, its vocalizations in the fall are rather infrequent. I have heard it singing on 4 occasions between September 5 and 27 and once on October 2—three of these five efforts were recorded as being only partial songs.

EVENING GROSBEAK—*Hesperiphona vespertina*

The first record of Evening Grosbeaks within Great Smoky Mountains National Park was on December 15, 1951, when a flock of 12 to 15 of these strikingly-plumaged birds was observed on the lawn close to the Park Headquarters Building by Superintendent Preston, Chief Ranger Mernin, and Ranger Morrell [Stupka, 1954a]. Seeds of yellow-poplar that littered the ground had, apparently, served to attract the birds. Fifteen days later, on December 30, 1951, while participating in the Christmas Bird Count, I observed 1 Evening Grosbeak at Newfound Gap; a flock of 14 were recorded the same day near Pigeon Forge, a few miles north of Gatlinburg, by Yambert, Ogden, and Beasley of the Tennessee Ornithological Society. Since weather conditions, along with overpopulation and food scarcity, have been suggested as factors that may account for an invasion of these birds [Chamberlain, 1952], it should be mentioned that the preceding month (November 1951) had been exceptionally cold, in fact it proved to be colder than any of the three winter months that followed it.* These erratic finches, in numbers up to an estimated 150 birds, were observed in either the Gatlinburg or the Park Headquarters areas on 23 occasions between January 7 and May 4, 1952, chiefly by Manley and me.

Two and one-half years later, on November 9, 1954, Evening Grosbeaks returned to the park and vicinity and,

* The first Tennessee record for this species was on November 22, 1945, near Elizabethton, in the northeast corner of the state [Behrend, 1945]. The birds remained in that vicinity in numbers totaling up to more than 100 birds until May 4, 1946 [Behrend, 1946a, b]. In North Carolina, Evening Grosbeaks were observed for the first time in March 1922; they reappeared at six localities from January through April 1946, and four birds were recorded at Warrenton on April 1, 1950. [Pearson, Brimley, and Brimley, 1959]

beginning on December 22, 1954, and continuing until their departure on May 3, 1955, these birds were reported almost daily. Most of the records were from Gatlinburg (Manley) and the Park Headquarters area (Stupka), but the Grosbeaks were also noted at Emerts Cove (1650 ft.), Newfound Gap (5040 ft.), and the Oconaluftee meadows (2100 ft.) just north of Cherokee, North Carolina. The largest flock, estimated as 250 birds, was observed by Manley on February 23, 1955, in Gatlinburg. It was this considerable invasion that brought the first record for this species to Knoxville, Tennessee, in mid-January 1955 [Stupka and Tanner, 1955] and to the state of Georgia on February 18, 1955 [Burleigh, 1958].

After an absence of slightly more than seven months, Evening Grosbeaks returned to the park. On December 11, 1955, approximately 30 birds were reported at Newfound Gap (Ealy), and thereafter the species was noted on numerous occasions by various observers throughout the winter and early spring. On December 26, 1955, I watched a flock of about 30 birds feeding in yellow birch trees at Collins Gap, 5720 ft.—the highest elevation at which they have been reported here. The largest flock, estimated at 200 birds, was reported March 19, 1956, in Gatlinburg (Manley); on the following day I recorded a flock of the same size near Emerts Cove. The latest departure date in the spring of 1956 was on May 5 when Manley noted 3 birds in Gatlinburg.

Evening Grosbeaks failed to return during the winter of 1956–57. They reappeared October 30, 1957, when Gilbert observed one bird at Newfound Gap. On January 8, 1958, a flock estimated at about 200 birds was reported from Gatlinburg (Manley)—this was the largest flock among the numerous records of this species during the early months of 1958. The grosbeaks frequented a number of bird-feeding stations in Gatlinburg, and their rather late departure during that spring (May 16, 1958—Manley) may have been influenced by the availability of such unnatural food.

The unpredictable Evening Grosbeaks were absent from the park and vicinity during the winter of 1958–59. On November 18, 1959, eighteen months after their last appearance, Manley's observation of 3 birds, in Gatlinburg, proved to be the forerunner of the fifth invasion by this species. Again they were reported almost daily in the Gatlinburg and Park Headquarters areas in numbers up to approximately 300 birds (January 28–29, 1960). The latest departure date was May 13 (1960, Gatlinburg—Manley).

During the winter of 1960–61 Evening Grosbeaks failed to appear in our area.* They returned November 1, 1961, when I watched a flock of 30 birds feeding in a boxelder in the Park Headquarters area. Two days later Manley reported a flock of perhaps 200 birds in Gatlinburg.

The following is a summary of Evening Grosbeak occurrences in the park and vicinity:

Earliest arrival date (fall)	Latest departure date (spring)
1951, Dec. 15—Hdqrs. (Morrell)	1952, May 4—Gatlinburg (Manley)
1952, (Absent)	1953, (Absent)
1953, (Absent)	1954, (Absent)
1954, Nov. 9—Emerts Cove (Stupka)	1955, May 3—Gatlinburg (Manley)
1955, Dec. 11—Newfound Gap (Ealy)	1956, May 5—Gatlinburg (Manley)
1956, (Absent)	1957, (Absent)
1957, Oct. 30—Newfound Gap (Gilbert)	1958, May 16—Gatlinburg (Manley)
1958, (Absent)	1959, (Absent)
1959, Nov. 18—Gatlinburg (Manley)	1960, May 13—Gatlinburg (Manley)
1960, (Absent)	1961, (Absent)
1961, Nov. 1—Hdqrs. (Stupka)	1962, May 14—Emerts Cove (Stupka)

Wild fruits eaten by Evening Grosbeaks in the park and vicinity include yellow-poplar, boxelder, yellow birch, red maple, flowering dogwood, and shining sumac.

PURPLE FINCH—*Carpodacus purpureus*

The Purple Finch is a fairly common winter resident, being much more plentiful some years than others. The earliest arrival date in the fall is October 9 (1954, Stupka), and from 1939 to 1952 there are 8 years when the first birds were noted between October 19 and 25. The latest spring departure date is May 5 (1940, Manley).

Purple Finches were scarce or absent during the three winters beginning late in 1934. Their scarcity was again evident

* Chamberlain [1961] records single birds in 3 cities in eastern North Carolina, in February and March 1961.

in the winters of 1938–39, 1942–43, 1944–45, 1955–56, 1956–57, and 1958–59. The winters when these birds were common to plentiful included 1940–41, 1941–42, 1945–46, and seven consecutive winters beginning late in 1948.

During their sojourn in the park Purple Finches may occur at all altitudes, and some singing has been noted every month from October through April.

Among the food items known to be acceptable to Purple Finches in this area are fruits of yellow-poplar, winged elm, American elm, and flowering dogwood; flowers of American elm, beech, and red maple; and insects (aphids).

Christmas Bird Count parties, during the years 1935–61, observed an average of 15 Purple Finches per count. This species was recorded on 23 of the 27 years.

In his "An Ornithological Reconnaissance in Western North Carolina," William Brewster [1886] wrote that on May 23, 1885, "the Purple Finch was abundant, in full song, and apparently breeding" at Old Fort, approximately 50 miles east of Great Smoky Mountains National Park. But, he continues, "to my surprise it was not afterwards met with, although I searched for it carefully, especially in the balsam forests on the Black Mountains." The A.O.U. *Check-list of North American Birds* [1957] gives southeastern West Virginia as the southernmost breeding range of this species.

PINE SISKIN—*Spinus pinus*

This vagrant is so erratic and unpredictable that it is with some hesitancy one attempts to designate its status in the park. Certainly it is not nearly as scarce as is generally supposed, for beginning in 1937 [Stupka, 1937] the Pine Siskin has been reported here in greater or less numbers every year for 26 consecutive years. In 1944, these birds were noted every month of the year, while for a period of 16 consecutive years, beginning in 1940, these finches were observed on an average of almost 8 months per year. For the most part Pine Siskins are irregular winter residents. On some occasions they may be quite abundant while there are times when the birds are very scarce or absent.

Fleetwood, who, beginning on May 27, 1934, spent 13 consecutive months in the park recording birds in the field, observed no Pine Siskins. My sojourn in the area began in mid-October 1935, and it was not until March 21, 1937, that I noted them here for the first time.*

Based only on those years when there were no summer records of Pine Siskins, the earliest arrival date in the fall is October 10 (1951) when Manley noted 8 birds in Gatlinburg and I heard a few on the summit of Mt. LeConte. There are 10 additional earliest arrival dates ranging from October 15 (1937, 1938, and 1946) to November 8 (1949 and 1953). The latest spring departure date is May 16 (1950 and 1951), with 4 records ranging from May 2 (1955) to May 14 (1952).

Flocks of 100 or more birds have been recorded only during the months of October through April (1937–61); for October there are 4 such reports, 6 for November, 5 for December, 4 for January, 2 for February, 2 for March, and 4 for April. These include flocks estimated at 1,000 or more birds observed in November 1948 and 1957; February 1938 and 1949; and April 1938.

Siskins were present in exceptionally large numbers during the winters of 1937–38, 1948–49, and 1952–53, and for a period of 10 years, beginning in the fall of 1946, these birds were quite plentiful from middle fall to middle spring. From 1941 through 1944 there are anywhere from 1 to 5 records of siskins during each July, August, and September, but that is a most unusual state of affairs since the species is normally absent during those three months.** Siskins were absent in 1935 and 1936, scarce in the winters of 1938–39 (6 records— October, February, and March) and 1939–40 (3 records— November, April, and May), scarce during 1956 (2 records— April and October), scarce in the winter of 1956–57 (3 records—October, April, and May), and scarce again during 1959 (2 records—December).

* The only previous park record appears to be by E. V. Komarek who, on April 11, 1933, collected a specimen in Greenbrier; this is now in the Chicago Academy of Sciences. In a letter dated February 2, 1939, the late C. S. Brimley of Raleigh, North Carolina, informed me that a flock of Pine Siskins had been reported on a lawn in Bryson City, North Carolina (on the park's boundary), on March 28, 1923, by J. C. Crawford.

** The exceptions are July 2, 1937, when one was taken near Cosby, 2700 ft. [Wetmore, 1939]; July 18, 1940, one at Cherokee Orchard, 2600 ft. (Stupka); August 19, 1940, two at Newfound Gap, 5040 ft. (Stupka); July 25 and 31, 1945, one at Newfound Gap (Stupka); August 3 and 8, 1945, one at Newfound Gap (Stupka); and July 28, 1953, two in Gatlinburg (Manley).

Reference to the tabulation "Number of Records of Pine Siskins and Red Crossbills for the 20-year Period, 1936–55" reveals that the four months beginning with June have the fewest records of Pine Siskins and the greatest number of records of Red Crossbills, the former representing less than 11 percent and the latter approximately 65 percent of the total number of records of these two erratic finches.

NUMBER OF RECORDS OF PINE SISKINS AND RED
CROSSBILLS FOR THE 20-YEAR PERIOD, 1936–55

Month	Pine Siskin	Red Crossbill
January	42	27
February	56	29
March	68	17
April	140	25
May	61	14
June	26	93
July	13	99
August	13	137
September	13	119
October	37	74
November	79	25
December	69	37
Total	617	696

With very few exceptions, all the summer and early fall (June through September) occurrences of Pine Siskins are at altitudes above 4800 ft.* During the other months, these birds have been found at all altitudes.

There is still (1962) no positive proof of Pine Siskins nesting in the Southern Appalachian Mountains although the evidence indicates that this may have taken place.** In

* These exceptions, excluding the records for Newfound Gap, are given in the preceding footnote.
** Brewster [1886] found them rather numerous and in full song in the Black Mountains on June 2, 1885. Cairns [1889] regarded them as resident and common in the Black Mountains. Burleigh [1941] in his report on the birds of Mt. Mitchell, North Carolina, stated that Pine Siskins bred there sparingly, as "evidenced by two birds seen June 4, 1930, and a single bird August 16, 1931, flying by overhead." Stevenson [1957] regards the Pine Siskin as "a very rare breeding bird in the mountains of the Southeast, . . . singles were encountered only in the Black Mountains . . . one at Mount Craig at 6650 feet, June 14, (1956), and one near Mount Mitchell Inn at 6300 feet, July 2 (1956)." The A.O.U. Check-list [1957] gives northern Pennsylvania, New York, and Connecticut as the southern limits of their breeding range but adds that Pine Siskins have been recorded in summer from eastern Tennessee (Cosby) and western North Carolina (Black Mountains).

a series of birds collected in the park by U. S. National Museum personnel is a Pine Siskin taken on July 2, 1937, at 2700 ft., four miles southeast of Cosby. Wetmore [1939] describes the specimen as "a young female barely grown and must have been reared at some nearby point." On June 13, 1938, I had 3 siskins under observation at Indian Gap (5266 ft.). The birds were occupied in feeding on some minute objects, possibly aphids, in the new terminal growth of a small fir tree when suddenly one of the trio made its way close beside another and began fluttering its wings. The bird for whom this display was intended stopped its feeding and, after pausing a few seconds, extended its bill to where it appeared merely to touch the bill of the demonstrative individual. No actual food-offering was detected, however, and the birds soon took wing. A few minutes later, in the same area, I came upon 2 siskins that I took to be young birds; their plumage, with more yellowish or buff color, appeared lighter than in the adults, and the notes they uttered were unlike any I had ever heard from mature birds [Stupka, 1938b].

The buzzing or wheezing notes of this bird have a rising inflection which is quite distinctive. I have heard the song, which resembles that of the goldfinch, on April 13 and May 2 and 9, 1945 (Newfound Gap) and on May 30, 1940 (Indian Gap).

In addition to the seeds of red spruce, eastern hemlock, and various pines, this bird has been observed feeding on the seeds of sweetgum, sycamore, elms, and yellow birch. Like the goldfinch, it feeds on the seed heads of dandelions and other low-growing plants. Occasionally siskins will come to bird-feeding stations. On November 30, 1937, a flock of these birds were feeding on the ground in the Sugarlands at a spot where salt had been strewn.

Pine Siskins were listed on 17 of the past 27 Christmas Bird Counts (1935–61); the largest number, approximately 1,000 birds, was noted on December 19, 1937.

AMERICAN GOLDFINCH—*Spinus tristis*

Goldfinches are common summer and winter residents whose numbers become augmented by migrants during the spring and fall. Although this bird is most common at the lower and middle altitudes, it has been observed in the high mountains at all seasons excepting late winter—Collins Gap, 5720 ft., 4 records (April, May); Andrews Bald, 5800 ft., 8 records (April, June–September, November); Clingmans Dome Parking Area, 6311 ft., 4 records (April, July, October, December); Mt. LeConte Lodge vicinity, 6300 ft., 2 records (January, August).

It is mostly in April when large flocks may be encountered. At that time the birds are exceptionally vociferous and, if Pine Siskins happen to be in the area, these two related finches may intermingle to form a noisy company. Large flocks have also been observed in March and November. There is one record of a flock of approximately 100 birds in Cades Cove on January 14, 1950, and a flock of perhaps 200 birds on Russell Field (4400 ft.) on July 1, 1937 (Stupka).

The earliest date when the males assume the attractive gold and black breeding plumage is March 21 (1938) when I observed one such male in a flock of approximately 300 birds. During most years this plumage transformation was noted in April.

The American Goldfinch is one of the latest birds to nest, as illustrated by the following observations: On September 18, 1956, upon being notified that a bird was incubating eggs in a nest, in Gatlinburg, I investigated and found a female goldfinch sitting on 4 eggs in a nest located 8 ft. from the ground in a small tree. The young birds hatched on September 20 and left the nest on October 5. On October 26, 1938, in the Park Headquarters area, I observed a flock of goldfinches in which were two juveniles that were fed by adult birds following a demonstration of wing-quivering. In the same area on September 9, 1954, a young bird running about on the lawn was not yet capable of flight.*

In May, when the abundant dandelions along the road-side between Newfound Gap and Clingmans Dome are con-

---

* There are a number of records of late nesting from western North Carolina: Ogburn [1931] reports a nest and eggs on September 10, 1930, at Highlands; Burleigh [1941] found a nest with 4 slightly-incubated eggs on September 1, 1932, at 5800 ft., on Mt. Mitchell; Murray [1946] and Sprunt came upon a fledgling at Blowing Rock on August 31, 1929, that had apparently just left the nest; Mrs. Grinnell [1946] records 3 or 4 young birds that left their nest in Arden on October 5, 1946.

spicuous with bloom, goldfinches are often to be seen there feeding on those plants already in seed. Numerous other seeds are eaten, such as birch, elm, sycamore, yellow-poplar, sweetgum, eastern hemlock, pine, and various common weeds. Aphids appear to be a favorite among the insects these birds consume.

An average of 106 goldfinches per count were listed during the 27 Christmas Bird Counts taken in this area, beginning in 1935. The largest number reported was 330 birds on January 3, 1954.

RED CROSSBILL—*Loxia curvirostra*

During the 20-year period 1936–55, a total of 696 observations of the Red Crossbill were made in the park. This bird was noted on an average of eight and one-half months per year, and at no time was it recorded less than six months per year throughout that period. In view of these and the additional statistics, the Red Crossbill may be regarded as a fairly common summer and early fall visitant and an occasional summer resident in this area; at other seasons the bird is unpredictable and very erratic in its occurrence, being common in some years and scarce, or absent, in others.

NUMBER OF RECORDS OF RED CROSSBILLS, 1936–55

Month	Six or more birds	All records
January	9	27
February	5	29
March	2	17
April	2	25
May	1	14
June	7	93
July	10	99
August	6	137
September	13	119
October	15	74
November	6	25
December	14	37
Total	90	696

Red Crossbills were observed every month from June through October for a period of 12 consecutive years, beginning in 1942. The birds were noted the fewest number of

times during May, just prior to the sudden early-summer up-
surge in their population; also May is the only month wherein
there were no flocks of 10, or more, birds. These figures
reveal that a person interested in these finches has a better
chance of finding them in the Great Smokies in August than
in any other month, with September the next best month.
Since these birds are known to breed during any month of the
year [Bailey, Niedrach, and Baily, 1953], the large number of
summer records do not indicate breeding at that season. Red
Crossbills, as shown by the tabulation comparing their numbers with those of the Pine Siskins, were here in greatest
profusion during those months when siskins were most scarce
(see Pine Siskin).

The question as to whether there is a breeding population
of Red Crossbills in the Southern Appalachian Mountains
is still unsolved, and the statements made by Griscom
[1937] in his excellent monograph are still valid: "My
answer to these questions is (1) that it is probably true in
small part, but that (2) the evidence is nowhere nearly ample
enough for finality, and (3) that there are specimens in
existence which cannot be referred to any known subspecies." * Since 1937 there have been a number of reports
of young birds that must have been reared in the vicinity,
but, as Tanner [1957a] has indicated, "these birds present
a challenge, for no one has yet discovered a nest of the red
crossbill in the Smokies."

On April 10, 1938, attracted to a grove of pines, in Gatlinburg, by the familiar notes of a Red Crossbill, I came upon
two heavily-streaked birds with uncrossed mandibles that I
did not recognize until an adult female crossbill appeared
and started feeding one of them. I then recalled that the
mandibles of young crossbills remain uncrossed for some

* During the years 1931–33, seven Red Crossbills were collected here by personnel of the Chicago Academy of Sciences. Griscom [1937], who examined
the series, concluded that four of the birds were of uncertain status, possess-
ing characters unlike any described race. Wetmore [letter] agreed with Griscom's decision, and both these authorities recommended that any description
of a new subspecies be postponed. When the 5th edition (1957) of the A.O.U.
Check-list appeared, *Loxia curvirostra minor* (Brehm) was given as the race
that "Breeds, and probably resident, . . . south irregularly to . . . eastern
Tennessee and western North Carolina (Great Smoky Mountains) . . ."

weeks after they leave the nest [Griscom, 1937], and I realized that the brief episode it was my good fortune to witness deserved to be recorded [Stupka, 1938a]. Next day, upon receiving a call from Manley suggesting I come to his home, less than a mile from the aforementioned locality, to look at a couple of birds that somewhat resembled female Purple Finches, Manley and I became witnesses to another instance of a parent Red Crossbill feeding young out of the nest, for that is what the birds with the streaked plumage proved to be. A number of days later, on April 19, 1938, among the birds I observed at Indian Gap (5266 ft.) was a male Red Crossbill accompanied by a young bird—the latter grayish and heavily streaked, with short tail and uncrossed bill. Upon returning to Gatlinburg I was informed by Manley that he had just witnessed another feeding of an immature by an adult crossbill near his residence.

The following year, on March 29, 1939, Manley was in Cades Cove when, at a distance of approximately 20 ft., he again watched a young crossbill being fed by a grown bird. This took place after the wing-fluttering act by the juvenile bird. From 1940 through 1944, during which time I recorded Red Crossbills on numerous occasions, the following observations involved what I took to be immature birds:

September 23, 1940—2 immatures with 3 adults at Newfound Gap (5040 ft.).

September 12, 1942—2 immatures with 5 adults at the tunnel overpass on the transmountain road (3500 ft.).

September 22, 1943—2 immatures with 2 adults at Newfound Gap.

June 14, 1944—1 immature with 1 adult at Newfound Gap.

August 2–15, 1944—mixed flocks of immatures and adults noted on several days at the tunnel overpass on the transmountain road.

On May 5, 1945, in Gatlinburg, within a few hundred yards of where I first noted an adult feeding a young bird, Lewy [1945] and I came upon what appeared to be a family group of Red Crossbills—an adult male, an adult female, and two grayish young, the latter streaked and with uncrossed mandibles. The chattering of the juveniles led me to believe they were begging for food; but as they soon departed this could not be proved.

On April 26, 1952, in a grove of pines approximately two miles west of Park Headquarters, H. C. and H. K. Land [letter] watched a male Red Crossbill feed two "quite dully marked" birds with which it associated. The observation was made during a rain at a distance of 15 to 20 ft.

Thus there is additional evidence that points to the breeding of Red Crossbills in the Great Smoky Mountains, for, as Griscom [1937] has indicated, the species must have nested in the immediate vicinity if young birds with short tails and uncrossed mandibles were present.

The song of this bird has been heard in April, June, July, and September (Tanner, E. O. Henry, Stupka).

In addition to the seeds of red spruce, Fraser fir, eastern hemlock, and the various native pines, Red Crossbills have been observed feeding on the seeds of yellow-poplar. On numerous occasions they have been flushed from areas where the ground was bare but where the birds appeared to be feeding. Their fondness for salt was well known by a few of the local people who referred to them as "saltbirds" or "saltpeter birds"; in the days when cattle were grazed on the high-mountain meadows these birds would pay frequent visits to the "lick-logs" where salt was placed in depressions chopped along the top of a log. Later, when camps of the Civilian Conservation Corps were established in the park (mostly 1934–41), crossbills appeared at some of these camps and fed upon salt if it was available. At the camp in the Sugarlands, approximately a mile south of the Park Headquarters area, salt blocks were in the horse-stalls, salt was placed in outside water barrels, and rock salt was strewn on the ground after it had been used in the making of ice cream. The latter supply of salt in particular was in great favor with the crossbills who, for months at a time, made daily visits to this camp where, while feeding, they were very approachable. These birds likewise resorted to the cliff at Alum Cave Bluffs where some mineral salts are available.

On January 13, 1954, while on the Appalachian Trail approximately three miles east of Newfound Gap, I observed two separate flocks each numbering about 100 crossbills. Bellrose [1938] reported a flock of about the same size in early September 1937, at Newfound Gap. All other reports are of 60, or fewer, birds.

Christmas Bird Count parties listed the Red Crossbill on 11 of 27 counts (1935–61) ; the total number is 269 birds and the largest number per count is 90 birds (January 3, 1954).

WHITE-WINGED CROSSBILL—*Loxia leucoptera*

Two observations, both made at Newfound Gap (5040 ft.) in December 1955, represent the sum total of our records for the White-winged Crossbill. Lix, using binoculars, watched one of these birds at a distance of 40–50 ft. on December 6. It was with a flock of Red Crossbills. Liles, on December 24, reported three birds in the same area.

RUFOUS-SIDED TOWHEE—*Pipilo erythrophthalmus*

This bird is a common permanent resident throughout the lower altitudes; at middle and high elevations, towhees * have the status of fairly common summer residents.

On December 20, 1942, Goddard reported a towhee at 5800 ft., approximately two miles east of Newfound Gap. In addition there are 3 observations in January—on January 24, 1935, Fleetwood reported 3 birds above 3000 ft. near Mt. Sterling Gap; I observed one at Indian Grave Flats, 3500 ft., on January 20, 1938; and a Christmas Bird Count party listed 2 birds along the Alum Cave Trail (3800–4900 ft.) on January 1, 1950. Otherwise there appear to be no winter records of towhees at middle or high altitudes in the park.

The migration to the higher elevations begins in March in some years. I observed the bird at the Alum Cave Parking Area, 3800 ft., on March 15 (1948), and Fleetwood reported

* Two races of this bird have been collected in the park which is within a broad area of overlap and integration of two subspecies of *Pipilo erythrophthalmus*. Specimens of *P. e. erythrophthalmus* were taken on October 18 and 23, 1933, at 2500 ft. in the Greenbrier area by R. V. Komarek; specimens of *P. e. canaster* were taken on December 16, 1932, at 2000 ft., in the Greenbrier area, and on May 6, 1933, at 4300 ft., on Russell Field by E. V. Komarek. These were determined by Wetmore and are in the Chicago Academy of Sciences. U. S. National Museum collectors took specimens of *P. e. canaster* on June 19, 1937, at 5000 ft. on Cosby Knob, and on June 29, 1937, at 6100 ft., on Old Black Mountain [Wetmore, 1939].

it from the summit of Cove Mountain, 4091 ft., on March 17 (1935). On April 2 (1939) Walker saw a towhee at the Clingmans Dome Parking Area, 6311 ft.; I heard one singing there on April 13 (1945). The birds remain in the higher altitudes until some time in October; my latest record from along the Appalachian Trail is on October 22 (1940) near Charlies Bunion, 5375 ft.

Towhees breed in brushy clearings throughout the spruce and fir forests and on the grass balds along, or near, the state-line divide. These birds are summer residents to 6500 ft. on Mt. LeConte [Stevenson and Stupka, 1948]. Ganier [1926] did not record this species from high altitudes during the four trips he made to these mountains in 1920–25, although Brewster [1886] regarded it as being generally distributed in the nearby mountainous areas of western North Carolina.

On July 6, 1934, Fleetwood came upon a towhee's nest and eggs along the trail from Low Gap (4242 ft.) to Mt. Cammerer (5025 ft.). The location was 5 ft. from the ground in a clump of chestnut sprouts. This bears out the statement by Todd [1940] that "The nest for the second family is generally placed from one to five feet above the ground in a low bush," the first nesting being on the ground. The ground nest of this species that I found on June 5, 1945, on Gregory Bald (4948 ft.) held 3 young approximately one week old. At the same place on June 17, 1961, I came upon a young towhee only a day or two out of the nest. On May 14, 1959, Muller discovered a nest with 4 eggs at the edge of Andrews Bald (5800 ft.).

The earliest singing date is February 12 (1945, Gatlinburg —Stupka).

Christmas Bird Count parties listed an average of 11 towhees per count (1935–61), the largest number being 45 birds on December 28, 1947.

SAVANNAH SPARROW—*Passerculus sandwichensis*

This bird is an uncommon spring and fall transient. In Cades Cove, and in the vicinity of our area in Tuckaleechee, Wears, and Emerts Coves, the Savannah Sparrow is also an uncommon winter resident. Being an inhabitant of open fields where long grasses prevail, this bird is often overlooked. When flushed it flies but a short distance before dropping down into the grass again where it may run like a mouse or remain motionless, thus making observation of it difficult.

Fleetwood moved into Cades Cove on March 18, 1935, where he remained for approximately 11 weeks. He reported Savannah Sparrows there on the day of his arrival and for 7 days during the remainder of March. He listed this species there on 7 days of April, the latest being April 23.

The northward migration of this sparrow begins in late March and continues well into May. There are the following records:

March 27 (1960) —1 at my bird-feeding station near Emerts Cove.

March 28 (1936) and March 29 (1949) —1 in the vicinity of Elkmont.

April 15–29 (1942–53) —5 records of 1 or 2 birds (each) on the lawn at Park Headquarters.

May 15 (1941) —1 at Park Headquarters.

During the spring migration, Savannah Sparrows have been noted at such high altitude localities as Newfound Gap, 5040 ft. (April 17, 1945, and May 3, 1952—Stupka; May 1, 1954—Tanner); Indian Gap, 5266 ft. (April 26, 1952—Stupka); and Thunderhead, 5530 ft. (May 22, 1935—Fleetwood).

E. V. Komarek's record of this sparrow from Pine Grove, near Pigeon Forge, on October 17 (1933) represents the earliest of the fall arrivals. From October 27 to 31, 1933, Komarek collected a series of 14 Savannah Sparrows, 11 of which were taken in Cades Cove.*

Here, as in Georgia [Burleigh, 1958], wintering Savannah

* Twelve of these birds were made available to Peters and Griscom [1938] and are listed among the material they examined in describing the new race of these sparrows which they called *Passerculus sandwichensis oblitus*. In January 1943, it was the opinion of Wetmore [letter] that 3 subspecies were represented in this series. Aldrich [letter] informed me that he identified 5 races of Savannah Sparrows among the specimens collected in and around Asheville, North Carolina, by Burleigh. This should serve to emphasize the futility of attempting to identify most subspecies in the field.

Sparrows have not been known to sing. Tanner's report of a flock of 18 in the Pigeon Forge region on December 28, 1947, is the largest number among our records. Altogether 72 of these sparrows were listed by Christmas Bird Count parties in the years 1935–60, an average of less than 3 per count.

GRASSHOPPER SPARROW—*Ammodramus savannarum*

This secretive little sparrow is a fairly common summer resident in Cades Cove, the Oconaluftee meadows area, and along the park boundary where there are cultivated or fallow fields. It appears to be restricted to the lower altitudes during the nesting season, there being no records from the grass balds. The earliest spring arrival date is April 3 (1935) when Fleetwood observed the bird in Cades Cove. On April 16, 1945, I heard this sparrow singing in Cades Cove, Wears Cove, and Tuckaleechee Cove. On October 15, 1938, Manley and I saw one of these birds along Little River, above Elkmont, at an elevation of 3200 ft.—the highest altitude it has been noted here.

My record of one of these sparrows on November 9, 1938, in the Park Headquarters Area, may represent a very late fall migrant. There is one winter record—in 1938, at a bird-feeding station I maintained in the Park Headquarters area, a Grasshopper Sparrow appeared on January 27–29, February 1–4, and February 25.*

HENSLOW'S SPARROW—*Passerherbulus henslowii*

The first record of this rare transient sparrow came on October 28, 1933, when E. V. Komarek collected a specimen in Cades Cove (1800 ft.). This was later sent to Wetmore who identified it as belonging to the western race *henslowii*. Ganier [1948] stated that this was the first Henslow's Sparrow collected in Tennessee.

There are but 2 additional records. On October 28, 1947, McCamey reported 2 birds at 2600 ft. in Greenbrier, at the

---

* Howell and Monroe [1957] give 5 winter records for Knox County, Tennessee, while Pearson, Brimley, and Brimley [1959] mention 1 winter record (December 29, 1931) for Buncombe County, North Carolina.

beginning of the trail to Ramsey Cascades. In Gatlinburg, Manley obtained a specimen on April 21, 1958, which is now in the park's collection.

VESPER SPARROW—*Pooecetes gramineus*

The Vesper Sparrow is a rather uncommon spring and fall migrant and a scarce winter visitant. The earliest spring arrival date is February 22 (1949, Park Headquarters—Stupka) and there are 11 years when the first arrivals appeared between March 10 and 21 (1933–52). A bird I noted in Wears Cove on May 17 (1939) represents the latest departure date in the spring. The earliest and latest fall dates are October 13 (1944, Gatlinburg—Koch), and November 23 (1940, Park Headquarters—Manley), respectively.

Fleetwood, who reported the Vesper Sparrow in Cades Cove on 15 days during March–April 1935, counted up to 40 birds in one day (March 25). March 24, 1938, was another day these sparrows were quite plentiful for I observed a total of at least 25 birds—at Park Headquarters, along the transmountain road at 4500 ft., along Straight Fork at 3000 ft., and at Pin Oak Gap (4428 ft.). On March 17, 1945, I noted a few birds at Park Headquarters, a flock of 8 at Newfound Gap (5040 ft.), and another flock of 12 at Indian Gap (5266 ft.). Fleetwood reported Vesper Sparrows from Parson Bald (4760 ft.) and Spence Field Bald (5000 ft.) in late March 1935.

Keating [letter] reported a Vesper Sparrow in Cades Cove on June 9, 1937, and another on Gregory Bald (4948 ft.) the following day. The Metcalfs [1938] reported one at Indian Gap (5266 ft.) on August 26–27, 1937. In view of the known breeding range of the species, these observations are of interest. According to the A.O.U. *Check-list of North American Birds* [1957], the southern limits of the breeding range are in part at Tate Springs, Tennessee, and Weaverville, North Carolina—the former located 40 miles north of the park boundary and the latter 30 miles east. Consequently, if the Vesper Sparrow were to expand its breeding range southward to any appreciable extent, as has happened with the House Wren and Solitary Vireo in recent years, it would include the Great Smoky Mountains National Park.

The scattering of winter records of this sparrow are all at altitudes below 1900 ft.—7 in December, 4 in January, and 2 in February. Christmas Bird Count parties listed a total of 11 birds over a period of 27 years (1935–61).

BACHMAN'S SPARROW—*Aimophila aestivalis*

This secretive sparrow is an uncommon spring migrant and a rather scarce summer resident in our area. The records * for the period 1935–60 consist of 12 for April, 4 for May, 2 each for June and July, and 1 each for August and September. The earliest arrival in the spring is April 9 (1935, Cades Cove—Fleetwood); vanguards arrived from April 21 to 29 on 6 years. The last record in the fall is September 5 (1937, Greenbrier—Bellrose [1938]).

In 1935, Fleetwood observed this sparrow on 4 days in April and 2 days in May—all but one of his records being in Cades Cove. McCamey and I saw one of these birds there April 24, 1947, and I noted it there again and heard its excellent song on April 28, 1948. Close to my home near Emerts Cove, less than a mile north of the park line, I have noted this species during the breeding season in 1947, 1949, 1950, 1951, and 1953. It is possible that its failure to return since 1953 is due to a gradual change in the habitat—from one of fairly open sterile hillsides where sumacs and small pines prevailed to one where there was an increase in the size and numbers of pines.

There are no high-altitude records in the park during the breeding season, but during its spring migration I have observed it at Newfound Gap, 5040 ft., on April 27, 1943; along the transmountain road (Tennessee side) at 4700 ft., on April 13, 1944; and at Collins Gap, 5720 ft., on April 13, 1945. Watkins also reported this sparrow from near the last-named locality on April 21, 1957.

I have heard the fine song of this bird from the time of its appearance in April until August 1 (1953, Emerts Cove).

* M. Brooks [1948] notes the listing of this bird among 33 species from the higher elevations of the Great Smoky Mountains in Robert Lindsay Mason's [1927], *The Lure of the Great Smokies*. As the result of a discussion I had with the late Mr. Mason some years ago, the list in question is unacceptable for use in the present manuscript.

SLATE-COLORED JUNCO—*Junco hyemalis*

No bird is as abundant or as characteristic of the higher mountains throughout the Southern Appalachian region as the Slate-colored Junco. So prevalent and, ordinarily, so approachable is this dark gray sparrow-size bird that even park visitors who habitually pay little or no attention to birds will often notice it and comment on it. Along the Appalachian Trail and other trails in the higher elevations and at those parking areas, picnic grounds, and other such places that are located above the 3000 ft. altitude, the Slate-colored Junco is usually the most commonly-observed form of wildlife. Just as the high-altitude forests of the park are symbolized by spruce and fir, so the bird life in these uplands is typified by the ubiquitous Slate-colored Junco.*

During the breeding season juncos range from the highest elevations down to approximately 3000 ft. In a few watersheds, such as the West Prong of the Little Pigeon River (Chimneys Campground) and Forge Creek (Gregory Ridge Trail), these birds occur down to approximately 2600 ft. In the south-facing valleys, such as along the Oconaluftee River, they may not be found below 3200 ft. [Tanner, 1958]. Generally, juncos are most plentiful at the highest altitudes; of the 106 nests I recorded, 78 are above 4900 ft. and 28 are below that elevation.

In the spring, the juncos disappear from the lower altitudes during April, although a few stragglers may linger into early May. Over a 25-year period, beginning in 1937, there are 12 years when the last of the juncos departed from the

* Two races of this bird inhabit the park during the late fall and on throughout the winter months, but, as with most subspecies, they look so much alike and have so much in common that most persons visiting the park at that time of year should be content to call them Slate-colored Juncos, a practice followed by parties who conduct the Christmas Bird Counts. For those people who visit the park during the May through September period, comprising 75% of the annual visitation, there is no problem concerning which race of this bird is to be found here; at that time of year practically all juncos are referable to the local breeding form usually called the Carolina Junco or, more properly, the Carolina Slate-colored Junco (*Junco hyemalis carolinensis*). This is the junco whose migration is, essentially, a vertical one in contrast to the northern subspecies (*J. h. hyemalis*) whose migration is horizontal (i.e. north and south). In this account, the junco referred to, unless otherwise specified, is the Carolina subspecies.

lowlands (mostly the Park Headquarters area, 1460 ft.) between April 12 and 23. There are but 6 low-altitude records later than April 23, including 3 in May (May 2, 1956; May 3, 1940 and 1950).*

During October, most juncos leave their high-altitude breeding grounds, but it is not unusual to find a few of these hardy birds on or near the summits of the highest mountains throughout the winter months. The earliest date in the fall for their appearance at a low altitude is September 16 (1944) when I observed one bird at 1400 ft. along Little River. On October 2 (1953) two juncos were noted at Park Headquarters, and during the 24-year period 1938–61 there are 12 years when the earliest arrivals appeared between October 5 and 16.

Our breeding juncos are permanent residents of the Southern Appalachian region, wintering in the foothills and nesting at middle and high altitudes. The A.O.U. *Check-list of North American Birds* [1957] gives northeastern West Virginia and western Maryland as the northern limits of their breeding range, which extends south through extreme eastern Kentucky, western Virginia, and western North Carolina to eastern Tennessee, northern Georgia, and northwestern South Carolina. As Tanner has stated [1958], these birds apparently do not nest in the Cumberland Mountains, "even though the highest mountains there would seem to be high enough."

During late spring and early summer one who hikes along the high-altitude trails of the park is likely to come upon more nests of the junco than of all other kinds of birds combined. This is due not only to the abundance of juncos but also to the site usually selected for the nest—in the side of a bank beside the trail, sheltered and normally well concealed by

* Information as to the arrival and departure dates of the northern race (*J. h. hyemalis*) is relatively scarce since the birds would have to be collected to determine their true identity. E. V. Komarek, representing the Chicago Academy of Sciences, collected one of these northern birds at 3800 ft., "near Indian Gap," on October 3, 1933, and another in Greenbrier (1800 ft.) on March 2, 1933. These were identified by Wetmore. Sennet [1887], in his study of the juncos on Roan Mountain, 60 miles northeast of the park, concluded that the northern birds had departed before April 15. Burleigh [1958] gives April 15 (1944) as the last date for their spring occurrence at Dalton, Georgia, 80 miles southwest of the park.

overhanging grasses and other low-growing plants. The mother bird, who does all the incubating [Tanner, 1958], sits so closely that she may remain on the nest while the hiker passes by, but frequently she will fly up almost at one's feet whereupon the finding of the nest is usually accomplished quite readily.

Occasionally the nest is in a tree or shrub, but in my experience, such sites are uncommon.* Ganier [1926], however, reports that on Mt. LeConte, "several nests were as high up as 30 feet." On Hemphill Bald on July 19, 1934, Fleetwood discovered one young junco in a nest 3 ft. from the ground in a coniferous tree. On July 23, 1942, I found 3 very small juncos in a nest 4 ft. from the ground in a fir tree on Mt. LeConte. Lovell and Lovell [1952], while walking along the trail from the Clingmans Dome Parking Area to Andrews Bald, flushed a junco from a nest that was placed in a flat grassy plot.**

Tanner [1958], who for seven years (1951–57) was engaged in a study of this bird in the park, found that "clutches which are started in April, May, or June generally have four eggs; 75% of the 92 nests for which I have data from these months had this number of eggs or young. The remainder had three except for one containing only two young and no unhatched eggs. Of 18 nests begun in July, only 22% had four eggs and 61% had three." Such information as I have available, based on 106 nests, largely confirms Tanner's data. On June 19, 1953, I discovered a junco's nest with 5 eggs at Sheep Pen Gap (4610 ft.) ; Tanner found his first set of 5

* Laurent [1892], who left Philadelphia July 5, 1892, and traveled to western North Carolina where he spent two weeks studying the breeding habits of the junco, located 46 nests, 44 of which were in natural depressions in the banks of wagon roads and railroad cuts. One was in the crevice of an old tree trunk and one was placed on a ledge of rocks. Sprunt [1924] describes a nest he examined in July 1921, that was built in a large tin can on the edge of a tennis court. In July 1930, Sprunt [1930] discovered one junco nest placed on a rafter of a garage and another built in a fern basket on the porch of a large house. All three of Sprunt's unusual nest sites were in Blowing Rock, North Carolina. Nicholson [letter, 1955], who favored me with photographs of nests and nesting sites, stated that he had discovered about 30 tree nests ranging up to 17 ft. from the ground, the majority of which were built against the trunk of the tree.

** Nicholson furnished me with a photograph of a similarly-located nest he found at Craggy Gardens, North Carolina, on July 1, 1955.

eggs on June 10, 1960, at 5700 ft., between Indian Gap and Collins Gap.*

Should the season be advanced, as it was in the spring of 1945, juncos may be incubating a full clutch of eggs before the end of April. On April 25, 1945, Miss Chiles while walking along the upper three miles of the Thomas Ridge Trail (5000–5200 ft.) flushed 6 juncos from as many trailside nests which held 4, 4, 4, 4, 3, and 2 eggs, respectively. Both March and April of that year were exceptionally mild, the former month being the warmest March on record. Again on May 1, 1954, following a 13-day period when the temperature at Park Headquarters rose to 80° or higher, I found 2 nests, each with 4 eggs, along the Appalachian Trail between Newfound Gap (5040 ft.) and Indian Gap (5266 ft.). Tanner's [ibid.] earliest record for the laying of the first egg is April 20, "in a warm spring and at a low altitude. The average date of laying the first egg is about eleven days later for each thousand feet increase in altitude."

Tanner [ibid.] states that "The majority of Juncos in the Smokies will nest a second time." The latest nest he found in the park "had a first egg date sometime between July 19 and July 30." A photograph in the park files, made July 31, 1939, by H. C. Wilburn, reveals 3 very young (sightless) juncos in a nest on Hemphill Bald. Three late nests found August 3, 1955, near Heintooga Overlook (5325 ft.) by Nicholson were reported to me as follows: One held 2 young, about 5 days old, and 1 infertile egg; another had 1 naked young and 2 infertile eggs; in the third were 2 young, about 4 days old, and 1 egg with a dead embryo. Both Sprunt and Burleigh believe that occasionally 3 broods are reared.**

Juncos sing but rarely during the late fall and early winter. By late February, however, the song period commences

---

* Laurent [1892], based on an examination of 46 nests found in the vicinity of Cranberry, North Carolina, in July 1892, said, "I am led to believe that the full set of eggs is generally four, never five, but very often three." Tyler [1936], whose studies were centered near Roan Mountain, mentions seeing one clutch of 5 eggs.

** Sprunt [1933a] records the finding of a nest with fresh eggs on August 11 on Grandfather Mountain. Burleigh's [1941] latest date for fresh eggs on Mt. Mitchell is August 2, 1932.

both at the lower and the higher altitudes and singing may then continue on through July.

Among several records of abnormally colored juncos are 2 relating to birds with entirely white plumage. The first appeared in the Smokemont Campground area during late December 1943, where it remained in association with a flock of juncos until early March 1944. What appeared to be the same individual was observed at the same place by Ealy on November 24, 1944, and he continued to report it from there until January 15, 1945. This bird, which I had under observation in January 1944, had what appeared to be normally-colored eyes, but all the plumage was white, the bill an ivory color, and the legs pinkish. It appeared to be larger than the normally-plumaged birds with which it associated, but this may have been an illusion. The other record of an entirely white bird of this species was reported to me by Burns who discovered it at Park Headquarters on February 7, 1951.

Aldrich and Goodrum [1946] found 7 pairs of juncos in the 23-acre virgin hardwood forest area they censused June 23–28, 1946, in Porters Flat, 2950–3200 ft. This is near the lower limits of the range of these birds. Christmas Bird Count parties listed an average of 293 juncos per count in the course of 27 such events conducted annually in the park and vicinity beginning in 1935. The largest count, an estimated 750 birds, was on December 19, 1937.

CHIPPING SPARROW—*Spizella passerina*

Chipping Sparrows are common summer residents, especially throughout the lower altitudes. There are 3 December records in the Park Headquarters area and 1 at Pigeon Forge. The earliest arrival date in spring is February 22 (1949) when I observed 2 birds in the Headquarters area. The only other February arrival date was on the 26th, in 1951, at the same locality. From 1939 to 1961 there are 12 years when the first arrivals appeared between March 4 and 13. The latest fall departure date is November 20 (1951, Park Headquarters area—Stupka). At Pigeon Forge, Tennessee, in 1938, Hay reported 1 of these birds on the day of the Christmas Bird Count (December 18). I noted single birds in the Park Headquarters area on December 16, 1943, and December 10, 1951. Burns and I observed 4 birds at that place on December 4, 1950.

Occasionally this little sparrow occurs and may breed at high altitudes in open situations. At Cataloochee Ranch (4888 ft.), I discovered its nest and eggs on May 28, 1952, and the species was present there again on June 4–5, 1961. At Soco Gap (4300 ft.), this sparrow was noted June 8, 1954, and July 1, 1961. Fleetwood recorded it June 11, 12, 13, and 16, 1935, in the vicinity of Black Camp Gap (4522 ft.). At these places and on the high Cataloochee Divide in that vicinity, Chipping Sparrows are regular summer residents in all probability. Trautman reported 2 birds from Mt. LeConte on June 20, 1940, one of which was in the clearing near the lodge (6300 ft.); two days later he observed 2 birds at the edge of Andrews Bald (5800 ft.) and 6 additional Chipping Sparrows between Newfound Gap (5040 ft.) and the Clingmans Dome Parking Area (6311 ft.).

Two, and possibly three broods are raised during the year. On July 10, 1947, at Park Headquarters, adult birds were mating while young were hopping about the lawn crying to be fed.

On infrequent occasions, this sparrow has been known to sing in the night. In Gatlinburg, I heard the unmusical song at 2 o'clock on a morning in May (1943) and at 11 P.M. on June 21, 1950.

In the Park Headquarters area I have noted flocks of 50–70 birds on October 27, 1947; November 2, 1945; and November 3, 1948.

FIELD SPARROW—*Spizella pusilla*

Field Sparrows are common permanent residents at low and middle altitudes. However, some movement takes place during the early spring since these birds then may appear in localities where they are not known to breed, such as the Alum Cave Parking Area (3800 ft.), Indian Gap (5266 ft.), and elsewhere. A few breed on the more isolated high-altitude grass balds such as Russell Field, Parson Bald and Gregory Bald, but they are more common in the southeastern corner of the park at essentially the same altitudes but in open areas of greater extent, such as the Cataloochee Divide and the grazed highlands just to the east. Trautman reported this sparrow from Andrews Bald (5800 ft.) on June 22, 1940, but that is our only record from such a high altitude. Field Sparrows are most abundant at the lower altitudes, especially in Cades Cove, the Oconaluftee meadows, the Cataloochee area, and on lands along much of the park boundary.

Fleetwood discovered a nest with 2 young birds in Cades Cove on May 30, 1935. The nest and 3 small fledglings I found in Emerts Cove on July 4, 1952, probably represented the second brood.

The pleasing, though somewhat plaintive song of this bird serves as a welcome announcement of the coming spring. Usually Field Sparrows begin their singing by the third week of February, although I have heard some singing as early as January 27 (1937). From 1942 to 1961 there are 12 years when I noted the first songs between February 17 and 25. Should March prove to be one of mild temperatures, as happened in 1945, Field Sparrows will be heard singing throughout that month. If, on the other hand, the season is delayed, with subnormal temperatures prevailing, as happened in March 1947, these birds do little or no singing, indulging in a few trial songs late in the month. After the nesting season, these common sparrows sing but rarely.

Parties taking the Christmas Bird Count (1935–61) listed an average of 128 Field Sparrows per count. The largest number recorded was a total of 440 birds on December 28, 1947.

WHITE-CROWNED SPARROW—
Zonotrichia leucophrys

This sparrow is a rare transient in the park and a very uncommon winter resident in the vicinity. Near the Oconaluftee Visitor Center it has been reported by Watkins on April 29, 1958, and by Lewy [1945] on May 2, 1945. McCamey's observation of 2 of these birds in the Park Headquarters area on October 14 (1947) represents our only fall record from within the park. In Pigeon Forge, a few miles north of Gatlinburg, Howell and Tipton came upon 4 of these large sparrows on December 28, 1952; on January

3, 1954, Howell observed 7 birds in the same area. The only additional report is by Highbaugh who, on January 1, 1961, listed a lone White-crowned Sparrow in the Dry Valley section of Tuckaleechee Cove.

Since this bird resembles the common White-throated Sparrow, it may have been overlooked. In Georgia, Burleigh [1958] says that "In recent years, it has been noted in increasing numbers," and the same situation prevails in North and South Carolina, according to B. R. Chamberlain [1953].

WHITE-THROATED SPARROW— *Zonotrichia albicollis*

This bird is a very common winter resident. During the times of its arrival and departure the White-throated Sparrow may occur at all altitudes, but from November through March it frequents the lower elevations almost invariably. The earliest arrival date in the fall is September 27 (1939, Manley); from 1934 to 1960 there are 14 years when the first birds were noted between October 8 and 16. The latest spring departure date is May 18 (1950, Tanner; 1953, Stupka); from 1936 to 1952 there are 9 years when the latest stragglers were recorded between May 2 and 9.

There is one record of a lone bird during the summer. On July 15, 1955, at approximately 4200 ft. along the Bull Head Trail to Mt. LeConte, Liles observed a White-throated Sparrow for several minutes; at times he was within 10 ft. of the bird which he saw to very good advantage. From the detailed description in his report, the sparrow was probably an immature.*

White-throated Sparrows have been heard singing every month from October until May. Ordinarily, songs are rather infrequent during the winter months, but there is considerable singing in the fall and again in the spring.

Christmas Bird Count parties listed an average of 95 White-throated Sparrows per count during the years 1935–61. The

---

* South of the park, at Blairsville, Georgia, Burleigh [1958] mentions one bird on the unusually late date of June 11, 1936. East of the park, Pearson, Brimley, and Brimley [1959] record unusual occurrences at Wilmington, North Carolina, on June 25 and at Raleigh, North Carolina, on July 6 (no years given). West of the park, Clarke [1949] reports on the singing of a White-throated Sparrow in Memphis, Tennessee, on July 6, 1949.

largest number of these birds was 280, recorded on January 3, 1960.

FOX SPARROW—*Passerella iliaca*

This large sparrow is an uncommon winter resident whose numbers appear to vary from one year to the next. Normally a rather shy and retiring bird, it exhibits a marked tendency to frequent the vicinity of houses and other buildings during snowfalls and while the snow covers the ground. The earliest arrival date in the fall is October 24 (1934) when Fleetwood reported one from near Cades Cove. My earliest record is October 26 (1943) at Chimneys Campground, and Howell observed it October 26 (1951) at Indian Gap, 5266 ft.—the latter being the highest altitude from which it has been reported. In 1935, Fleetwood noted 2 birds at approximately 4000 ft. on the slopes of Mt. Cammerer on February 4, and 2 at 5000 ft. below Inadu Knob on March 4. Most records of this sparrow are from the low altitudes. From 1935 to 1955 there are 10 years when the last of these northbound birds were recorded between March 14 and 26; the latest spring-departure date is April 5 (1959) when I heard the fine song of this species at Park Headquarters.

Ordinarily the sight of more than 1 or 2 of these birds is rather unusual. However, on March 20, 1935, Fleetwood listed 13 in Cades Cove. From November 25 to 30, 1950, during a period of record-breaking cold and snow, 12 to 24 Fox Sparrows frequented an area close to the Park Headquarters Building where some grain was scattered.

It is in March or early April, just prior to its departure for the north, that this bird may favor us with bits of its melodious song. On one occasion I heard it sing in December.

On the annual one-day count of winter birds for the years 1935–61, an average of 3 Fox Sparrows per count was listed from the park and vicinity. The largest number—20 birds—was observed on January 1, 1961.

LINCOLN'S SPARROW—*Melospiza lincolnii*

Our only record of this rare retiring bird was on April 24, 1952, when one was observed and reported by Sutton and party along the Roaring Fork Road, in Gatlinburg. It is regarded as a rare spring and fall migrant in nearby Knox County, Tennessee [Howell and Monroe, 1958]; in Buncombe County, North Carolina, Burleigh [Pearson, Brimley, and Brimley, 1959] "found it almost plentiful each fall about Asheville," but he had no records of it during the spring.

SWAMP SPARROW—*Melospiza georgiana*

Decidedly localized in the habitat for which it was named, the Swamp Sparrow is a fairly common winter resident in a few areas at the lower altitudes, but mostly outside the park. In the fall I observed the earliest arrivals on October 8 (1943, Stupka) ; the latest departure date in the spring is May 10 (1935, Cades Cove—Fleetwood) .

On January 1, 1961, Tanner and party while engaged in the Christmas Bird Count in Tuckaleechee Cove listed 111 Swamp Sparrows in the wet meadows along the road from Laurel Lake to the Kinzel Springs bridge. Howell and party, while counting birds in the same area on December 31, 1961, estimated 150 of these sparrows.

SONG SPARROW—*Melospiza melodia*

This sparrow * is a common permanent resident at the lower altitudes, but it breeds at any altitude wherever it finds the proper habitat. Only a few species of our birds have a breeding range of such a considerable extent. This distribution, however, may have come about only in recent decades. In 1885, Brewster [1886] noted the absence of the Song Sparrow in western North Carolina. Cairns [1902], in 1891, regarded it only as a winter visitor in Buncombe County, North Carolina. A. H. Howell [1909] observed none during 10 days spent in the mountains of north Georgia in July 1908. Burleigh [1958] mentions that the nest and eggs he found at Young Harris, in Towns County, Georgia, on July

---

* According to Wetmore [1939, 1941], the common breeding race of the Song Sparrow in Tennessee and in the elevated section of North Carolina is *Melospiza melodia euphonia*. Eight specimens collected in the park by E. V. Komarek in 1932–33 for the Chicago Academy of Sciences were identified by Wetmore [letter] as belonging to that subspecies.

10, 1922, represents the first verified nesting record for that state. Ganier [1926] reported Song Sparrows only from the low and middle altitudes in the course of four visits he made to the park from 1920 to 1925. It appears unlikely that a bird as persistent in its singing as the Song Sparrow would have been overlooked. Fleetwood observed the birds above 5000 ft. in June 1934 (Sawteeth), and June 1935 (Hemphill Bald), and since then they have been found regularly in the breeding season at or near the summits of some of our highest mountains. As mentioned in the comments relating to the Chestnut-sided Warbler, it is Odum's [1945] belief that this warbler and the Song Sparrow have extended their breeding ranges in recent years due to large-scale changes in habitat (destruction of overstory trees resulting from lumbering operations and chestnut blight).

On February 28, 1945, I observed a Song Sparrow at 6000 ft. on Mt. Collins and another at the Clingmans Dome Parking Area (6311 ft.). Since these appear to be the only winter records at a high altitude, it would be of interest to know whether the abnormally mild temperatures of the preceding 7 days had anything to do with these unusual occurrences.

Fleetwood, on August 9, 1934, discovered a nest with 2 young in the vicinity of Smokemont (2200 ft.); this may have been a third brood. In Cades Cove (1800 ft.) I found 2 half-grown birds in a nest on June 28, 1938. It is not unusual to find Song Sparrows at altitudes in excess of 6000 ft. during the summer where, in certain brushy openings in these moist highlands the birds will breed. In the forest clearing about the lodge on Mt. LeConte, at 6300 ft., the birds were noted in June on 4 consecutive years (1940–43). After 1943 I made dozens of visits to that part of the park but did not record the Song Sparrow there again until August 30, 1957. On June 15, 1940, five young birds left a nest which Mr. and Mrs. Jack Huff discovered near the lodge and which they had under observation for some time. These young were hatched on June 6. In the same vicinity, on July 4, 1940, I found 3 young birds about ready to leave a nest. My earliest record for the appearance of Song Sparrows on Mt. LeConte was May 11 (1942); the latest date was October 23 (1940).

There are a number of summer records of this bird from

Clingmans Dome where, in the old burn on the southwestern slope (6000–6400 ft.), I observed it over a number of years. Stevenson [letter] also noted it there on June 12, 1957. Nearby, on Andrews Bald (5800 ft.), I have one summer record—June 14, 1940. In the region of the Sawteeth, along the Appalachian Trail east of Newfound Gap, my records of Song Sparrows during June and July are for 8 of the years between 1936 and 1948.

During February, when the long song period of this bird is already under way, I have heard the familiar trill when the temperature was near the zero mark—February 1 (1945), February 2 (1951), and February 9 (1947).

The average number of Song Sparrows listed on the annual one-day count of winter birds (1935–61) is 93. The largest number totaled in one day is 274 birds (January 3, 1950).

SNOW BUNTING—*Plectrophenax nivalis*

Our only record of this bird came on December 22, 1957, when a party * engaged in the Christmas Bird Count reported a total of 8 Snow Buntings on and in the vicinity of Spence Field Bald. On or near Big Bald Mountain in the northeastern corner of Tennessee, Behrend [1948, 1953, 1955, 1960] observed from 1 to 15 Snow Buntings since his initial discovery of this species at that place (November 21, 1948).

* Paul S. Purdue, Mr. and Mrs. Harold Garlinghouse, Mrs. E. E. Overton, Mary Enloe, Bernard and Audrey Kaiman, and David Highbaugh—members, East Tennessee Ornithological Society.

...union and the Sawteeth on state line, E. of New-
...3'
...ades Cove
...W. of Park Hdqrs. (Tenn.)
...x. 1600'
...E. of Gatlinburg (Tenn.)
...—2320'
...oad, 4 miles W. of Park Hdqrs. (Tenn.)
...2729' (lowest)
...e River, S.E. of Elkmont (Tenn.)
...4000–5000'
...Overlook near S.E. boundary (N. C.)
...s—approx. 2000'
...ntain road, between Cherokee, N. C., and Oconaluftee
...prox. 1700'
...dary of park (N.C.)
...approx. 2000'
...dary (N. C.)
...rox. 1800–2000'
...ic. Gregory Bald to Cades Cove (Tenn.)
...700' (lowest)
...m vic. Clingmans Dome to Fontana Reservoir (N. C.)
...3'
...ral boundary of park (Tenn.)
...1700'
...Emerts Cove (E. of Gatlinburg, Tenn.)
...80'
...iles E. of Gatlinburg, Tenn.
...nacle—4805'
...ier, near N.E. boundary (Tenn.)
...nacle Trail—2647–4805'
...junction of Ramsey Prong with Middle Prong of Little
...ver; in N.E. part of park (Tenn.)
...dge—approx. 4500–5300'
...rom Greenbrier Pinnacle (Tenn.)
...—4948'
...e ridge S.W. of Cades Cove
...e Trail—1930–4600'
...Cades Cove to state-line ridge (Tenn.)
...ntain Trail—approx. 2500–4600'
...Parsons Branch, S.W. of Cades Cove, to Sheep Pen Gap on
...e ridge (Tenn.)
...y—1332'
...ndary near Chilhowee Mt. (Tenn.)

Appendixes

Localities, with Altitudes

Abrams Creek, mouth of—857'
  W. boundary (Tenn.)
Abrams Creek Ranger Station—1200'
  W. boundary (Tenn.)
Abrams Falls—approx. 1500'
  2 miles W. of Cades Cove
Alum Cave Bluffs—4900'
  S. slope of Mt. LeConte (Tenn.)
Alum Cave Parking Area—3800'
  Transmountain road (Tenn.)
Alum Cave Trail—3800–6300'
  S. slope of Mt. LeConte (Tenn.)
Andrews Bald—5800'
  S. of Clingmans Dome (N. C.)
Andy McCully Ridge—2000–2300'
  W. of Cades Cove (Tenn.)
Anthony Creek Trail—2000–3500'
  S.E. of Cades Cove (Tenn.)
Appalachian Trail—mostly 5000–6000'
  Approx. along Tenn.–N. C. line
Arch Rock—4200'
  Along trail to Alum Cave Bluffs (Tenn.)
Big Cove—2500'
  Cherokee Indian Reservation, E. of Smokemont (N. C.)
Big Creek—mostly 1500–3000'
  Vic. N.E. boundary (N. C.)
Black Camp Gap—4522'
  Vic. S.E. boundary (N. C.)
Blanket Mountain—4609'
  S.W. of Elkmont, Tenn.
Blanket Mountain Trail—approx. 2500–4609'
  Vic. Elkmont (S.W. of Gatlinburg, Tenn.)
Blue Ridge Parkway (southern terminus) —2000'
  Between Cherokee, N. C., and the Oconoluftee Visitor Center
Bote Mountain—approx. 2500–4800'
  E. of Cades Cove (Tenn.)

Hazel Creek—approx. 2100′ (lowest)
   Flows into Fontana Reservoir between Eagle Creek and Forney Creek
      (N. C.)
Heintooga Bald—approx. 5200′
   S. of Heintooga Overlook near S.E. boundary (N. C.)
Heintooga Overlook—5325′
   Terminus of Blue Ridge Parkway spur which leaves Parkway at Mile
      458.2; vic. S.E. boundary (N. C.)
Heintooga Ridge—approx. 4000′
   S.W. of Heintooga Overlook near S.E. boundary of park (N. C.)
Hemphill Bald—5573′
   On S.E. boundary of park (N. C.)
Hughes Ridge—mostly 4000–5500′
   From Pecks Corner, on state-line, S. into Cherokee Indian Reserva-
      tion (N. C.)
Huskey Gap Trail—approx. 1900–3000′
   Starts from along transmountain road, approx. 2 miles beyond Park
      Hdqrs. (Tenn.)
Ice Water Spring Shelter—approx. 5600′
   Along Appalachian Trail, 3 miles E. of Newfound Gap (Tenn.–N. C.)
Inadu Knob—5941′
   On state-line ridge, N. of Mt. Guyot; in N.E. part of park
Indian Creek—2000′ (lowest part)
   Tributary of Deep Creek near boundary, N. of Bryson City (N. C.)
Indian Gap—5266′
   West of Newfound Gap, along road to Clingmans Dome
      (Tenn.–N. C.)
Indian Grave Flats—4091′
   On Road Prong, along the Old Indian Gap "Road", N.W. of Indian
      Gap (Tenn.)
Injun Creek—1470′ (at mouth)
   Tributary of Middle Prong of Little Pigeon River; near Greenbrier
      Ranger Station (Tenn.)
Jenkins Ridge—approx. 3000–5000′
   S. of Thunderhead (N. C.)
Jump Off—6100′
   N. of Mt. Kephart near Boulevard Trail (Tenn.)
Kephart Prong—2800′, at mouth
   Tributary of the Oconaluftee River, above Smokemont (N. C.)
Kinzel Springs bridge—approx. 1100′
   Crosses Little River in N.W. corner of Tuckaleechee Cove (Tenn.)
Lake Junaluska—2612′
   Approx. 10 miles S.E. of park boundary (N. C.)
Laurel Creek—approx. 1200–1800′
   Tributary of the Middle Prong of Little River; along spur road to
      Cades Cove (Tenn.)
Laurel Falls Trail—2320–2600′
   Starts from Fighting Creek Gap, along Little River Road (Tenn.)

Laurel Lake—approx. 1100'
Outside park in Tuckaleechee Cove; W. of Townsend, Tenn.
Laurel Top—5900'
On state line between Charlies Bunion and Pecks Corner
LeConte Creek—1300' (at mouth)
Flows from Mt. LeConte into Gatlinburg, Tenn.
Ledge Bald—5175'
On Balsam Mountain range between the state line and Heintooga
Overlook (N. C.)
Lickstone Fire Tower—4500'
In Cherokee Indian Reservation in vic. Soco Bald, near S.E. bound-
ary (N. C.)
Little River Gorge—1100–1600'
That part of the Little River Rd. area below Metcalf Bottoms (Tenn.)
Little River Road—approx. 1100–2320'
From Sugarlands Visitor Center to vic. Townsend, Tenn.
Little Tennessee River Valley—approx. 850–1700'
In vic. S.W. boundary (Tenn.)
Locust Ridge—approx. 4000'
Ridge to W. of Hazel Creek (N. C.)
Look Rock—2650'
Near W. boundary on Chilhowee Mountain (Tenn.)
Low Gap—4242'
On state line, N. of Cosby Knob, in N.E. part of park
Lynn Camp Prong—1925' (mouth)
Tributary of Middle Prong of Little River, S. of Blanket Mt. (Tenn.)
Meigs Post Prong Trail—approx. 3200–5000'
Follows one of the higher tributaries of Little River, N. of Clingmans
Dome (Tenn.)
Metcalf Bottoms—1679'
Picnic area along Little River, 2 miles above Sinks Bridge (Tenn.)
Middle Prong of Little Pigeon River—1374–1680'
Flows from Greenbrier to Emerts Cove (Tenn.)
Middle Prong of Little River—1147' (mouth)
Tributary of Little River, entering that stream about 3 miles above
Townsend, Tenn.
Miller's Cove—1000'
Includes Walland, Tenn.—along road from Townsend to Maryville,
Tenn.
Miry Ridge—approx. 4500–5200'
Meets state line S. of Blanket Mt. (Tenn.)
Mollie's Gap—5358'
Along spur road from Blue Ridge Parkway to Heintooga Overlook,
near S.E. boundary (N. C.)
Mt. Buckley—6582'
1 mile W. of Clingmans Dome on state line
Mt. Cammerer—5025'
Near state line in extreme N.E. corner of park (Tenn.)

Mt. Collins—6188'
   On state line between Indian Gap and Clingmans Dome
Mt. Guyot—6621' (2nd highest peak in park)
   On state line E. of Greenbrier
Mt. Kephart—approx. 6300'
   On state line 3 miles N.E. of Newfound Gap
Mt. LeConte—6593'
   Third-highest peak in park, S.E. of Gatlinburg, Tenn.
Mt. LeConte Lodge—approx. 6300'
   Near summit of Mt. LeConte, at junction of trails
Mt. Mingus—5800'
   N. of Indian Gap (Tenn.)
Mt. Sterling (summit) —5835'
   Near E. boundary, S. of Mt. Sterling, N. C.
Mt. Sterling Gap—3894'
   Along road on E. boundary, S. of Mt. Sterling, N. C.
Mt. Sterling, N. C.—1557'
   On N.E. boundary, near state line (N. C.)
Narrows, The—approx. 5250'
   Near Silers Bald on state line
Newfound Gap—5040'
   Highest point on transmountain road; on state line and on Appa-
   lachian Trail
Newton Bald—5142'
   On Thomas Ridge, E. of Smokemont, N. C.
Noland Divide Trail
   From E. of Clingmans Dome S. to Deep Creek Campground (N. C.)
Oconaluftee meadows (See Floyd–Enloe Bottoms)
Oconaluftee Visitor Center—approx. 2100'
   Along transmountain road 2 miles N. of Cherokee, N. C.
Old Black Mountain—6356'
   On state line 1 mile N. of Mt. Guyot
Park Headquarters—1460'
   Area 2 miles S. of Gatlinburg, Tenn.
Park Headquarters Building—1460'
   Administration Building, 2 miles S. of Gatlinburg, Tenn.
Parson Bald—4730'
   On state line W. of Gregory Bald
Pecks Corner—approx. 5600'
   On state line E. of Charlies Bunion
Peregrine Ridge—approx. 4800'
   Near Alum Cave Bluffs, on S.W. slope of Mt. LeConte
Pigeon Forge—approx. 1000'
   Community, a few miles N. of Gatlinburg on road to Sevierville,
   Tenn.
Pinnacle Creek—1791' (mouth)
   Tributary of Eagle Creek, between Thunderhead and Fontana Res-
   ervoir (N. C.)

Pin Oak Gap—4428'
On Balsam Mountain N. of Heintooga Overlook (N. C.)
Porters Creek—1680' (mouth)
Tributary of Middle Prong, Little Pigeon River, S. of Greenbrier (Tenn.)
Porters Flat—2242'
S.W. of Greenbrier, along Porters Creek (Tenn.)
Pretty Hollow Gap—5176'
S.W. of Mt. Sterling tower on Mt. Sterling Ridge (N. C.)
Rabbit Creek—1300–2600'
Tributary of Abrams Creek, W. of Cades Cove (Tenn.)
Rainbow Falls—approx. 4200'
Along LeConte Creek near trail from Cherokee Orchard to Mt. LeConte, via Rocky Spur (Tenn.)
Rainbow Falls Trail—2581–6300'
From Cherokee Orchard to Mt. LeConte via Rocky Spur (Tenn.)
Ramsey Cascades—4750'
Along Ramsey Prong, E. of Greenbrier
Ramsey Cascades Trail—2647–4750'
E. of Greenbrier, along Ramsey Prong
Raven Fork—2100' (mouth)
Tributary of Oconaluftee River which it enters near Ravensford; flows N.E. through Cherokee Indian Reservation and N. into park
Ravensford—2100'
Near junction of Ravens Fork and Oconaluftee River, in vic. Oconaluftee Visitor Center (N. C.)
Revenue Hill—2150'
Near W. boundary, approx. 3 miles E. of Calderwood, Tenn.
Rich Mountain—approx. 2750'
On park boundary N. of Cades Cove (Tenn.)
Roaring Fork—approx. 1300' (mouth)
Enters W. Prong of Little Pigeon River in Gatlinburg; its upper reaches are below Cliff Top on Mt. LeConte (Tenn.)
Rocky Spring Gap—approx. 5500'
Along road between Indian Gap and Clingmans Dome (N. C.)
Rocky Spur—5587'
Part of Mt. LeConte trending N.W. from near Cliff Top (Tenn.)
Roundbottom—3022'
On Straight Fork, at junction with Roundbottom Creek; S.E. part of park (N. C.)
Rowans Creek—approx. 1800' (mouth)
Flows N. from near Russell Field (state line) to Cades Cove (Tenn.)
Russell Field—4250'
On state line S.E. of Cades Cove
Sam Gap—approx. 2600'
Point where Parsons Branch truck trail crosses Hannah Mt.; start of trail to Gregory Bald in W. end of park (Tenn.)
Sawteeth—approx. 5500'
On state line E. of Charlies Bunion

Schoolhouse Gap—approx. 2000'
> On N. boundary of park on old road between White Oak Sink (vic.) and Dry Valley in Tuckaleechee Cove (Tenn.)

Sheep Pen Gap—4610'
> On state line W. of Gregory Bald

Silers Bald—5620'
> On state line W. of Clingmans Dome

Sinks (or Sinks Bridge) —1565'
> Along Little River Road below Metcalf Bottoms (Tenn.)

Smokemont (and Campground area) —2198'
> On transmountain road above Oconaluftee Visitor Center (N. C.)

Soco Gap—approx. 4300'
> Point where Blue Ridge Parkway overpasses N. C. 19; S. of Black Camp Gap (on S.E. boundary) (N. C.)

Spence Field (same as Spence Field Bald) —approx. 5000'
> Just W. of Thunderhead on state line

Spence Field Bald (Same as Spence Field)

Spruce-Fir Nature Trail—approx. 6000'
> A $\frac{3}{4}$ mile loop trail on Mt. Collins, between Indian Gap and Clingmans Dome (Tenn.–N. C.)

Straight Fork—approx. 2400' (mouth)
> Tributary of Raven Fork, between Hyatt Ridge and Balsam Mt., in E. part of park (N. C.)

Sugarlands—1500–2700'
> Valley from near Sugarlands Visitor Center to Chimneys Campground (Tenn.)

Sugartree Gap—4435'
> On state line 3 miles E. of Thunderhead

Sunkota Ridge—approx. 3900'
> Between Deep Creek and Thomas Divide (N. C.)

Sunup Knob—5000'
> On state line, S. of Mt. Cammerer in N.E. corner of park

Tabcat Creek—952' (mouth)
> N. of Calderwood Dam in extreme W. end of park (Tenn.)

Thomas Ridge—mostly 4000–5000'
> The main divide W. of the Oconaluftee River (N. C.)

Thomas Ridge Trail—mostly 4000–5000'
> Trail along crest of Thomas Ridge (N. C.)

Three Forks—4202'
> Junction of Left, Middle, and Right Forks of Raven Fork, the main watershed S. of Mt. Guyot (N. C.)

Thunderhead—5530'
> On state line S.E. of Cades Cove

Transmountain road—1300–5040'
> Road from Gatlinburg, Tenn., to Cherokee, N. C., via Newfound Gap

Tremont—1925'
> On Middle Prong of Little River near junction with Lynn Camp Prong (Tenn.)

Tricorner Knob—approx. 6100′
    On state line, 1 mile S. of Mt. Guyot
Trillium Gap—4717′
    Between Mt. LeConte and Brushy Mt. (Tenn.)
Tuckaleechee Cove—approx. 1100′
    Relatively flat area on park boundary N. of Cades Cove; includes
    Townsend and Laurel Lake (Tenn.)
Tuckasegee River—approx. 1700–2000′
    Flows through Bryson City, N. C., and W. along park boundary. Its
    impoundment created Fontana Reservoir
Tuckasegee River Valley (See Tuckasegee R.)
Twentymile Creek—1313′ (mouth)
    Flows into Cheoah Lake on Park boundary W. of Fontana
    Dam (N. C.)
Walland—approx. 1000′
    Between Maryville and Townsend, Tenn., 4 miles N. of park
Walnut Bottoms—3042′
    On Big Creek, in N.E. part of park (N. C.)
Walters Dam—approx. 2300′
    S.E. of Mt. Sterling, N. C.
Waterrock Knob—6292′
    On Blue Ridge Parkway between Soco Gap and Balsam Gap (N. C.)
Wears Cove—1454′
    On park boundary W. of Cove Mt. (Tenn.)
Welch Bald—approx. 4800′
    On Welch Ridge S.W. of Silers Bald (N. C.)
Welch Ridge—approx. 2500–5400′
    Main ridge E. of Hazel Creek (N. C.)
West Prong of Little Pigeon River (same as West Fork of Little Pigeon
    River) —approx. 1300–4600′
    The main stream along road from Gatlinburg, Tenn., to near New-
    found Gap
Whiteoak Sink—approx. 1750′
    Small cove just inside park boundary N.E. of Cades Cove (Tenn.)
White Rock (see Mt. Cammerer)
Wooly Tops—5500′
    3 miles S.E. of Greenbrier; 1 mile N. of state line (Tenn.)

Contributors Mentioned in Text

I wish to acknowledge my indebtedness to all who contributed lists, records, specimens, and other pertinent information. Those whose names appear in this report are listed below. However, there are many others whose cooperation has been helpful, and the names of most of these are in the bird files in the Sugarlands Visitor Center near the Park Headquarters Building.

Names of contributors are grouped as follows:

Gatlinburg and Vicinity
National Park Service Employees
        (Present and Former)
Tennessee Ornithological Society Members
Other Contributors

GATLINBURG AND VICINITY

Gervin, Mrs. Harry A.
Hadley, Dr. and Mrs. J. B.
Huff, Mr. and Mrs. Jack
Huff, Philip
Liles, James E.
MacLean, Dorothy J.
Manley, Joe F.

McCarter, Curtis
Ogle, Mrs. Sheril
Rawlings, Rush
Reagan, Jack
Snowden, George L.
Stupka, Mrs. Arthur
Whittle, M. M.

NATIONAL PARK SERVICE EMPLOYEES
(PRESENT AND FORMER)

Atchison, Alan L.
Burns, Richard C.
Chiles, Mary Ruth
Cole, Julius
Condon, David deL.
Davis, Carl
Ealy, Dewey R.
Earnst, John R.
Fleetwood, Raymond J.
George, John L.
Gilbert, Vernon C., Jr.
Grossman, Charles S.
Hannah, Mark E.
Henry, Samuel W.
King, Willis
Kirkland, Jack J.
Light, James B.

Lix, Henry W.
McCamey, Franklin
Morrell, John O.
Muller, Hugh B.
Myers, D. Labe
Myers, William H.
Needham, John T.
Ogle, Elmer J.
Ogle, Wesley E.
Oliver, Frank W.
Overly, Fred J.
Owenby, T. Lee
Pfitzer, Donald W.
Price, J. Melvin
Quay, Thomas L.
Rauhuff, Mack
Reid, Neil J.

Rogers, John B.
Rolen, William T.
Royce, Rodney D.
Russell, Richard W.
Savage, Wilbur L.
Shields, A. Randolph
Smith, Homer E.
Smith, Mr. and Mrs. J. Clyde

Stark, Jack
Sullivan, Maurice
Wear, Sheridan H.
Whaley, David O.
White, Robert G.
Wilburn, Hiram C.
Worthington, William S.

TENNESSEE ORNITHOLOGICAL SOCIETY MEMBERS

Baird, Charles O.
Beasley, Jon
Behrend, Fred W.
Coffey, Ben B., Jr.
Crouch, Brockway
Dunbar, Mr. and Mrs. Robert J.
Enloe, Mary
Foster, George
Ganier, Albert F.
Garlinghouse, Mr. and Mrs.
   Harold
Goddard, Frelan
Henry, Earl O.
Herndon, Lee R.
Highbaugh, David
Howell, Joseph C.
Janson, Mrs. Elsie
Johnson, Mr. and Mrs. Wm. M.

Kaiman, Bernard and Audrey
Leonhard, Mrs. Frank
Maslowski, Karl
Mayfield, George R.
Meyer, Henry
Monroe, Mrs. Robert A.
   (Muriel B.)
Ogden, S. A.
Overton, Mrs. E. E.
Pardue, Paul S.
Tanner, James T.
Tipton, Dr. and Mrs. Samuel R.
Walker, William M., Jr.
West, Mrs. Eugene M. (Adele H.)
Wilkinson, Mr. and Mrs. Jack
Yambert, William
Zaenglein, Ralph J.

OTHER CONTRIBUTORS

Alexander, Thomas W.
   (Waynesville, N. C.)
Amadon, Dean
   (New York City)
Appleby, Mrs.
   (Morristown, Va.)
Baldwin, Dr. and Mrs. S. Glidden
   (Danville, Ill.)
Bowen, Richard
   (Cambridge, Mass.)
Brimley, C. S.
   (Raleigh, N. C.)
Brooks, Maurice
   (Morgantown, W. Va.)
Burleigh, Thomas D.
   (Washington, D. C.)

Chamberlain, B. Rhett
   (Wadmalaw Island, S. C.)
Downer, C. T.
   (Cleveland, O.)
Edwards, R. E.
   (McClellanville, S. C.)
Eifert, Mrs. Virginia S.
   (Springfield, Ill.)
Fawver, Ben
Fisher, James
   (Northampton, England)
Frizzell, G.
   (Knoxville, Tenn.)
Gordon, Robert B.
   (West Chester, Pa.)

Gunn, W. W. H.
(Toronto, Ont.)
Hardy, William
(Murphysboro, Ill.)
Hebard, Frederick V.
(Philadelphia, Pa.)
Hicks, Lawrence E.
(Columbus, O.)
Hill, Norman P.
(Cambridge, Mass.)
Hyder, Albert
(Nashville, Tenn.)
Ijams, Elizabeth
(Knoxville, Tenn.)
Keating, F. R., Jr.
(Philadelphia, Pa.)
Kent, Deane F.
(Washington, D. C.)
Kincaid, Mr. and Mrs. B. J., Sr.
(Miami, Florida)
Koch, Peter
(Cincinnati, O.)
Komarek, E. V.
(Chicago, Ill.)
Komarek, R. V.
(Chicago, Ill.)
Land, H. C.
(Huntington, W. Va.)
Land, H. K.
(Huntington, W. Va.)
Landis, Harry, Jr.
(Memphis, Tenn.)
MacArthur, Edward
(Cleveland, O.)
Maher, Robert T.
(Knoxville, Tenn.)
Miller, D. S.
(Toronto, Ont.)
Miller, Eugene J.
(Loudenville, O.)
Miller, Gerrit S., Jr.
(Washington, D. C.)
Moore, Edward M.
(Cleveland, O.)
Nicholson, Donald J.
(Tuxedo, N. C.)

Oberholser, Harry C.
(Cleveland, O.)
Peterson, Roger Tory
(Old Lyme, Conn.)
Phillips, Richard E.
(Lafayette, Ind.)
Robbins, Chandler S.
(Laurel, Md.)
Saunders, Aretas A.
(Canaan, Conn.)
Savage, Thomas
(Mt. Rainier, Md.)
Schweinfurth, Charles
(Wellesley Farms, Mass.)
Scott, Frederick R.
(Ann Arbor, Mich.)
Seeber, Edwin L.
(Buffalo, N. Y.)
Seibert, Henri C.
(Athens, O.)
Spofford, Walter R.
(Syracuse, N. Y.)
Stevenson, Henry M., Jr.
(Tallahassee, Fla.)
Stimson, Louis A.
(Miami, Fla.)
Street, Phillips B.
(Chester Springs, Pa.)
Sutton, George M.
(Norman, Okla.)
Thomas, Edward S.
(Columbus, O.)
Thomas, John
(Columbus, O.)
Trautman, Milton B.
(Columbus, O.)
Watkins, John O.
(Spartanburg, S. C.)
Weig, Mrs. Melvin J.
(Morristown, Va.)
Wetmore, Alexander
(Washington, D. C.)
Wilson, Gordon
(Bowling Green, Ky.)
Wilson, R. G.
(Lookout Mountain, Tenn.)

References Cited in Text
(Indicated by date of publication within brackets)

Aldrich, John W. and Phil Goodrum
1946. Breeding Bird Census in a Virgin Hardwood Forest. *Aud. Mag. Sec. 2, Aud. Field Notes* pp. 144–145.

Allen, Mrs. Juanita
1946. Courtship Behavior of Whip-poor-wills. *Migrant* 17:28–29.

American Ornithologists' Union
1957. *Check-list of North American Birds. 5th ed.* Baltimore: Am. Ornithol. Union. 691 pp.

Bailey, Alfred M., Robert J. Niedrach, and A. Lang Baily
1953. The Red Crossbills of Colorado. *Museum Pictorial No. 9*, Denver Museum of Natural History. 63 pp.

Behrend, Fred W. and Mary Fern Behrend
1945. Evening Grosbeaks in Northeast Tennessee. *Migrant* 16:53–55.

Behrend, Fred W.
1946a. Wintering of the Evening Grosbeak in Northeast Tennessee. *Migrant* 17:1–4.

1946b. Departure of the Eastern Evening Grosbeak from Elizabethton. *Migrant* 17:25.

1948. A Record of the Snow Bunting in East Tennessee. *Migrant* 19:64–66.

1953. Second Record of Eastern Snow Bunting on Big Bald Mountain in East Tennessee. *Migrant* 24:85–86.

1955. Evening Grosbeaks and Snow Buntings on Roan and Big Bald Mountains, Tenn.–N. C. *Migrant* 26:14–16.

1960. The 1960 Christmas Season Bird Count: Big Bald Mountain and Roan Mountain. *Migrant* 31:73, 78.

Bellrose, Frank, Jr.
1938. Notes on Birds of the Great Smoky Mountains National Park. *Migrant* 9:1–4.

Bendire, Charles E.
1892. Life Histories of North American Birds. *U. S. Nat. Mus. Spec. Bull.* 1

Bent, Arthur Cleveland
1932. Life Histories of North American Gallinaceous Birds. *U. S. Nat. Mus. Bull.* 162:490 pp.

1938. Life Histories of North American Birds of Prey (Part 2). *U. S. Nat. Mus. Bull.* 170:482 pp.

1939. Life Histories of North American Woodpeckers. *U. S. Nat. Mus. Bull.* 174:334 pp.

1940. Life Histories of North American Cuckoos, Goatsuckers, Hummingbirds, and their Allies. *U. S. Nat. Mus. Bull.* 176:506 pp.

1946. Life Histories of North American Jays, Crows, and Titmice. *U. S. Nat. Mus. Bull.* 191:495 pp.

1948. Life Histories of North American Nuthatches, Wrens, Thrashers, and their Allies. *U. S. Nat. Mus. Bull.* 195:475 pp.

1949. Life Histories of North American Thrushes, Kinglets, and their Allies. *U. S. Nat. Mus. Bull.* 196:454 pp.

1953. Life Histories of North American Wood Warblers. *U. S. Nat. Mus. Bull.* 203:734 pp.

Brewster, William
1886. An Ornithological Reconnaissance in Western North Carolina. *Auk* 3:94–112, 173–179.

Brimley, C. S.
1940. The Birds of Buncombe County. *Chat* 4:21–36.

Brimley, H. H.
1926. The Sooty Tern in North Carolina. *Auk* 43:535.

Brooks, A. B.
1933. West Virginia Breeding Record for the Saw-whet Owl. *Auk* 50:361–362.

Brooks, Maurice
1936. The Canadian Component of West Virginia's Bird Life. *Cardinal* 4:53–60.

1938. Bachman's Sparrow in the North-central Portion of its Range. *Wilson Bull.* 50:86–109.

1940. The Breeding Warblers of the Central Allegheny Mountain Region. *Wilson Bull.* 52:249–266.

1944. A Check-list of West Virginia Birds. *Bull. 316, Agric. Exper. Sta., W. Va. Univ.*

Burleigh, Thomas D.
1935. Two New Birds from the Southern Appalachians. *Proc. Biol. Soc. Wash.* 48:61–62.

1941. Bird Life on Mt. Mitchell. *Auk* 58:334–345.

1944. The Bird Life of the Gulf Coast Region of Mississippi. *Occ. Papers, Mus. Zool., La. State Univ.* No. 20. pp. 329–490.

1958. *Georgia Birds.* Norman: Univ. of Oklahoma Press, 746 pp.

Cain, Stanley A.
1930. Certain Floristic Affinities of the Trees and Shrubs of the Great Smoky Mountains and Vicinity. *Butler Univ. Bot. Studies,* Vol. 1, Paper No. 9. pp. 129–150.

Cairns, John S.
1889. The Summer Birds of Buncombe County, North Carolina. *Orn. and Ool.* 14:17–23.

1902. List of the Birds of Buncombe County, North Carolina. (List dated July 6, 1891.) Privately printed.

Campbell, Carlos C.
1936. Raven's Nest. *Am. Forests* 42:454—.

Castles, Ruth
1957. T. O. S. Annual Meeting, 1957. *Migrant* 28:33–34.

Chamberlain, B. R.
1952. Evening Grosbeaks in the Carolinas. *Chat* 16:30–33, 64–65.

1953. Status of the White-crowned Sparrow in North and South Carolina. *Chat* 17:47–50.

1961. (compiler) Evening Grosbeaks. *Chat.* 25:75.

Chapman, Frank M.
1926. *Handbook of Birds of Eastern North America*. N. Y.: D. Appleton and Co. 530 pp.

Clarke, Herbert
1949. Some Unusual Notes from Memphis. *Migrant* 20:53–54.

Coues, Elliott
1897. Characters of *Dendroica caerulescens cairnsi*. *Auk* 14:96–97.

Darnell, Elva
1956. Baltimore Oriole near Greeneville. *Migrant* 27:59.

Dixon, Joseph S.
1933. The Falcons of the Great Smokies. *Am. Forests* 39:256.

Fleetwood, Raymond J.
1936. The Red-cockaded Woodpecker in Blount County, Tennessee. *Migrant* 7:103.
1937. A Woodcock at High Altitude in Great Smoky Mountains National Park. *Migrant* 8:42.
1943. Blue Goose in Eastern Tennessee. *Migrant* 14:62.

Forbush, Edward Howe
1929. *Birds of Massachusetts and Other New England States*. Mass. Dept. of Agric. 3 vols.

Fox, William H.
1886. List of Birds found in Roane County, Tennessee, during April, 1884, and March and April, 1885. *Auk* 3:315–320.

Ganier, Albert F.
1926. Summer Birds of the Great Smoky Mountains. *Journ. Tenn. Acad. Sci.* 1:31–40.
1929. Some Unusual Water Bird Visitors to Tennessee. *Wilson Bull.* 41:96–100.
1931. Nesting of the Duck Hawk in Tennessee. *Wilson Bull.* 43:3–8.
1935. (compiler) Spring Migration at Athens, Tennessee. *Migrant* 6:2–5.
1940. Notes on Tennessee Birds of Prey. *Migrant* 11:1–4.
1946. Additional Records of the Saw-whet Owl. *Migrant* 17:67–68.
1948. Western Henslow's Sparrow in East Tennessee. *Migrant* 19:28–29.
1952. Ring-billed Gull in the Great Smoky Mountains National Park. *Migrant* 23:30.
1954. A New Race of the Yellow-bellied Sapsucker. *Migrant* 25:37–41.
1956. Nesting of the Black-throated Blue and Chestnut-sided Warblers. *Migrant* 27:43–46.
1962. Some Nesting Records from the Smokies. *Migrant* 33:1–6.

Ganier, Albert F. and Alfred Clebsch
1938. Some June Birds of the Great Smokies. *Migrant* 9:41–45.
1944. Summer Birds of the Unicoi Mountains. *Migrant* 15:61–65.

Ganier, Albert F. and G. R. Mayfield
1946. A June List from the Smoky Mountain Summits. *Migrant* 17:67.

Green, Charlotte Hilton
1949. Carolina Bird Club Fall Meeting held at Fontana Village. *Chat* 13:70–72.

Grimes, Samuel A.
1952. Photographing the Red-breasted Nuthatch. *Chat* 16:80–81.

Grinnell, Mrs. Dodette
1946. Goldfinch Nests Late at Arden, North Carolina. *Chat* 10:86.

Griscom, Ludlow
1937. A Monographic Study of the Red Crossbill. *Proc. Bost. Soc. Nat. Hist.* 41:77–210.

1945. *Modern Bird Study.* Cambridge: Harvard Univ. Press. 190 pp.

Hamilton, Warren
1961. *Geology of the Richardson Cove and Jones Cove Quadrangles Tennessee.* Geological Survey Professional Paper 349-A. 55 pp.

Hawkins, Robert M.
1946. Bald Eagle Feeding on the Highway. *Auk* 63:85.

Henry, B. L. and R. R. Dickson
1959. *Climatological Summary, Gatlinburg, Tennessee.* U. S. Dept. of Commerce, Weather Bureau, Climatography of the U. S. No. 20–40.

Herndon, Lee R.
1958. Traill's Flycatchers Breeding in Tennessee. *Migrant* 29:37–42.
1959. Traill's Flycatcher. *Migrant* 30:40.
1960. Traill's Flycatcher. *Migrant* 31:55.
1961. Traill's Flycatchers. *Migrant* 32:52–53.

Howell, Arthur H.
1909. Notes on the Summer Birds of Northern Georgia. *Auk* 26:129–37.

Howell, Joseph C. and Muriel B. Monroe
1957. The Birds of Knox County, Tennessee. *Journ. Tenn. Acad. Sci.* 32:247–322.

1958. The Birds of Knox County, Tennessee. *Migrant* 29:17–27.

Howell, Joseph C. and James T. Tanner
1951. An Accident to Migrating Birds at the Knoxville Airport. *Migrant* 22:61–62.

Ijams, H. P.
1933. Field Days at Knoxville. *Migrant* 4:23.

Ijams, H. P. and L. A. Hofferbert
1934. Nesting Records of Birds at Athens, Tennessee. *Migrant* 5:1–4.

Jeffries, W. A. and J. A. Jeffries
1889. Notes on Western North Carolina Birds. *Auk* 6:119–122.

Johnson, I. H.
1926. Sooty Tern (*Sterna fuscata*) in West Virginia. *Auk* 43:535–536.

Kephart, Horace
1921. *Our Southern Highlanders.* New York: Macmillan Co. 395 pp.

King, Philip B., Jarvis B. Hadley, Robert B. Neuman, and Warren Hamilton
  1958. Stratigraphy of Ocoee Series, Great Smoky Mountains, Tennessee and North Carolina. *Bull. Geol. Soc. of Amer.* 69:947–966.
King, P. B. and A. Stupka
  1950. The Great Smoky Mountains—their Geology and Natural History. *Sci. Monthly* 71:31–43.
Klyce, Miriam A. (Mrs. T. I.)
  1936. Summer Tanager Behavior. *Migrant* 7:44.
Korstian, Clarence F.
  1937. Perpetuation of Spruce on Cut-over and Burned Lands in the Higher Southern Appalachian Mountains. *Ecol. Monog.* 7:125–167.
Langdon, F. W.
  1887. August Birds of the Chilhowee Mountains, Tennessee. *Auk* 4:125–133.
Langridge, H. P.
  1957. The Season—Elizabethton, Tennessee. *Migrant* 28:13.
Lanman, Charles
  1849. *Letters from the Alleghany Mountains.* New York: Geo. P. Putnam.
Laskey, Amelia R.
  1938. Bird Banding Activities—No. 13. *Migrant* 9:51–52.
  1941. An Indigo Bunting in December at Nashville. *Migrant* 12:60.
Laurent, Philip
  1892. Breeding Habits of *Junco Hyemalis carolinensis*, Br. *Orn. and Ool.* 17:116–117.
Lemoyne, Arthur
  1886. Notes on Some Birds of the Great Smoky Mountains. *Orn. and Ool.* 9:8–12.
Lesley, Sarah
  1953. White Pelicans at Lake Junaluska, Haywood County, North Carolina. *Chat* 17:69–70.
  1954. Loons and Mergansers. *Chat.* 18:52
Lewy, Alfred
  1945. A Week in the Great Smokies. *Aud. Bull.* (Ill. Audubon Soc.) No. 55, pp. 9–13.
Lovell, Harvey B.
  1947. Mountain Vireo Nests in the Great Smoky Mountains. *Migrant* 18:51–53.
Lovell, Harvey B. and Ethel W. Lovell
  1952. Nesting Sites of the Slate-colored Junco in the Southern Appalachians. *Chat* 16:38–39.
McCamey, Franklin
  1936. Six September Days in the Smokies. *Migrant* 7:57–59.
Mason, Robert L.
  1927. *The Lure of the Great Smokies.* New York: Houghton Mifflin Co. 320 pp.

Metcalf, Z. P. and Luella O. Metcalf
   1938.   Field Notes—Clingman's Dome. *Chat* 2:11.
Monroe, Mrs. R. A. (Muriel B.)
   1952.   An unusual Winter Visitor. *Migrant* 23:7–8.
   1959.   Round Table Notes. *Migrant* 30:56.
Murray, J. J.
   1940.   The Faunal Zones of the Southern Appalachians. *Va. Journ. of Sci.* 1: nos. 2 and 3.
   1946.   Some North Carolina Bird Notes. *Chat* 10:32–34.
National Park Service (Wildlife Division)
   1937.   *Check-list of Birds of Great Smoky Mountains National Park.* National Park Service. Mimeographed. 26 pp.
Nevius, Ruth Reed
   1950.   The Season—Greeneville, Tenn. *Migrant* 21:52–54.
   1955.   Blue Grosbeak in Greene County, Tennessee. *Migrant* 26:33.
Neuman, Robert B.
   1947.   Notes on the Geology of Cades Cove, Great Smoky Mountains National Park, Tennessee. *Journ. Tenn. Acad. Sci.* 22:167–172.
Oberholser, Harry C.
   1937.   Description of a New Chickadee from the Eastern United States. *Proc. Biol. Soc. Wash.* 50:220.
Odum, Eugene P.
   1944.   Summer Occurrence of the Oven-bird at Athens. *Oriole* 9:35.
   1945.   The Concept of the Biome as Applied to the Distribution of North American Birds. *Wilson Bull.* 57:191–201.
   1949.   Small Mammals of the Highlands (North Carolina) Plateau. *Journ. Mamm.* 30:179–192.
Ogburn, Charlton, Jr.
   1931.   Late Nesting of the Goldfinch in North Carolina. *Auk* 48:273.
Ogden, S. A.
   1933.   Raptore and Water Bird Records from East Tennessee. *Migrant* 4:46–48.
Pearson, T. Gilbert, C. S. Brimley, and H. H. Brimley.
   1942.   *Birds of North Carolina.* Raleigh, N. C., Department of Agriculture, State Museum Div. 416 pp.
Pearson, Thomas Gilbert, Clement Samuel Brimley, and Herbert Hutchinson Brimley. Revised by David L. Wray and Harry T. Davis.
   1959.   *Birds of North Carolina.* Raleigh: N. C. Dept. of Agric., State Mus. Div. 434 pp.
Peters, James L. and Ludlow Griscom
   1938.   Geographical Variation in the Savannah Sparrow. *Bull. Mus. of Comparative Zoology* 80:443–478.
Peterson, Roger Tory
   1947.   *A Field Guide to the Birds.* Boston: Houghton Mifflin Co. 290 pp.

Powers, Edwin B.
  1936. The Attachment of a Mountain Vireo to its Nest. *Migrant* 7:95.
Rhoads, Samuel N.
  1895. Contributions to the Zoology of Tennessee. No. 2. Birds. *Proc. Acad. Natural Sci. of Phila.* pp. 463–501.
Saunders, Aretas A.
  1935. *A Guide to Bird Songs.* New York: D. Appleton-Century Co. 285 pp.
Schultz, Vincent
  1955. Status of the Wild Turkey in Tennessee. *Migrant* 26:1–8.
Sennett, George B.
  1887. Observations in Western North Carolina Mountains in 1886. *Auk* 4:240–245.
Shanks, R. E.
  1954a. *Reference Lists of Native Plants of the Great Smoky Mountains.* Botany Dept., Univ. of Tennessee. Mimeographed. 17 pp.
  1954b. Climates of the Great Smoky Mountains. *Ecology* 35:354–361.
Skutch, Alexander F.
  1940. Social and Sleeping Habits of Central American Wrens. *Auk* 57:293–312.
Sprunt, Alexander, Jr.
  1924. Notes on the Breeding of the Carolina Junco (*Junco hyemalis carolinensis*) in the Mountains of North Carolina. *Auk* 41:610–612.
  1930. Two Unusual Nesting Sites of the Carolina Junco. *Auk* 47:568.
  1933a. Late Nesting of the Carolina Junco. (*Junco hyemalis carolinensis*) . *Auk* 50:122–123.
  1933b. Additional Notes from the North Carolina Mountains. *Auk* 50:233.
Sprunt, Alexander, Jr. and E. Burnham Chamberlain
  1949. *South Carolina Bird Life.* Univ. of S. C. Press. 585 pp.
Stevenson, Henry M.
  1941. Summer Residents of the Highlands, North Carolina, Region. *Oriole* 6:41–48.
  1950. Distribution of Certain Birds in the Southeastern United States. *Amer. Midland Nat.* 43:605–626.
  1957. Summer Notes on Altitudinal Distribution in the Mountains of the Southeastern States in 1956. *Chat* 21:2–8.
Stevenson, Henry M. and Arthur Stupka
  1948. The Altitudinal Limits of Certain Birds in the Mountains of the Southeastern States. *Migrant* 19:33–60.
Stupka, Arthur
  1937. Pine Siskins in the Great Smokies. *Migrant* 8:69–70.
  1938a. Red Crossbill Breeding in the Great Smoky Mountains National Park. *Auk* 55:675.

1938b. Additional Notes on Pine Siskins in the Great Smoky Mountains National Park. *Migrant* 9:93–94.

1943. Through the Year in the Great Smoky Mountains, Month by Month, in *The Great Smokies and the Blue Ridge,* Roderick Peattie, ed. New York: Vanguard Press. pp. 263–289.

1946a. Occurrence of the Saw-whet Owl in the Great Smoky Mountains during the Breeding Season. *Migrant* 17:60–62.

1946b. Blue Grosbeak in Great Smoky Mountains. *Migrant* 17:68.

1948. Snow Goose in Great Smoky Mountains National Park. *Migrant* 19:72–73.

1950. Recent Bird Mortality in Great Smoky Mountains National Park. *Migrant* 21:80–82.

1953. Some Notes Relating to the Mortality of Screech Owls in Great Smoky Mountains National Park. *Migrant* 24:3–5.

1954a. Evening Grosbeaks in the Great Smoky Mountains and Vicinity—1951 and 1952. *Migrant* 25:7–9.

1954b. Golden Plover Recorded from the Great Smoky Mountains National Park. *Migrant* 25:33.

1960. *Great Smoky Mountains National Park, Natural History Handbook Number Five.* Washington: Government Printing Office. 75 pp.

Stupka, Arthur and James T. Tanner

1955. Evening Grosbeaks in the Gatlinburg-Knoxville Area. *Migrant* 26:13–14.

Tanner, James T.

1948. Golden Eagle in the Great Smoky Mountains in July. *Migrant* 19:24.

1950a. First Record of Swainson's Warbler in the Great Smoky Mountains. *Migrant* 21:49.

1950b. Fall Flights of Broad-winged Hawks in the Southern Appalachians. *Migrant* 21:69–70.

1952. Black-capped and Carolina Chickadees in the Southern Appalachians. *Auk* 69:407–424.

1954. Bird Mortality during Night Migration. *Migrant* 25:57–68.

1955. The Altitudinal Distribution of Birds in a Part of the Great Smoky Mountains. *Migrant* 26:37–40.

1957a. Adventures for Bird-watchers in the Great Smoky Mountains. *Aud. Mag.* 59:118–123.

1957b. The Season—Knoxville Area and Vicinity. *Migrant* 28:10.

1957c. Sight Record of a Saw-whet Owl in the Great Smoky Mountains. *Migrant* 28:28.

1958. Juncos in the Great Smoky Mountains. *Migrant* 29:61–65.

Tennessee Valley Authority

1961. *Precipitation in Tennessee River System.* TVA Annual Report for 1960. Multilithed.

Todd, W. E. Clyde

1940. *Birds of Western Pennsylvania.* Univ. of Pittsburgh Press. 710 pp.

Trautman, Milton B.
　1940.　*The Birds of Buckeye Lake, Ohio*. Ann Arbor: Univ. of Mich. Press, Misc. Publications, Mus. of Zoology, No. 44. 466 pp.
Tyler, Bruce P.
　1922.　The Starling in Tennessee. *Bird Lore* 24:94–95.
　1936.　The Carolina Junco in Northeastern Tennessee. *Migrant* 7:89–90.
Tyler, Bruce P. and Robert B. Lyle
　1947.　Two New Birds for Shady Valley. *Migrant* 18:28–29.
Walker, William M., Jr.
　1935.　A Collection of Birds from Cocke County, Tennessee. *Migrant* 6:48–50.
Walker, W. M.
　1937.　The Season at Knoxville. *Migrant* 8:41–42.
　1946.　A Red Phalarope in Tennessee. *Auk* 63:102.
Wayne, Arthur T.
　1926.　The Sooty Tern and Audubon's Shearwater in South Carolina. *Auk* 43:534–535.
Wetmore, Alexander
　1939.　Notes on the Birds of Tennessee. *U. S. Nat. Mus. Proc.* 86:175–243.
　1941.　Notes on the Birds of North Carolina. *U. S. Nat. Mus. Proc.* 90:483–530.
　1950.　*The List of Birds of the Shenandoah National Park* (Third Revision). Bull. No. 1, Shenandoah Natural History Association, September.
Whittaker, R. H.
　1956.　Vegetation of the Great Smoky Mountains. *Ecol. Monographs* 26:80 pp.
Williams, Ellison A.
　1955.　Florida Gallinule in the Great Smokies. *Chat* 19:70.
Wing, Leonard
　1940.　A Study of Wintering Tennessee Crow Specimens. *Journ. Tenn. Acad. Sci.* 15:358–370.

Common and Scientific Names of Plants Mentioned in Text

American-mistletoe, Christmas—*Phoradendron flavescens*
Apple—*Malus* sp.
Basswood—*Tilia* sp.
Beech, American—*Fagus grandifolia*
Birch, yellow—*Betula alleghaniensis*
Blackgum—*Nyssa sylvatica*
Blueberry—*Vaccinium* spp.
Boxelder—*Acer negundo*
Buckeye, yellow—*Aesculus octandra*
Cherry, black—*Prunus serotina*
Cherry, pin—*Prunus pensylvanica*
Chestnut, American—*Castanea dentata*
Creeper, Virginia—*Parthenocissus quinquefolia*
Cucumbertree—*Magnolia acuminata*
Dandelion, common—*Taraxacum officinale*
Devils-walkingstick—*Aralia spinosa*
Dogwood, flowering—*Cornus florida*
Elder, scarlet—*Sambucus pubens*
Elm, American—*Ulmus americana*
Elm, winged—*Ulmus alata*
Fir, Fraser—*Abies fraseri*
Grape, wild—*Vitis* spp.
Hackberry—*Celtis* spp.
Hemlock, eastern—*Tsuga canadensis*
Holly, American—*Ilex opaca*
Huckleberry—*Gaylussacia* spp.
Magnolia, Fraser—*Magnolia fraseri*
Maple, red—*Acer rubrum*
Maple, sugar—*Acer saccharum*
Mistletoe (see American-mistletoe, Christmas)
Mountain-ash, American—*Sorbus americana*
Mountain-laurel—*Kalmia latifolia*
Oak, black—*Quercus velutina*
Oak, chestnut—*Quercus prinus*
Oak, northern red—*Quercus rubra*
Oak, scarlet—*Quercus coccinea*
Oak, white—*Quercus alba*
Persimmon, common—*Diospyros virginiana*
Pine, eastern white—*Pinus strobus*
Pine, pitch—*Pinus rigida*
Pine, Table-Mountain—*Pinus pungens*
Pine, Virginia—*Pinus virginiana*
Poison-ivy, common—*Toxicodendron radicans*
Pokeberry, common—*Phytolacca americana*

Privet—*Ligustrum* sp.
Redcedar, eastern—*Juniperus virginiana*
Rhododendron, rosebay—*Rhododendron maximum*
Serviceberry—*Amelanchier* spp.
Silverbell, mountain—*Halesia monticola*
Smilax—*Smilax* spp.
Spruce, red—*Picea rubens*
Sumac—*Rhus* spp.
Sumac, shining—*Rhus copallina*
Sumac, staghorn—*Rhus typhina*
Sweetgum—*Liquidambar styraciflua*
Sycamore, American—*Platanus occidentalis*
Walnut, (black) —*Juglans nigra*
Willow—*Salix* spp.
Witch-hazel—*Hamamelis virginiana*
Yellow-poplar—*Liriodendron tulipifera*

Species Index

A

Accipiter cooperii, **33**
  striatus, **32,** 33
Accipitridae, 32
Actitis macularia, **61,** 62
Aegolius acadicus, **72,** 73, 74
Agelaius phoeniceus, **172,** 173
Aimophila aestivalis, **200**
Aix sponsa, **27,** 28
Alaudidae, 95
Alcedinidae, 80
Alectoris graeca, 3
Ammodramus savannarum, **198**
Anas acuta, **26**
  carolinensis, **26**
  discors, **26,** 27
  platyrhynchos, **25**
  rubripes, **25**
Anatidae, 23
Anthus spinoletta, **131,** 132
Apodidae, 77
Aquila chrysaetos, **37,** 38, 39
Archilochus alexandri, 79
  colubris, **79,** 80
Ardea herodias, **20**
Ardeidae, 20
Aythya affinis, 28
  collaris, **28**
  sp., **28,** 29

B

Baldpate. See Widgeon, American
Bittern, American, **22,** 43
Blackbird, Redwinged, **172,** 173, 175, 176
Blackbird, Rusty, **174,** 175
Bluebird, Eastern, 124, **128,** 129
Bobolink, **170**

Bobwhite, 44, **48,** 49, 50
Bombycilla cedrorum, **132,** 133, 134
Bombycillidae, 132
Bonasa umbellus, **45,** 46, 47, 48
Botaurus lentiginosus, **22**
Brant, 24
Branta bernicla, **24**
  canadensis, **23**
Bubo virginianus, **70,** 71
Bufflehead, 3
Bunting, Indigo, **182,** 183
Bunting, Snow, **212**
Buteo jamaicensis, **33,** 34
  lineatus, **34,** 35
  platypterus, **35,** 36, 37
Butorides virescens, **20,** 21

C

Canvasback, 3
Capella gallinago, **61**
Caprimulgidae, 74
Caprimulgus carolinensis, **74,** 75
  vociferus, **75,** 76
Cardinal, **179,** 180
Carpodacus purpureus, **185,** 186
Catbird, 119, 120, 121, 129
Casmerodius albus, **21,** 22
Cathartes aura, **30,** 31, 32
Cathartidae, 30
Centurus carolinus, **83,** 84
Certhia familiaris, **110,** 111
  familiaris americana, 110
  familiaris nigrescens, 9, 110
Certhiidae, 110
Chaetura pelagica, **77,** 78
Charadriidae, 58
Charadrius vociferus, **58,** 59
Chat, Yellow-breasted, 14, **165,** 166
Chen caerulescens, **24,** 25
  hyperborea, **24**

G

H

I

J

K

L

M